Multidisciplinary Assessment of Children with Learning Disabilities and Mental Retardation

Multidisciplinary Assessment of Children with Learning Disabilities and Mental Retardation

edited by

David L. Wodrich, Ph.D.
Child Psychology
Division of Behavioral Pediatrics
Phoenix Children's Hospital
Phoenix, Arizona

and

James E. Joy, M.D.
Child Psychiatry
Division of Behavioral Pediatrics
Phoenix Children's Hospital
Phoenix, Arizona

·P A U L·H·
BROOKES
PUBLISHING CO

Baltimore • London

Paul H. Brookes Publishing Co.
Post Office Box 10624
Baltimore, Maryland 21285-0624

Typeset by The Composing Room, Grand Rapids, Michigan.
Manufactured in the United States of America by
The Maple Press Company, York, Pennsylvania.

Library of Congress Cataloging-in-Publication Data
Main entry under title:
Multidisciplinary assessment of children with learning
  disabilities and mental retardation.

Includes bibliographies and index.
  1. Learning disabilities—Diagnosis. 2. Mental retardation—
Diagnosis. I. Wodrich, David L., 1948–   . II. Joy, James E. [DNLM:
1. Learning Disorders—diagnosis. 2. Mental Retardation—diagnosis. WS 110
M961]
RJ506.L4M85   1986   618.92'89   86-2323
ISBN 0-933716-62-1 (pbk.)

Contents

Contributors

~

Anthony Bashir, Ph.D.
Hearing and Speech Division
The Children's Hospital Medical Center
300 Longwood Ave.
Boston, MA 02115

Timothy A. Cavell, M.S.
Doctoral Student in Clinical Psychology
Psychology Department
Louisiana State University
Baton Rouge, LA 70803

Michael J. Hannafin, Ph.D.
Associate Professor of Education
176 Chambers
The Pennsylvania State University
College of Education
University Park, PA 16802

Deborah Hayes, Ph.D.
Director
Department of Audiology and Speech
  Pathology
The Children's Hospital
1056 East 19th Avenue
Denver, CO 80218

Rebecca Ichord, M.D.
Assistant Professor of Child Health &
  Development
George Washington University Medical
  School
Assistant Director of Pediatric
  Residency Training
Children's Hospital, National Medical
  Center
Washington, DC 20010

James E. Joy, M.D.
Division of Behavioral Pediatrics
Phoenix Children's Hospital
Phoenix, AZ 85062

Michael E. Msall, M.D.
Robert Warner Rehabilitation Center
The Children's Hospital of Buffalo
936 Delaware Avenue
Buffalo, NY 14209

Trudi Norman-Murch, Ph.D.
Department of Speech Pathology
Good Samaritan Medical Center
1111 E. McDowell Road
Phoenix, AZ 85062

Peter Rosenberger, M.D.
Director, Learning Disorders Unit
Massachusetts General Hospital
Boston, MA 02114

**Margaret A. Short-DeGraff, Ph.D.,
  OTR/L**
Department of Education
Fellow at Center for Child Study
Skidmore College
Saratoga Springs, NY 12866

Joseph C. Witt, Ph.D.
Assistant Professor
Psychology Department
Louisiana State University
Baton Rouge, LA 70803

David L. Wodrich, Ph.D.
Division of Behavioral Pediatrics
Phoenix Children's Hospital
Phoenix, AZ 85062

Preface

$\sim$

When is it acceptable for a practitioner to proceed alone? When is a multidisciplinary effort required? With whom should one consult and under what conditions? All of us have, at one time or another, recognized that we need more and different information than our discipline's techniques and perspectives afford if we are to fully assess and plan for delayed learners. Yet, too often, we have been ignorant of the knowledge, techniques, and perspectives possessed by colleagues from other professions. We have not known when multidisciplinary collaboration was appropriate, nor have we known how to do it.

This book is designed to encourage and guide multidisciplinary assessment by providing the most essential information that one set of professionals needs to work with another: ways in which the training and background of one profession differ from another; descriptions of the assessment techniques peculiar to each profession; accounts of the logical, empirical, and research bases that substantiate the worth of those techniques; and descriptions of children with the types of problems each profession believes it should see for assessment. Possessing this information, diagnosticians from all disciplines can better coordinate assessment efforts and ultimately produce more effective treatment plans.

Children who are failing to learn or develop properly, whether categorized as having learning disabilities or mental retardation, are the focus of this book. Also included are those who fit neatly into neither category, but who are clearly deficient in the development of basic psychological skills such as language, perception, or cognition. For example, children with autism, hyperactivity, language and motor disorders, and family or emotional problems that prevent acceptable academic progress are discussed. Included as well are explanations of certain biomedical conditions, and their pathological processes, that are likely to cause delayed development.

The book contains ten chapters. The first defines mental retardation, learning disabilities, and the associated learning and developmental problems to be addressed in the text, and examines goals of the assessment process. The book's next eight chapters cover the various professionals who might be involved in the assessment process. Each of these chapters details professional training, diagnostic techniques, research and logical bases justifying the techniques used, and rules for making referrals to each discipline. The book's final chapter examines practical considerations in the multidisciplinary assessment of children, and contains illustrative cases to show how multidisciplinary collaboration might actually occur in clinical practice.

The primary aim of the book is to help the clinician, whether he or she is still in training or presently practicing. Accordingly, each chapter is written by an experienced practitioner and reflects issues most pertinent to clinicians, rather than primarily theoretical or research concerns. Where possible, we have included information deemed most helpful in the day-to-day practice of diagnosing children with delays; but we have, by necessity, left out some less critical, but perhaps useful, information. For instance, occupational therapy and physical therapy overlap to a considerable extent in that both involve the evaluation of physical and motor handicaps. Only occupational therapy was included here because individuals in this profession are more apt to identify learning and development problems, rather than more narrow physical conditions. Similarly, no ophthalmology or optometry chapter exists, not because these professions are unimportant, but because relatively few children receive assessment in these areas.

A book such as this cannot be completed without the assistance of many people. Thanks go to Melissa A. Behm, vice president at Brookes Publishing Company, for her initial interest and continuing support; and to Susan Hughes Gray, production editor at Brookes Publishing Company, for her conscientious and insightful work on the text. We would also like to thank our colleagues at Phoenix Children's Hospital, Dan Field and Tom DiBartolomeo, for their encouragement. Finally, the typing assistance we received from Margaret Frost and Joyce Bartels was indispensable in the completion of this project.

We dedicate our efforts
in this volume
to Susan and Judy.

Multidisciplinary Assessment of Children with Learning Disabilities and Mental Retardation

Chapter 1

The Terminology and Purposes of Assessment

~~~~~~~

David L. Wodrich

Few tasks are as intellectually demanding as discerning why a child is not developing properly or is failing to learn in school. This is so because children fail for an infinite variety of reasons and in an infinite variety of ways. Sometimes genetic coding is defective, resulting in the birth of a baby who is destined to be mentally retarded from the outset. Other children suffer central nervous system impairments at birth that jeopardize later development. Still others have medical conditions, such as epilepsy or hearing problems, that make school learning difficult. Many children have no identifiable physical or medical problems, but fail because they lack sufficient ability to compete in school or lack the unique combination of abilities to learn complex school tasks, such as reading. The individual diagnostician faces a formidable task in even the simplest case.

The complex nature of diagnostic cases is only one reason assessment is so difficult. The assessment process is further complicated because so many different disciplines are involved and because each is prone to use its own terminology, to view the purposes of assessment from its own perspectives, and to employ its own diagnostic techniques or procedures. Consider the issue of terminology. Mental retardation might connote one thing to a special educator, and something else to a pediatrician. Aphasia might convey considerable meaning to a speech-language pathologist, but mean little to a psychologist. A term such as glycogenosis bewilders nonmedical diagnosticians, while failure to acquire the "silent e rule" in reading and spelling is meaningful to those instructing children in school but to few others. Diagnosticians from the various disciplines must be able to share information with one another effectively if multidisciplinary assessment is to proceed; a commonly understood language system is a prerequisite for such sharing.

The varied educational, behavioral science, and medical professionals who assess children are trained in divergent ways, often absorbing very different traditions regarding diagnosis and assessment. Seldom is there unanimity about what assessment is to accomplish or in what the assessment process is to culminate. For instance, some medical professionals might confine their evaluation to a search for biological anomalies or disease states, with relatively little concern for the behavioral manifestations of the anomaly, such as the degree of intellectual impairment the child might have. In contrast, some behavioral scientists might be content to describe a child's current functional level and set of adaptive skills, but consider no biological causes for the child's delay. Diagnosing biomedical conditions is a legitimate goal of medicine, consistent with tradition and proven effective in the treatment of innumerable diseases. Detailed description of a child's behavioral repertoire, including precisely what the child can and cannot do, has proven effective as the first step in programming learners. Coordinated and comprehensive multidisciplinary assessment, however, is impossible until diagnosticians recognize their different perspectives and agree upon a common set of assessment goals.

Besides talking and thinking differently, each discipline's diagnosticians often act differently. That is, they use assessment techniques with which professionals in allied disciplines are unfamiliar or that they do not understand. A psychologist might use a mental test when evaluating a child in whom a neurologist had located a lesion using a CT (computerized tomography) scan. To integrate information fully, each professional must know something of the nature of the other's techniques. Knowledge of the capabilities and limitations of the diagnostic procedures and tools used by each discipline is an important factor in competent multidisciplinary assessment.

This book's goal is to facilitate effective multidisciplinary assessment. Toward that end, this first chapter begins by addressing the issues of common terminology and by defining the two central labels applied to learners who are delayed or disabled: mental retardation and learning disabilities. Other considerations related to terminology, specifically the relation of behavioral and descriptive labels to labels denoting biomedical conditions, are also examined. The chapter also discusses why assessment of students who have delays in learning need occur and outlines suggested goals of assessment that might be common to all diagnosticians, regardless of discipline. Subsequent chapters (Chapters 2–9) define additional, less general, terms and discuss the most important assessment techniques used by each discipline. The final chapter

(Chapter 10) presents a practical discussion about coordinating multidisciplinary assessment and several illustrative cases that reveal how such assessment can occur.

DEFINITION OF MENTAL RETARDATION

History and Background

Mental retardation has been present throughout human history, as Scheerenberger's (1983) detailed account on the topic shows, but understanding of its exact nature and diagnosis was slow to develop. Contemporary definitions of mental retardation continue to be influenced by thinking developed over a period of several hundred years. Three historical trends are most pertinent to the present discussion of definitions.

First, the concept of mental retardation arose out of a social need, originally the protection of property rights for the wealthy. According to the King's Act of 1324, individuals incapable of managing their own affairs could be designated "idiots," their property then going to trusteeship of the Crown until assumed by heirs (Scheerenberger, 1983). Incompetence in meeting life's demands was the first attribute that was noted in the history of the mental retardation concept.

Second, the King's Act also distinguished "idiocy" (assumed to be congenital and unremitting) from "lunacy" (assumed to be transient). Deficient mental ability came to be recognized as the characteristic that distinguished the two conditions. Mental ability thus required an assessment technique, prompting attempts at intelligence testing, such as the efforts of Sir Anthony Fitzherbert in 1534:

> and he who shall be said to be a sot and idiot from his birth, is such a person who cannot account or number twentypence, nor can tell who was his father or mother, nor how old he is, etc., so as it may appear that he hath no understanding of reason what shall be for his profit, nor what for his loss. But if he hath such understanding, that he know and understands his letters, and do read by teaching or information of another man, then it seemeth he is not a sot nor a natural idiot. (Scheerenberger, 1983, p. 36)

The diagnostic importance of limited mental ability was solidified by the scientific work on the measurement of intelligence by Alfred Binet in France at the turn of the century. Lack of general cognitive ability became recognized as a second element defining mental retardation.

Third, physicians, who historically were the ones most involved in assessing mental retardation, long assumed that the condition was caused by organic pathology but were consistently unable to locate objective markers distinctive to mental retardation. In 1838, the physician Esquirol spoke of "imperfect development . . . based upon structures visible at autopsy"

(Bialer, 1977, p. 71). By 1866, the physician Edouard Seguin included in his definition of mental retardation that idiocy is a "specific infirmity of the cranio-spinal axis, produced by deficiency of nutrition in utero or neo-nati" (Bialer, 1977, p. 71). Later diagnosticians (Jervis, 1960) continued to speak of physiological etiology when asserting that "mental deficiency" is caused "by disease or genetic constitution." It is now clear, though, that vague references to etiology which fail to provide actual observable signs are of no help to the clinician charged with identifying mental retardation.

Contemporary Definition

In the 19th and 20th centuries, numerous formal definitions evolved for reliably identifying the presence of mental retardation, most incorporating the points mentioned above: intellectual subnormality, and social incompetence, with little or no reliance on biological signs. In the United States, the most widely accepted definition comes from the American Association on Mental Deficiency (AAMD). Although alternative definitions are offered by other groups (e.g., American Psychiatric Association, *DSM-III*, 1980) or are incorporated into laws regulating services for children with handicaps, for practical purposes those definitions are equivalent to the AAMD definition listed below.

> Mental retardation refers to a significantly subaverage general intellectual functioning existing concurrently with deficits in adaptive behavior and manifested during the developmental period. (Grossman, 1983, p. 1)

An examination of each element of the definition is in order.

"Significantly subaverage general intellectual functioning" refers to scores on standard intelligence tests, such as the Wechsler Scales or Stanford-Binet Intelligence Scale, that are 70 or below (Grossman, 1983). While IQ values are not directly comparable among all tests because of statistical differences (some standard deviations equal 15, while others equal 16; Sattler, 1982), scores of 70 fall at or below the third percentile. Children scoring in this range are typically lacking in reasoning, problem-solving, and thinking skills to a degree that they are destined to fall behind children of the same age, either before or after entering school. It is this lack of cognitive ability that is the core handicap common to all individuals with mental retardation. The importance of intelligence tests in identifying children with mental retardation is discussed in Chapter 2.

"Deficits in adaptive behavior" refers to "significant limitations in an individual's effectiveness in meeting the standards of maturation, learning, personal independence, and/or social responsibility that are expected for his or her age level and cultural group, as determined by clinical assessment and, usually standardized scales" (Grossman, 1983, p. 11). Stated more simply, individuals with mental retardation fail to meet environmental demands adequately. In adults, who are expected to adapt to the world around them independently, deficits are noted relatively easily. In children, who are expected to be dependent even when developing normally, adaptive deficits are less obvious. Consequently, diagnosticians evaluate each child's adaptive competence compared to the developmental tasks normally expected for a child of that age. For instance, infants might be appraised for sensorimotor competence in crawling and walking, preschoolers for age-appropriate use of language in conversation and mastery of more complex motor tasks, such as dressing, and school-age children for academic proficiency and competence in increasingly complex life tasks such as telling time and managing money (Grossman, 1983). Objective, pencil-and-paper adaptive behavior inventories have been developed to aid the clinician in determining the presence of adaptive delays and in indexing their severity. Chapter 2 reviews the content, organization, and use of some of these instruments.

"Manifested during the developmental period" indicates that deficiencies must be noted at or before 18 years of age. This criterion limits the mental retardation designation to deficits arising during childhood and adolescence, thus excluding the consequences of neurological disease or post-traumatic states that have occurred later in life.

Severity of mental retardation can be summarized by broad level designation as seen in Table 1.1. Level designations are indexed behaviorally by degree of cognitive and adaptive impairment. These descriptions have some implications for programming. Mild mental retardation, for instance, generally denotes those persons thought to be capable of learning academics (in educational terms, "educable"), while those in lower ranges receive instruction in adaptive and life skills to the exclusion of basic academics (hence designated educationally as "trainable"). As one might suspect, classifications have some prognostic value. For instance, a typical child with "moderate" mental retardation might attain vocational competence in sheltered settings as an adult, while a child with "severe" mental retardation might acquire no vocational skills, instead developing only to the level of assisting in his or her own dressing and feeding (Grossman, 1983).

The AAMD definition offers much to clinicians because it specifies a set of replicable, standard procedures that produce objective results that either unequivocally meet or fail to meet the terms of the definition. If the child scores below the 70 IQ cutoff (assuming valid testing), has adaptive delays, and is younger than 18 years, he or she is classifiable as mentally retarded. If the child fails to meet any of the three conditions, he or she is not so classifiable. Although these explicit criteria have helped objectify the mental retardation construct, several sources of confusion remain that sometimes create problems among diagnosticians. Each warrants brief consideration.

Points of Confusion

First, both low intelligence test scores and accompanying adaptive delays must be present if mental retardation is to be diagnosed. Deficient intellectual ability, while recognized as a characteristic common to all individuals with

Table 1.1. Intelligence test scores and levels of mental retardation

Term	IQ range for level
Mild mental retardation	50–55 to approx. 70
Moderate mental retardation	35–40 to 50–55
Severe mental retardation	20–25 to 35–40
Profound mental retardation	Below 20 or 25

Adapted from Grossman (1983).

mental retardation, is by itself never sufficient to make the diagnosis. In the past, some children (especially those of ethnic minority groups) have been categorized as mentally retarded solely on the basis of IQ test scores. This has led to judicially imposed restraints on the use of intelligence tests and set aside the issue of whether labeling and placement are helpful or deleterious (*Larry P. v. Riles*, 1979). The independent use of intelligence tests is technically inconsistent with the definition of mental retardation; low IQ scores always must be buttressed by confirmation of self-care and social inadequacies. That is, children with mental retardation must appear socially/developmentally incapable when compared to standards of their own cultural and ethnic groups. Similarly, adaptive delays alone are insufficient to diagnose mental retardation. Some children have severe delays in dealing with the environment because of sensory or motor deficits, or because of emotional problems. If assessed as intellectually capable, such children are not mentally retarded. Figure 1.1 is a graphic representation of the relationship between IQ and adaptive skills when diagnosing mental retardation.

Second, the mental retardation definition is dependent solely on the individual's present behavior and concerns itself with neither etiology nor prognosis. Thus, individuals may be diagnosed as mentally retarded at one point and nonretarded at another, with each diagnosis being technically accurate. Belief that the individual possesses "potential," a not infrequent intuition among diagnosticians, is insufficient to avoid the mental retardation diagnosis if this potential is not manifested in actual test performance or day-to-day adaptive behavior.

Third, mental retardation cannot be diagnosed by the presence of physical signs alone. Thus, children with identifiable genetic anomalies, inborn errors of metabolism, documented brain damage, or a variety of other conditions that consistently cause mental retardation should be designated as mentally retarded only when the above criteria have been met in the standard assessment fashion. (The criteria are met only by the actual or attempted administration of standardized intelligence tests, which normally necessitates the involvement of a psychologist in the diagnosis, as is suggested in Chapter 2.)

Fourth, the definition avoids differentiating mental retardation from a variety of other childhood conditions, such as autism, childhood schizophrenia, brain damage, and language disorders. That is, a child may be simultaneously categorized as demonstrating any of the aforementioned conditions as well as mental retardation, should he or she meet the necessary criteria. In clinical practice it is common for youngsters with autism to have an accompanying diagnosis of mental retardation. In fact, the diagnostic and statistical manual (*DSM-III*) of the American Psychiatric Association (1980) notes that approximately 60% of children diagnosable as autistic are also mentally retarded.

Biomedical Classification: Values and Limitations

While the AAMD definition helps clinicians agree upon terms to describe the functioning of persons with mental retardation on a behavioral level, it should not obscure the fact that much is also known about the biomedical causes and correlates of mental retardation. The AAMD system allows classification on two levels: one that is behavioral and identifies the presence or absence of mental retardation and accompanying degree of disability, and a second that includes physical causes of mental retardation, such as trauma, metabolic errors, nutritional deficiencies, and chromosomal anomalies (some of which are discussed in Chapter 7). While an accurately diagnosed biomedical classification is of considerable importance, as is discussed later in this chapter, vague hypothesizing about causation has been criticized.

The clearest example of this vague hypothesizing occurs when clinicians attempt to differentiate "organic" from "familial" or "functional" retarda-

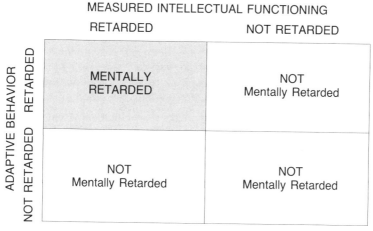

Figure 1.1.   Intellectual functioning and adaptive behavior. (From Grossman, H. J. [Ed.]. [1983]. *Classification in mental retardation* [p. 12]. Washington, DC: American Association on Mental Deficiency. Reproduced by permission.)

tion. Children with organic mental retardation are assumed to be handicapped as a result of brain pathology, even though, in many cases, conclusive evidence from a medical history or examination is lacking. These children are assumed to fall toward the severe end of the retardation continuum and to have the least capacity to profit from instruction because their brains are damaged or defective (Gordon, 1977). By contrast, children with "familial" or "functional" mental retardation are believed to be delayed because of limited inherited ability (their parents were limited intellectually and as offspring they inherited this characteristic) or because they were raised in impoverished environments (Gordon, 1977). Because this latter group is assumed to have undamaged brains, they are felt to possess more potential to profit from instruction than their "organic" counterparts (Gordon, 1977). This position has been attacked on several points, some of which are relevant to the upcoming discussion of learning disabilities as well as to the present topic.

First, Gordon (1977) notes that the anticipated agreement between significant brain injury and severe mental retardation has not been borne out. For example, postmortem examinations have shown that even significant neuropathology sometimes shows only mild (or even less) cognitive/adaptive impairment. Persons with mental retardation who are proven postmortem to have had brain damage, though they are more likely to have been severely intellectually impaired, were not categorically severely impaired. Proponents of the organic-familial distinction do not expect children with severe brain injury to have only mild intellectual impairments or children with no identifiable organic involvement to be severely handicapped, even though such cases do occur (Robinson & Robinson, 1976). These findings question whether present evidence is sufficient for clinicians to assume a one-to-one correspondence between severe intellectual impairment and brain injury among persons with mental retardation.

Second, Gordon points out that assignment of individuals to either organic or familial categories may simply reflect current scientific ignorance rather than genuine etiological differences. For example, until genetic and metabolic errors were fully understood and widely recognized, children so afflicted might well have been assumed to be nonorganic and were thus incorrectly categorized as familial or functional. Research likely will uncover additional "organic" causes of mental retardation, some of which may be manifested as mild retardation and follow family lines, and which now are possibly being miscategorized as familial.

Third, the conclusion that some children with mental retardation are "organic" is an invalid generalization, based on behavior assumed to be caused by brain injury, but not proven to be so. Influential research by Strauss (Strauss & Lehtinen, 1947) demonstrates that known brain injury (e.g., encephalitis) resulted in heightened incidence of certain behavior problems, most notably: disturbed visual-motor perceptual skills, emotional lability, and hyperactivity. It was subsequently reasoned that children who exhibited these symptoms were "organic," even when history and examination showed no conclusive evidence of neurological damage. Gordon and several others have pointed out the faulty logic on which this hypothesis is based. That is, evidence that some children are labile and hyperactive because of brain injury does not prove that all labile and hyperactive children are brain injured. In clinical practice, the observance of hyperactivity, emotional lability, and perceptual disturbances fails to prove organicity. Still, practitioners should expect to hear the description "organic" applied to such children and should recognize which behaviors the labels denote, even though nothing conclusive is said about the child's neurological status.

Fourth, recent conceptualizations have attacked the functional-organic dichotomy at its very core by questioning the viability of separating physical and environmental factors. For instance, research has shown that animals denied early stimulation have resultant physical, structural, and biochemical brain deficiencies as compared to animals raised in more stimulating environments (Rosenzweig, 1984). These animals subsequently performed more poorly than normally stimulated animals—a finding that presents classification problems for a system that assigns causation exclusively to either physical or environmental factors. Causation in this case cannot be neatly assigned to a deficient environment or to a neurological deficiency, which shows that the two categories are not mutually exclusive. With humans as well, environmental effects are reflected in neural changes at some level, in that the nervous system is the ultimate repository of habits, skills, and knowledge. Consequently, simplistic separations of functional from organic factors in humans may be similarly questioned.

Finally, and perhaps most important, beyond the ambiguity and lack of reliability of the distinctions, this categorization has been challenged as having little practical significance in planning. Ross (1974), for example, argues that a detailed analysis of the current behavioral repertoire of children with mental retardation (such as the behavioral assessment discussed in Chapter 2 or the task analysis detailed in Chapter 3) serves as a starting place for planning remediation. Knowing this, organic or familial/functional labels are largely inconsequential.

Without doubt, many children have mental retardation as a result of organic nervous system damage or impairment. When the exact nature of the causative biomedical condition is known, it should be specified, perhaps using systems that allow for simultaneous description of the degree of retardation (behavioral) and causative agents (biomedical), such as the AAMD system. But for the approximately 75% of cases with no known causative factor

(Grossman, 1983), it is not justifiable to assume familial/functional etiology. In these cases, a designation of "unknown etiology" is probably more justified.

In conclusion, although the term mental retardation is used throughout this book, it should be noted that this designation alone says little. The unique profile of cognitive, adaptive, and educational abilities as well as the biomedical status associated with each child is essential for intelligent planning and remediation.

DEFINITION OF LEARNING DISABILITIES

Mental retardation is characterized by interindividual differences: the child's skills are inferior across-the-board to age-peers. Learning disabilities, by contrast, are characterized by intraindividual differences: the child has problems such as perceptual, cognitive, or academic skill deficits, with overall intelligence presumably unaffected.

History and Background

Learning disabilities, because they affect nonacademic social competence little, if at all, and because their manifestations are so subtle that they are often unnoticed in any setting other than formal academic settings, have not been as apparent in human history as mental retardation. Not until late in the 19th century did clinical reports appear in the professional literature that described the inability in otherwise bright children to learn academics (Morgan, 1896). These early reports generally described extreme and atypical learning problems, such as virtually complete inability to read despite normal intelligence and regular instruction. Investigators in this era, most of whom were physicians, were influenced by reports of post-illness loss of previously acquired skills among adults. Reasoning by analogy, these thinkers hypothesized that similar focal lesions (or underdeveloped brain zones) must account for the pattern of uneven skill development seen in children. Specific sites of these lesions were often cited in the speculative works of this time (Shapiro, 1979). For example, Morgan (1896) suggested that underdevelopment of the angular gyrus produced the congenital "word blindness" observed in one of his patients, a rather perceptive hypothesis given contemporary speculation of the role of the angular gyrus in dyslexia (Hynd & Cohen, 1983).

While early clinical studies, generally conducted by physicians, were important in introducing the possibility that children can have unique learning problems (perhaps resulting from nervous system dysfunction), the notion took on special significance when embraced by educators. In the educational world, the concept of learning disabilities came of age. It was a special educator, Samuel Kirk, who first used the term "learning disabilities" to denote the problems of otherwise capable children who failed to learn in school because of intrinsic deficiencies (Kirk, 1962; Kirk & Kirk, 1983). The fact that the term has acquired such widespread recognition among the general public and such wide application in schools is telling of society's eagerness to accept the concept.

Learning disabilities gained prominence in the 1960s after special education was well entrenched in many schools in the form of special classes for students with mental retardation (Scheerenberger, 1983). These special classes for children with mental retardation promoted an implicit assumption that some learners were unsuitable for regular instruction. The idea of learning disabilities opened the door to the notion that pupils other than those with mental retardation required special education services. Confronted with the demand to educate all pupils to acceptable standards, schools found an appealing concept in learning disabilities: some nonretarded children were struggling because of inherent deficiencies in perceptual or cognitive skills. The educational system had not failed; instead, pupils incapable of learning with regular instruction were being recognized. That these children were difficult to identify (e.g., precise IQ cutoff scores and distinctive physical stigmata were unavailable) was not seen as a problem. A broad concept, or one with nebulous defining criteria, would provide services for a maximum number of children, while simultaneously absolving the school of instructional failure.

When federal legislation was passed to fund services for children with handicaps, including children with learning disabilities, many varied and often strongly held views were expressed. Some sought a broad definition with behavioral wording; others desired neurological terminology and insisted that the condition be assigned to brain dysfunction. The result was a compromise that, in fact, was similar to Kirk's original definition. It was widely criticized. For instance, McLeod's (1983) oblique reference to the committee's definition indicated it was "designed to appease every pressure group and offend none" (p. 23).

Contemporary Definition

The federally promoted definition of learning disability has subsequently become a standard, largely because it is used in school programs that depend on federal funding. The definition is as follows:

> "Specific learning disability" means a disorder in one or more of the basic psychological processes involved in understanding or in using language, spoken or written, which may manifest itself in an imperfect ability to listen, think, speak, read, write, spell, or do mathematical calculations. The term includes such conditions as perceptual handicaps, brain injury, minimal brain dysfunction, dyslexia, and developmental aphasia. The term does not include children who have learning problems which are primarily the result of visual, hearing, or motor handicaps, of mental retardation, or emotional disturbance, or of environmental, cultural, or economic disadvantage. (*Federal Register,* 1977)

Problems with the Federal Definition

First, the child with a learning disability suffers from a disorder of "basic psychological processes" related to written or spoken language. The requisite processes for language use, especially when the written form is included (i.e., reading and spelling) are many. Among those most frequently implicated as deficient are skills of: attention/concentration, memory, retrieval, language comprehension, language reasoning, language expression, visual perception, and visual-motor coordination. It is often these deficits in the processing of information for which diagnosticians search when conducting an assessment.

Researchers and mental test developers have sought to locate the most critical of these processing skills and to develop tests to examine each. For example, Kirk, McCarthy, and Kirk (1968) developed the Illinois Test of Psycholinguistic Abilities to locate auditory-vocal (language-related) or visual-motor (nonlanguage) abilities involved in receiving, reasoning with, or expressing information. Kaufman and Kaufman (1983) developed the Kaufman Assessment Battery for Children (K-ABC) to measure simultaneous and sequential processing skills, consistent with the research of neuropsychologist A. R. Luria and cognitive psychologist J. P. Das (Das, Kirby, & Jarman, 1979).

While tests such as these may ultimately lead to better assessment, the heavy emphasis on the measurement of processing skills causes some confusion. In some instances, clinicians assume that a relatively depressed score on a measure of processing explains why a child is not learning properly and is itself sufficient to label the child as having a learning disability. Clinicians must interpret mental tests with some degree of caution (partially because of reliability considerations; see Chapter 2) and must examine all of the definitional conditions before diagnosing learning disabilities, even when a child has a major processing problem.

Second, the learning disabilities definition calls for an "imperfect ability" to perform academic or academic-related skills such as adding or subtracting, reading, or listening. The federal guidelines accompanying the definition clarify "imperfect ability" by requiring a "severe discrepancy between achievement and intellectual ability" (*Federal Register,* 1977). Intelligence tests were to be used to establish expected levels of achievement. Thus, those with high IQs were assumed to be performing with "imperfect" academic skills if they were only slightly below grade level, while much greater academic problems were required for those with average or low average IQs to be considered performing "imperfectly." Some psychometric theorists have contended that this is too simple a solution to the problem of identifying underachievement and that existing intelligence and academic achievement tests are too similar in content to allow valid comparisons to be made (Das, 1983; Kaufman & Kaufman, 1983). Others have noted the lack of a uniform method for determining the degree of discrepancy between intelligence and achievement that is sufficient to meet the definition of "imperfect ability." On this latter point, a review of over a dozen formulae designed to determine the magnitude of ability-achievement differences concluded that each formula was deficient psychometrically or statistically, and thus the legal determination remained imprecise (Berk, 1984).

Third, the learning disabilities concept is designed to subsume a variety of other terms and conditions such as "minimal brain dysfunction" and "dyslexia." Unfortunately, the clinician is helped minimally by the inclusion of these terms. Consider a dyslexia definition as evidence of how little is added. The World Federation of Neurology's 1968 research group defined dyslexia as "a disorder manifested by difficulty in learning to read despite conventional instruction, adequate intelligence, and socio-cultural opportunity. It is dependent on fundamental cognitive disabilities which are frequently of constitutional origin" (Pirozzolo, 1979, p. 9). This specifies dyslexia as a reading learning disability, but accomplishes nothing to help the diagnostician determine whether the learning disability label should be applied to a specific child.

Linking learning disabilities with such a confusing notion as minimal brain dysfunction could be worse, in that such an arrangement might not only fail to clarify, but might confuse. While many writers, both medical and nonmedical, have questioned the utility of the minimal brain dysfunction concept, perhaps none has been so clear as psychiatrist Michael Rutter (1982). Rutter examines in detail, and challenges, two positions central to the minimal brain dysfunction concept. The first assertion that Rutter attacks is that minimal brain dysfunction is a lesser variant of major brain injury that is characterized by soft neurological signs (e.g., clumsiness, perceptual problems), rather than the hard neurological signs (e.g., abnormal EEG) that are associated with more severe neuropathology. Rutter contends that available research suggests that subclinical neurological damage (i.e., damage without hard signs such as impaired reflexes, abnormal EEG, or abnormal CT scan) occurs only rarely; when such damage occurs, it usually follows severe insult, is not capable of being reliably diagnosed from soft neurological signs, and does not produce a homogeneous syndrome. In Rutter's words, "The diagnosis of minimal brain dysfunction, at best, is just an uncertain hypothesis, which is usually not open to testing in the individual child and, at worst, creates a neuromythology, which provides a rather pretentious cloak to cover ignorance" (1982, p. 26). Rutter also investigates minimal brain dysfunction as a genetically determined, biochemically mediated syndrome that is characterized by hyperactivity, impulsivity, and attention deficits, but does not presume any brain "injury." He concludes that these symptoms are not exclusive to the minimal brain dysfunction syndrome, and that there is insufficient evidence to attribute this syndrome to biochemical abnormalities.

Speaking of hyperactivity, attention deficits, and learning problems, Rutter (1982) concludes that "it is both unhelpful and invalid to group them all together under the umbrella of minimal brain dysfunction" (p. 31). Symptoms that are referred to as "minimal brain dysfunction" or "organicity" are often encountered in clinical practice, but they offer little assistance in the identification of children with learning disabilities.

A fourth condition of the definition stipulates that the child's difficulties are not due to sensory, motor, cultural-environmental, or emotional factors. The intent is to limit learning disabilities to those conditions inherent in the child, problems resulting from improper functioning of the nervous system or immaturity of cognitive, memory, or perceptual skills requisite to school learning. Excluding children with major sensory or motor handicaps is fairly easily accomplished and is, indeed, logical. Children with hearing impairment have needs not necessarily met by learning disabilities programs. Similarly, children with cerebral palsy require special techniques and equipment not necessarily available in classes designed for academic remediation.

However, separating cultural-environmental and emotional factors from inherent deficits is difficult diagnostically and of questionable value programmatically. For instance, is a child from an impoverished home (i.e., one that contains no books or minimizes the merit of reading) failing to read because his or her environment is understimulating, or might the child have inherited cognitive characteristics (apart from low IQ) that destined failure regardless of environment? Inherent and acquired influences are hopelessly confounded in this case, as in most such cases, making assignment of singular causation impossible. While some psychometric instruments (Kaufman & Kaufman, 1983; Mercer, 1979) have created norms for various ethnic and socioeconomic groups, these tools are used primarily in mental retardation diagnosis and so provide little or no help for the clinician who is trying to control for cultural factors in learning disability determination. To make matters worse, experts disagree among themselves about the relevance of considering environmental-cultural factors. A survey by Tucker, Stevens, and Ysseldyke (1983) found that some leading experts in the United States thought that experiential influences should not even be considered as exclusionary criteria for learning disabilities.

Separating school failures attributable to emotional problems from those due to inherent learning problems is an equally troublesome challenge for the diagnostician, because these factors, too, are often hopelessly entwined. For instance, a child with short-term memory impairment may fail in school despite possessing adequate intelligence and would, accordingly, be diagnosable as learning disabled. Frustration attendant to these memory problems throughout the preschool years, however, might eventuate in poor self-esteem and lack of social skills so that the child would appear to be emotionally disturbed on his or her first day of kindergarten. Does this child have learning disabilities or emotional handicaps? Much like the dilemma of separating functional from organic factors in mental retardation, separating emotional from learning problems results in the clinician recognizing that these are not mutually exclusive categories.

A final criticism of the learning disabilities definition results from its exclusionary nature in regard to causation. After eliminating all feasible reasons for school failure (e.g., low IQ, sensory problems, cultural deprivation), an unwarranted assumption is made that something is defective in the child, that it is *the child* who is learning disabled. An alternative explanation, equally plausible critics contend, is that the educational process is defective (Cohen, 1971). That is, if a capable learner has been provided and failure results, then it is the school, rather than the child, that has failed. Consequently, Cohen (1971) has suggested that labels accusatory of the child, such as "dyslexia," be replaced by labels accusatory of the school, such as "dyspedogogia." As pointed out later, the notion of single causation of school failures, either attributable to the child or the school, provides little value in planning for the child's future. (In Chapter 2, Witt and Cavell outline situational factors that may contribute to poor pupil performance and, therefore, might result in the incorrect assumption that the child is learning disabled.)

Notwithstanding the imprecision and epistemological problems of some of its conditions, the PL 94-142 learning disabilities definition offers something to the clinician. Children with learning disabilities are understood to be nonretarded pupils who have not profited from regular instruction and who will require special education services. Recognition that a child fits the criteria for a learning disability label, however, only begins the assessment process, as seen later in this chapter.

MENTAL RETARDATION AND LEARNING DISABILITIES: RELATION TO DISEASE

Sometimes clinicians behave as if mental retardation and learning disabilities are disease entities, when, in fact, they are legal concepts having primarily administrative value (Heber, 1962). "Disease," according to *Dorland's Medical Dictionary,* implies a definite morbid process, usually with common etiology, course, or prognosis (Friel, 1974). Chicken pox, as an example, is caused by the introduction of a specific virus in a host lacking immunity. There is no other cause. The disease is recognized by physical signs (e.g., characteristic pox) that follow a predictable course. Its effects are understood at a molecular, immunological, and molar level. Chicken pox is, therefore, a disease.

Both mental retardation and learning disabilities lack the requisite characteristics of a disease. Each is caused by a multitude of factors, mental retardation alone having over 80 identifiable causes (Grossman, 1983). The course and prognosis for each child varies enormously within the respective diagnostic categories; in many cases, an understanding of the pathological processes is absent. The meanings of the mental retardation and learning disabilities concepts are fixed only by consensus among experts, as seen from the foregoing discussion.

OTHER DIAGNOSTIC LABELS

Mental retardation and learning disabilities are the most frequently used and the most all-encompassing of the diagnostic labels assigned to children. If only these labels were used, such that children with learning problems were designated either "mentally retarded," or "learning disabled," there would be less confusion. Diagnosticians seem especially confused when children are labeled with any of a variety of less familiar terms. The following discussion describes the types of additional labels that might be affixed during assessment, and attempts to show their relationship to mental retardation, learning disabilities, and to each other. In subsequent chapters, the various diagnostic professionals define other terms and amplify the brief definitions provided here. The importance of the present discussion lies in the types of terms used and how they interrelate.

Behavioral Labels

Both mental retardation and learning disabilities are descriptive terms. As noted previously, each of the conditions lacks a unique etiology, course, and prognosis and, hence, is defined only by its present manifestations. The terms simply describe the child's status, without explaining how he or she became affected. Besides the broad designations of mental retardation and learning disabilities, there exist additional, more specific behavioral labels of childhood disorders. The more global of these can generally be thought of as "behavioral syndromes" (i.e., several interrelated symptoms), the less global as simply isolated "symptoms" that lack the multisymptom aspect necessary for syndrome designation.

Severe expressive language problems might be thought of as a behavioral syndrome (see Chapter 5). Children so designated have certain features (or symptoms) in common: normal intelligence (as evidenced by nonverbal tests or tests of receptive language) and adequate understanding and use of language, but impaired formulation of ideas into coherent sentences, word-finding problems, and performance that becomes increasingly compromised in pressure situations. Frequently, these children encounter early reading problems. While some researchers note higher rates of this condition among children with known or suspected neurological involvement, such involvement has failed to be shown as the exclusive cause.

Much the same situation exists with autism. Once assumed to be an emotional problem, establishment of a clear set of diagnostic conditions (see

Table 1.2.   Diagnostic criteria for autism

1. Onset before 30 months of age
2. Pervasive lack of responsiveness to other people (autism)
3. Gross deficits in language development
4. If speech is present, peculiar speech patterns such as immediate and delayed echolalia, metaphorical language, pronominal reversal
5. Bizarre responses to various aspects of the environment (e.g., resistance to change, peculiar attachment to objects)
6. Absence of delusions, hallucinations, loosening of associations, etc.

Adapted from American Psychiatric Association (1980).

Table 1.2) coupled with empirical studies has shown the condition to be a developmental problem, hence its discussion in the present text. Research has shown autism to be a developmental phenomenon; that is, there is considerable concordance with mental retardation (American Psychiatric Association, 1980), the condition lacks a clear psychogenic etiology (Rutter, 1978), and is not an equivalent or variant of schizophrenia (Rutter, 1978). Autism is discussed in more detail in Chapter 8; its present relevance derives from the fact that it is a multisymptom syndrome identified by behavioral features.

The condition called ''attention deficit disorder'' is similar to autism in that many diagnosticians assume a neurological or biochemical basis for both, but clear evidence for such is lacking (Rutter, 1982). A set of behavioral criteria has been established to define the condition (American Psychiatric Association, 1980). Whether one conceptualizes the problem as a syndrome (many behaviors related and occurring together), or merely a significant behavior excess (heightened activity level) or a behavior deficit (insufficient attention), assessment remains important when examining potential causes for academic failure.

Clinicians are sometimes confused about how these relatively specific terms are related to the broader mental retardation and learning disabilities labels. Some behavioral syndromes are subsumed fully under these terms and are essentially subtypes. Severe expressive language deficit, as an example, implies an aspect of language functioning considerably poorer than overall ability and implies that the condition is not primarily attributable to emotional or cultural factors. Accordingly, the affected child could be identified as having both expressive language impairment and learning disability, the expressive language label merely indicating a specific subtype of learning disability.

Other behavioral syndromes are not subtypes of mental retardation or learning disabilities labels, but show a high rate of concordance with mental retardation or learning disabilities. For example, approximately 70% of children with autism are also diagnosable as having mental retardation (American Psychiatric Association, 1980). Similarly, a percentage of children diagnosed as having learning disabilities are also diagnosable as having attention deficit disorder, an appreciably higher percentage than is the case with a control group of non-learning disabled children (Safer & Allen, 1976). In both the autism–mental retardation and the attention deficit disorder–learning disabilities examples, however, concordance is insufficient to allow the clinician to presume the diagnosis of mental retardation or learning disabilities based only on the presence of the behavioral syndrome. To do so would result in an unacceptably high rate of misclassification. In all cases, children must be fully assessed so as to meet the definitional conditions for mental retardation or learning disabilities if such labels are applied.

Relatively isolated deficits or behavioral peculiarities are sometimes observed that are too narrow to constitute a syndrome. Diagnosticians, particularly those with medical backgrounds, frequently attach labels to these symptoms. The labels are medical (Latin or Greek) in form, though they denote observable behaviors. Examples are: tactile agnosia—"impaired ability to recognize familiar objects by touch," perseveration— "persistence of a previous response in spite of its lack of relation to the present situation," and monoplegia—"paralysis of one limb." Many of these symptoms have a heightened incidence among children with learning disabilities or mental retardation, but are not actual subtypes of mental retardation or learning disabilities. Some of the symptoms, especially when observed unequivocally in older children or adults, indicate organic brain injury requiring medical assessment. In young children, however, the symptoms are often difficult to interpret because developmental norms are imprecise. Confusion sometimes results because diagnosticians mistakenly assume that learning disabilities or mental retardation can be diagnosed by observing symptoms (e.g., perseveration, figure-ground confusion), and if several symptoms are present, then the label can be affixed without meeting the conditions of the definition.

Biomedical Conditions

Sometimes the underlying biological process or condition that caused failed development or disabled learning is understood and the child may be diagnosed medically. Clinicians must appreciate, however, that these biomedical labels (diagnoses) are qualitatively different from behavioral labels. Delineating the faulty biomedical condition explains to some degree how the child came to be affected, whereas the behavioral label only describes the child's current status. To treat behavioral and biomedical labels as identical confuses pathological processes with behavioral outcomes.

Some biomedical disorders are identifiable syndromes that cause mental retardation or learning disabilities. Others are physical diseases whose presence is likely to affect development or learning in school. In either case, it is often imperative that the disorder be assessed if appropriate plans and interventions are to occur.

Down syndrome is an example of a biomedical syndrome that causes mental retardation. This condition has specific etiology (trisomy 21, or, rarely, 14), pathological nervous system changes (e.g., smaller brain weight [Graham, 1983]), and a fairly specific course and prognosis (moderate to severe mental retardation [Graham, 1983]). Most of the biomedical syndromes presently diagnosable involve genetic defects or improper metabolism, and result in mental retardation more frequently than in learning disabilities (Robinson & Robinson, 1976). Their methods of causation and diagnosis are discussed fully in Chapter 7.

Seizure disorders are an example of medical conditions that can affect development. Seizures are of several types, ranging from easily recognized conditions that if severe enough can cause further neurological damage and impair subsequent development (Lombroso, 1974) to subtle dysfunctions that can interfere with attention and can mimic learning disabilities (O'Donohoe, 1979). Chapter 9 discusses seizure disorders and their diagnosis.

Summary

Classifications applied to children as part of the assessment process range from the broad labels of mental retardation and learning disabilities, to the narrower labels of behavioral syndromes and symptoms such as attention deficit disorder or perseveration, to the labels denoting biomedical conditions and disorders such as Down syndrome and seizures. Consensus among diagnosticians as to the meaning of each type of label facilitates communication and enhances assessment.

PURPOSES OF ASSESSMENT

Mutually understood language is one prerequisite for effective multidisciplinary assessment. Establishment of a common purpose for assessing is another. That assessment should somehow make a difference is essential; the process must be more than an intellectual exercise. What is the process of assessing children suspected of having learning or developmental delays intended to accomplish? Is the goal to arrive at a suitable label? If not, then what is the goal?

Assessment to Facilitate Remediation

Several writers (Reschley, 1980; Ross, 1974) have taken the extreme position that assessment is of value only if there is a direct transfer of assessment data to treatment plan. These writers contend that if assessment fails to culminate in a specific treatment plan, then it is without value. Moreover, because labels have negative social implications, they should be applied only when intervention with proven efficacy follows from their use (Reschley, 1980).

Assuming that successful treatment is the only goal of assessment, how much direction is attendant to the diagnostic labels of the types just discussed? The answer is, generally, little indeed. To say that a child has mental retardation or learning disabilities may imply that he or she requires special services, but does nothing to indicate the degree of intensity (resource program, self-contained classroom, special school, or residential facility). Nothing is specified about where remedial efforts should be focused (self-care skills of dressing and grooming, prevocational tasks of sorting and arranging, word attack skills, or memory rehearsal drills to facilitate reading comprehension), and a remedial method or technique is not indicated (physical prompting and modeling with immediate primary reinforcers, treatment with drugs, or remedial flashcard drills). Mental retardation and learning disabilities labels denote extremely heterogeneous problems and consequently offer little programming information.

Behavioral syndromes represent a more homogeneous grouping than the mental retardation or learning disabilities labels. Accordingly, diagnosticians might hope that similar needs and interventions are associated with each syndrome. To a limited extent this is the case, even though behavioral syndromes themselves are varied in nature. Children with autism, for example, present a wide array of self-care, social, and academic needs; noting the syndrome's presence does little to suggest precisely how to meet these needs. However, when autism is identified, diagnosticians can derive general planning direction, because they can predict the nature of problems that are likely to arise. For example, a 20-month-old child with autism is almost certain to show language difficulties ultimately, even if these are not yet recognizable. Intensive language services can begin as soon as possible, perhaps maximizing the child's prospect for later competence. Early identification of a behavioral syndrome such as autism does provide some intervention focus.

Likewise, children with severe expressive language deficits are sufficiently homogeneous to allow some degree of treatment prescription. For instance, each may be treated with drills in oral formulation and, perhaps, be taught to manage anxiety in speaking situations. However, individual cases vary so greatly in features evidenced, rate of improvement, and exact techniques that prove effective, that simply specification of a condition offers only general direction. For the most part, behavioral syndromes offer better hope of prescription than mental retardation or learning disabilities labels, but specifics of remediation are seldom derived from these diagnostic terms.

Biomedical syndromes and conditions, as mentioned previously, sometimes play etiological roles in delayed development that lend themselves to direct treatment. Phenylketonuria (PKU), as an example, is caused by inheritance of a specific genetic code, which follows an autosomal recessive pattern, and results in the body's inability to metabolize certain substances. If this condition is diagnosed, treatment consists of a modified diet so that toxic levels of unmetabolized substances do not accumulate and produce brain damage. Unfortunately, treatment is possible only with some disorders and tends to be biomedical in nature (e.g., dietary restriction for PKU, surgery for incipient hydrocephalus), designed to prevent or arrest undesirable behavioral expression of an underlying physiological problem. Seldom does such intervention preclude the need for training and education, the specifics of which do not follow from medical diagnosis. The importance of diagnosing treatable biomedical disorders, such as PKU, is such a primary goal of assessment as to be unchallenged. Should retardation already exist, however, additional information beyond a medical diagnosis is necessary if planning and remediation are to occur. The nature of this information is discussed later in this chapter.

Seizure disorders are a second example of biomedical conditions that must be diagnosed, even though the disorders lack a specific, singular etiology or homogeneous manifestation (O'Donohoe, 1979). Diagnosis is imperative because the conditions can produce behaviors that interfere with functioning in school and because the pathological seizure process often can be controlled medically. Should academic skills or developmental tasks persist once seizures are controlled, more specific assessment must occur so that training and education can proceed.

For many, if not most, of the biomedical syndromes that cause delayed development, the mechanism of causation is either not understood or is understood but is unalterable. No feasible medical remediation is available, and, more important, the particular behavioral and developmental characteristics of each affected child vary so greatly that the medical diagnosis itself offers nothing to the intervention effort.

Down syndrome is a case in point. The chromosomal anomaly underlying the condition is understood, but no corrective or ameliorative medical intervention exists. Affected children are characteristically cognitively retarded, but IQs may range from 20 to 70, with unique profiles of strength and weakness apparent in each child (Graham, 1983). Self-care competencies also vary, probably because of the unique life experiences, amount of and quality of special education, and severity of central nervous system impairment. Motivation, attention, and personality characteristics are similarly scattered (Baron, 1972). Fixing the cause of retardation as Down syndrome tells those charged with habilitating the child nothing about where to begin.

If delineating the handicapped learner's biomedical or behavior disorder in most cases fails to guide remediation, upon what is the assessment to focus? Beyond categorizing and labeling, assessment must collect specific information about learners that can provide the individuality of treatment necessary to develop training and education plans. The kinds of additional information that are sought and, consequently, the focus of assessment depend on the diagnostician's orientation toward education and training. Two broad approaches seem to prevail.

Behavior Analysis Approach   The behavior analysis approach contends that the primary goal of assessment is the precise delineation of a learner's current skills, which serves as a blueprint for determining the next academic or adaptive behaviors to be taught. Assessment provides a sufficiently detailed appraisal of academic and adaptive skills so that intervention can concentrate on modifying behaviors. Some proponents of this position contend that only the academic and adaptive behaviors require assessment and that behaviors believed to be incompatible with learning (e.g., impulsivity) are not to be addressed directly (Treiber & Lahey, 1983). Test-derived cognitive profiles are considered generally unimportant because they are too inferential and too imprecise to guide training (Ross, 1974).

For example, assessment reveals that a sixth grader has adequate oral reading scores, but poor comprehension. Without hypothesizing about the mental abilities that contribute to this skill deficit, a program of reading comprehension drills is outlined. Intelligence test scores, reports of superior nonlanguage to language functioning, and designations of learning disabilities have no impact on planning. Drills are designed to teach the deficient skill directly, and generally include a procedure to reinforce correct responses so as to provide feedback and enhance motivation. Observations that the youngster is inattentive or off-task do not receive specific programming, because the proponents of this approach, while noting that these associated behaviors are readily remedied by using conditioning techniques, believe that such improvements produce little positive impact on academics (Marholin & Steinman, 1977). If the child's reading comprehension improves to acceptable standards, the problem is considered to be alleviated, again without inferences about mental processes or speculation about causation.

In some instances, the desired behavior is totally absent from the learner's response repertoire, necessitating a detailed appraisal of prerequisite skills before determining where training is to begin. A youngster with mental retardation, for example, might lack handwashing skills. A survey of prerequisite behaviors shows that he cannot adjust hot and cold water faucets, cannot retrieve the soap from its tray, and fails to replace the towel on its holder. Training in this instance concentrates on essential precursor skills not yet acquired. Practice and reinforcement of the goal behavior of handwashing takes place only after the child masters each component skill. In cases such as this, assessment consists of extremely detailed behavior analyses (see Chapter 3).

Treiber and Lahey (1983) present data showing the efficacy of this approach with a variety of academic and nonacademic behaviors, though they point out a disconcerting lack of follow-up studies. Considering that alternative remedial approaches lack comparable empirical support, Treiber and Lahey advocate use of the behavioral method for all types of learning disorders. In practice, the exclusive use of the behavioral approach most often occurs with learners who have mental retardation. Clinicians concerned with learning disabilities tend to attribute academic failures to deficient information-processing skills and are therefore understandably reluctant to abstain from speculation about mental processes.

Modality Preference Approach In contrast to the indifference of the behavioral approach proponents to mental processing abilities, those who favor the modality preference approach hold assessment of these abilities to be indispensable to remediation (Strichart & Gottlieb, 1981). The goal of this approach is a detailed analysis of the learner's information-processing abilities so that a pattern of cognitive strengths and weaknesses (a "modality preference") can be discerned. Once a profile is determined, training efforts either avoid weaknesses and teach academics using the learner's stronger mode of learning, called "capitalization of strengths" (Cronbach & Snow, 1977) or "circumvention" (Hartlage & Telzrow, 1983), or they attempt to remedy weaknesses in the hope that rectified processing skills ultimately lead to more efficient academic learning (Kirk & Kirk, 1971). Operating from a neuropsychological perspective, Rourke, Bakker, Fisk, and Strang (1983) advocate an approach that strengthens or avoids deficits or does both when treating brain-impaired children.

For example, a failing reader is found to have poor auditory discrimination, short-term auditory memory, and confused syntax when speaking. However, she has good visual memory and excellent spatial/mechanical skills. This learner is said to show a preference for the visual-motor or nonlanguage mode of learning. Advocates of the modality preference approach then proceed by instructing in a way that capitalizes on strengths such as the "whole-word" or "look-say" reading method, a method thought to rely on visual-motor and spatial abilities (Jorm, 1979). Alternatively, remediation might provide auditory discrimination training and work on proper formulation of syntax, in the belief that enhanced processing skills will produce the aptitude necessary to learn reading.

To date, neither research that matches instruction to strengths nor that remedies information-processing weaknesses has produced consistently positive evidence of academic gains (Arter & Jenkins, 1977; Hammill & Larsen, 1974; Tarver & Dawson, 1978). However, much of this research has been criticized as depending on naive models of mental functioning, and when more sophisticated research-based neuropsychological and cognitive psychology models are employed, positive "capitalization of strengths" findings appear, as do some positive process-training findings (Brailsford, Snart, & Das, 1984; Hartlage & Telzrow, 1983). The importance for the present discussion is that the modality preference approach requires detailed analyses of mental abilities, including, in some cases, fairly specific processing skills.

Consequently, adherents of the modality preference approach view detailed measurement of mental abilities using psychometric instruments as a prime objective of assessment. The reader is referred to Chapter 2 for a discussion of some of these psychometric instruments.

Assessment to Facilitate Planning

Prescriptive treatment that teaches academics or important life skills and ultimately makes the child less handicapped is the foremost goal of assessment. Notwithstanding the preeminence of direct remediation, much can be accomplished by recognizing the child's condition and by planning intelligently for him or her in both the near and far term.

The labels of learning disabilities and mental retardation plus the behavioral and biomedical designations that provide little value in devising intervention strategies prove more helpful in anticipating the child's future course. Knowledge of the course of a disorder provides the cornerstone on which a logical plan for the future can be made.

Even the broad categorization of mental retardation, when properly affixed, even as early as infancy, allows for meaningful prediction. For instance, researchers have shown that significant delays before 18 months result in a high incidence of mental retardation in later childhood (Honzik, 1983). Similarly, those children designated as having mental retardation in the school years, especially moderate or severe retardation, are likely to continue to have special social, adaptive, and vocational needs as adults. Parents of preschoolers with mental retardation, armed with this information, may locate in school districts with favorable programs; parents of school-age children with mental retardation can begin searching for high school vocational programs for learners with handicaps, plan for the prospect of extended financial dependency, or consider appointment of a guardian should they not survive into their child's adult years. The same considerations of continued special education services are attendant to parents of children with learning disabilities, though there is somewhat less assurance of long-range academic disability and considerably less likelihood of adult vocational, financial, and social dependence (Schonhaut & Satz, 1983).

Behavioral syndromes, being more homogeneous than learning disabilities or mental retardation, generally offer even better planning utility. Children with expressive language deficits, for instance, may anticipate a need for continued language remediation, may expect to fare best in high school courses requiring little oral discussion, and, if bright enough, may attend college but probably not major in foreign languages. Children with autism can be expected to encounter lifelong problems. Those few with average ability can still be expected to have persistent social awkwardness and difficulty with interpersonal skills and vocational adjustment. They need to be directed toward life/vocational experiences with minimal demands for the use of sophisticated social skills and, generally, for the use of expressive language.

Biomedical conditions are sometimes manifested with more predictable outcomes than the behavioral conditions mentioned above. Children with Down syndrome, for instance, have IQs that decline with age, require special services throughout school, and often have a greatly increased incidence of cardiac problems (Graham, 1983; Robinson & Robinson, 1976).

Appropriate categorization of a learner with delays or disabilities may be invaluable in long-term planning, and the same is true in the short run. Knowing the characteristics and probable course of a learner with disabilities has tremendous value here as well, even when the core disability cannot be changed. This notion has been advanced in detail as the idea of environmental match or "goodness of fit" by Thomas and Chess (1977), as a way to maximize the adjustment of nonhandicapped children. The principles apply as well to those with special needs.

The central premise of the work of Thomas and Chess is that children differ on key traits (they enumerate nine personality-behavior characteristics, including activity level, adaptability, quality of mood, threshold of responsiveness, etc.). These traits are detectable early and continue to persist throughout childhood. Significant discrepancies between parental expectations and the child's characteristics lead to dissonance and increased prospects of the child manifesting behavior/emotional problems. Parental values and concerns that match inherent child traits lead to fewer problems—even though the child's characteristics may be viewed as difficult or undesirable.

Empirical studies have offered some support for this intuitively plausible notion. A longitudinal study found that children with difficult temperamental styles (those who react with strong emotions, adapt to change slowly, and have unpredictable sleep and eating habits) have a much higher chance of adjustment problems than children with easy styles (those who react with less intense emotions, adapt quickly, and have predictable biological habits). Significantly, however, parents who had traits compatible with their children, or who maintained equilibrium, modified their expectations, and avoided overreacting, ultimately had better adjusted children even when those children were temperamentally difficult. Environmental demands compatible with the child's characteristics seem to promote good adjustment.

Additional studies of children with mental retardation or brain injuries have concluded that a handicapping condition heightens the child's risk of adjustment problems by magnifying any incompatibility between the child's traits and parental values and expectations (Thomas & Chess, 1977). The authors contend that early detection of the temperaments of children with handicaps is imperative so that environmental modifications can produce an acceptable match. Whether one accepts a temperament-environment mismatch as a cause of adjustment problems is unimportant. What is important is the recognition that, logically and empirically, there is justification for identifying important learner characteristics and modifying the environment to match these characteristics in the hope that the child will adjust better and feel more subjective life satisfaction. This is true even when the disability is not able to be remedied.

If frustration is to be avoided, the environment needs to match not only the child's temperament, but also his or her cognitive abilities. A child who retains only the briefest verbal utterances and never follows directions involving more than three steps benefits enormously from an environment that keeps verbal statements succinct and limits directions to one step. The value of such planning, even though it involves no remediation, is so obvious that it sometimes escapes discussion. Yet one of the prime goals of assessment is to collect information about the child's skills and characteristics so that planning of the world around the child can occur. Toward this end, personality/emotional and cognitive data need to be secured as part of assessment.

Assessment to Inform Others

The final legitimate purpose for assessing is to provide information. Individuals and agencies involved in the child's life expect and deserve information about the child's status and condition, even if that information is negative, pessimistic, or unhelpful in the realm of planning and intervention. Child diagnosticians are approached with specific concerns: "Why can't this child read?" "Why is my son's language so delayed?" These concerns must be addressed. It would be the height of insensitivity and so ludicrous as to tax credibility to believe that a professional would say, "I think I know what is wrong with your son's language, but I don't want to talk about it because I have no plan to help him." There is an implicit but powerful recognition that the "significant others" in the child's life need as much information as possible.

Parents appreciate knowing that their child's language is at the second percentile, even if no clear etiological, prognostic, or intervention information is forthcoming. Similarly, parents are grateful if told that their child's reading problem is classifiable as a "reading learning disability" (setting aside the planning notion and focusing merely on description). Detailed explanations are better than simple labels. For example, a statement like the following might be made: "We believe Bobby does so poorly in class because he loses information from memory very quickly. We are unsure if this is a memory problem per se, or is related to difficulty concentrating. We have no plan to correct this problem at present, nor do we know what exactly will happen in the future." A diagnostician who fails to inform the child's significant others in a clear, comprehensive way is missing one important goal of assessment.

SUMMARY

This chapter defines two essential terms in the assessment of delayed and disabled learners: mental retardation and learning disabilities. Mental retardation is defined as general intellectual deficiency (IQs less than 70) and concomitant delays in adaptive behavior, noted before 18 years of age. The term learning disabilities refers to specific or circumscribed learning problems that are not due to emotional or experiential factors and prevent otherwise capable children from functioning normally, especially in school. Like mental retardation, learning disabilities is a general term used to describe the child's current status and does not explain etiology.

Besides the mental retardation and learning disabilities labels, diagnosticians sometimes describe children in less general terms by specifying syndromes or identifying individual problematic symptoms. Some syndromes are behavioral in nature, referring to only observable developmental delays or problems (e.g., expressive language problems, autism). Others are biomedical in nature and denote etiology or pathological process, such as Down syndrome or PKU, which are akin to diseases and are diagnosed medically.

The assessment process, however, requires more than simply assigning an appropriate diagnostic term. Diagnostic labels are valuable if they help with the broader goals of assessment: to formulate a remedial strategy, to predict the course of a problem so that planning can occur, or to inform concerned parties (such as parents) about the child's status or disorder. Besides labels or medical diagnoses, clinicians require detailed descriptions of the child's current complement of academic and adaptive skills, and, in many cases, an accounting of cognitive abilities, including a breakdown of information-processing skills, if they are to meet their information-dispensing, planning, and intervention purposes.

REFERENCES

American Psychiatric Association. (1980). *Diagnostic and statistical manual of mental disorders* (3rd ed.). Washington, DC: Author.

Arter, J. A., & Jenkins, J. R. (1977). Examining the benefits and prevalence of modality considerations in special education. *The Journal of Special Education, 11,* 281–298.

Baron, J. (1972). Temperament profile of children with Down's syndrome. *Developmental Medicine and Child Neurology, 14,* 640–643.

Berk, R. A. (1984). An evaluation of procedures for computing an ability-achievement discrepancy score. *Journal of Learning Disabilities, 17,* 262–266.

Bialer, I. (1977). Mental retardation as a diagnostic construct. In M. Sternlicht & I. Bialer (Eds.), *The psychology of mental retardation: Issues and approaches* (pp. 67–123). New York: Psychological Dimensions.

Brailsford, A., Snart, F., & Das, J. P. (1984). Strategy training and reading comprehension. *Journal of Learning Disabilities, 17,* 287–290.

Cohen, S. A. (1971). Dyspedogogia as a cause of reading retardation: Definition and treatment. In B. Bateman (Ed.), *Learning disorders: Vol. 4. Reading* (pp. 269–291). Seattle: Special Child Publications.

Cronbach, L. J., & Snow, R. E. (1977). *Aptitude and instructional methods.* New York: Irvington.

Das, J. P. (1983, August). *The essence of human intelligence.* Paper presented at the meeting of the American Psychological Association, Los Angeles, CA.

Das, J. P., Kirby, J. R., & Jarman, R. (1979). *Simultaneous and successive cognitive processes.* New York: Academic Press.

Federal Register. (1977, August 23). *42*(163).

Friel, J. P. (Ed.). (1974). *Dorland's illustrated medical dictionary* (26th ed.). Philadelphia: W. B. Saunders.

Gordon, J. E. (1977). Neuropsychology and mental retardation. In M. Steinlicht & I. Bialer (Eds.), *The psychology of mental retardation: Issues and approaches* (pp. 367–411). New York: Psychological Dimensions.

Graham, P. J. (1983). Specific medical syndromes. In M. Rutter (Ed.), *Developmental neuropsychiatry* (pp. 68–82). New York: Guilford Press.

Grossman, H. J. (Ed.). (1983). *Classification in mental retardation.* Washington, DC: American Association on Mental Deficiency.

Hammill, D. D., & Larsen, S. C. (1974). The effectiveness of psycholinguistic training. *Exceptional Children, 41,* 5–14.

Hartlage, L. C., & Telzrow, C. F. (1983). The neuropsychological basis of educational intervention. *Journal of Learning Disabilities, 16,* 521–528.

Heber, R. (1962). Mental retardation: Concept and classification. In E. P. Trapp & P. Himmelstein (Eds.), *Readings on the exceptional child: Research and theory.* New York: Appleton-Century-Crofts.

Honzik, M. P. (1983). Measuring mental abilities in infancy. In M. Lewis (Ed.), *Origins of intelligence: Infancy and early childhood* (2nd ed.) (pp. 67–105). New York: Plenum.

Hynd, G. W., & Cohen, M. (1983). *Dyslexia: Neuropsychological theory, research, and clinical differentiation.* New York: Grune & Stratton.

Jervis, G. A. (1960). Factors in mental retardation. In J. F. Magary & J. R. Einhorn (Eds.), *The exceptional child: A book of readings* (pp. 45–53). New York: Holt, Rinehart & Winston.

Jorm, A. F. (1979). The cognitive and neurological basis of developmental dyslexia: A theoretical framework and review. *Cognition, 7,* 19–33.

Kaufman, A. S., & Kaufman, N. L. (1983). *Kaufman Assessment Battery for Children* (K-ABC). Circle Pines, MN: American Guidance Service.

Kirk, S. A. (1962). *Educating exceptional children.* Boston: Houghton Mifflin.

Kirk, S. A., & Kirk, W. D. (1971). *Psycholinguistic learning and disabilities: Diagnosis and remediation.* Urbana: University of Illinois Press.

Kirk, S. A., & Kirk, W. D. (1983). On defining learning disabilities. *Journal of Learning Disabilities, 16,* 20–21.

Kirk, S. A., McCarthy, J. J., & Kirk, W. D. (1968). *Illinois Test of Psycholinguistic Abilities.* Urbana: University of Illinois Press.

Larry P. v. Riles, 495 F. Supp. 926 (N. D. Cal. 1979).

Lombroso, C. T. (1974). The treatment of status epilepticus. *Pediatrics, 53,* 536–540.

Marholin, D., & Steinman, W. M. (1977). Stimulus control in the classroom as a function of behavior reinforced. *Journal of Applied Behavior Analysis, 10,* 465–478.

McLeod, J. (1983). Learning disabilities is for educators. *Journal of Learning Disabilities, 16,* 23–24.

Mercer, J. R. (1979). *System of Multicultural Pluralistic Assessment, technical manual*. New York: Psychological Corporation.

Morgan, W. P. (1896). A case of congenital word blindness. *British Medical Journal, 2,* 1378.

O'Donohoe, N. (1979). *Epilepsies of childhood*. London: Butterworth.

Pirozzolo, F. J. (1979). *The neuropsychology of developmental reading disorders*. New York: Praeger.

Reschley, D. J. (1980). School psychologists and assessment in the future. *Professional Psychology, 11,* 841–848.

Robinson, N. M., & Robinson, H. B. (1976). *The mentally retarded child: A psychological approach* (2nd ed.). New York: McGraw-Hill.

Rosenzweig, M. R. (1984). Experience, memory, and the brain. *American Psychologist, 39,* 365–376.

Ross, A. O. (1974). A clinical child psychologist examines retarded children. In G. J. Williams & S. Gorden (Eds.), *Clinical child psychology: Current practices and future perspective* (pp. 67–79). New York: Behavioral Publications.

Rourke, B. P., Bakker, D. J., Fisk, J. L., & Strong, J. D. (1983). *Child neuropsychology: An introduction to theory, research and clinical practice*. New York: Guilford Press.

Rutter, M. (1978). Diagnosis and definition. In M. Rutter & E. Schopler (Eds.), *Autism: A reappraisal of concepts and treatment* (pp. 1–25). New York: Plenum.

Rutter, M. (1982). Syndromes attributed to "minimal brain dysfunction" in childhood. *American Journal of Psychiatry, 139,* 21–33.

Safer, D. J., & Allen, R. P. (1976). *Hyperactive children: Diagnosis and management*. Baltimore: University Park Press.

Sattler, J. M. (1982). *Assessment of children's intelligence and special abilities* (2nd ed.) Boston: Allyn & Bacon.

Scheerenberger, R. C. (1983). *A history of mental retardation*. Baltimore: Paul H. Brookes Publishing Co.

Schonhaut, S., & Satz, P. (1983). Prognosis for children with learning disabilities: A review of follow-up studies. In M. Rutter (Ed.), *Developmental neuropsychiatry* (pp. 542–563). New York: Guilford Press.

Shapiro, J. (1979). An historical overview of education and the learning-disabled child. In M. I. Gottlieb, P. W. Zinkus, & L. J. Bradford (Eds.), *Current issues in developmental pediatrics: The learning disabled child* (pp. 47–75). New York: Grune & Stratton.

Strauss, A., & Lehtinen, L. (1947). *Psychopathology and the education of the brain-injured child*. New York: Grune & Stratton.

Strichart, S. S., & Gottlieb, J. (1981). Learning disabilities at the crossroads. In J. Gottlieb & S. S. Strichart (Eds.), *Developmental theory and research in learning disabilities* (pp. 3–12). Baltimore: University Park Press.

Thomas, A., & Chess, S. (1977). *Temperament and development*. New York: Brunner/Mazel.

Traver, S. G., & Dawson, M. M. (1978). Modality preference and the teaching of reading: A review. *Journal of Learning Disabilities, 11,* 5–17.

Treiber, F. A., & Lahey, B. B. (1983). Toward a behavioral model of academic remediation with learning disabled children. *Journal of Learning Disabilities, 16,* 11–116.

Tucker, J., Stevens, L. J., & Ysseldyke, J. E. (1983). Learning disabilities: The experts speak out. *Journal of Learning Disabilities, 16,* 6–14.

Chapter 2

Psychological Assessment

~~~/

Joseph C. Witt and
Timothy A. Cavell

Over the past half century, the science of psychology has been applied with increasing frequency to a wide variety of human problems. Whether in schools, clinics, or hospitals, the activities of psychologists have expanded in both breadth and depth. This expansion has been nourished, encouraged, and facilitated by a strong research base documenting both diagnostic efficiency and intervention efficacy across a broad spectrum of applications. In addition, the clinical significance of input from psychologists has made them an integral component of many multidisciplinary teams.

Despite the risk of being perceived as presumptuous, the authors must state a bias at the outset: psychologists should be involved in most, if not all, decisions about children with deficits in perceptual, cognitive, or language processes. This bias is based on the supposition that deficits underlying these fundamental psychological processes can be understood better within the context of the multitude of complex factors that underlie these problems. The child with a language delay provides a good example. For such children, it is undesirable, if not impossible, to understand fully the nature of this language delay by focusing solely on language because many factors may contribute to the language problem. At one level, it is routine for such children to be evaluated by a psychologist to determine cognitive ability in order to examine the possibility that the language delay may have resulted from a general cognitive delay. At another level, psychologists may be in a unique position within a multidisciplinary arena to minimize the miscommunication and lack of synthesis that can result when several highly specialized disciplines contribute information to the resolution of a child's problem. Each specialty may use language that means little to other multidisciplinary team members. Utilizing information provided by a specialist can be difficult if the conceptual underpinnings are unclear. Because of their background and training, psychologists may have more overlap in their knowledge base with other specialists on the multidisciplinary team. This overlap may allow psychologists not only to contribute information to multidisciplinary decision-making but also to facilitate the process itself. Without a good process for interaction among specialists, individual contributions are not integrated and are often overlooked. Psychologists are in a relatively unique position to facilitate multidisciplinary communication and problem resolution because of the overlap they share with other disciplines.

Despite some overlap of expertise with other disciplines and some compatibility of language and jargon, obvious differences between psychology and other specialties still exist. The purpose of this chapter is to inform professionals within these disciplines of the possibilities and limitations of psychological assessment.

BACKGROUND AND TRAINING OF PSYCHOLOGISTS

For psychologists, the most typical model of training for practitioner specialties has come to be known as the "Boulder Model" (Raimy, 1950). The model derives its name from a conference held in 1949 in Boulder, Colorado, which advocated that psychologists be trained as scientist-practitioners. On the scientist dimension, the Boulder Conference advocated that psychologists be trained as knowledgeable contributors to and consumers of the research literature. It is perhaps surprising to applied practitioners in other disciplines how much coursework in experimental design, research methodology, and statistics each psychologist completes and the amount of independent research needed to fulfill the doctoral dissertation requirements. In addition, the scientific orientation to psychological practice implied an ongoing empirical evaluation by individual practitioners of assessment and treatment methods. The practitioner dimension of this model called for an adequate knowledge and experiential base in assessment, intervention, and consultation so that individuals possess the requisite skills for diagnosis and treatment of the problems they will face in everyday practice.

A major outcome of the Boulder Conference was the development of guidelines specifying the 4-year doctoral program as the optimal arrangement for the training of professional psychologists. Training programs for psychologists generally consist of educational experiences in the following areas: 1) coursework in the fundamental "core" areas of psychology, such as biological bases of behavior and individual differences; 2) coursework in research design, statistics, measurement, and evaluation; and 3) coursework and experience relative to a professional specialty, such as clinical, school, or medical psychology. Following a sequence of university-based courses and practical experiences, psychologists complete a 1-year internship in a setting similar to that in which they plan to work. For certain specialties within psychology, a year or more of postdoctoral experience and training may be necessary.

It should be mentioned that the training described above pertains to doctoral level psychologists. However, a number of psychologists employed in various settings have been trained at a subdoctoral level. Typically, psychologists at this level have received approximately 60 hours of graduate training in psychology. For the most part, the function of subdoctoral psychologists is to provide information (e.g., psychological testing) to doctoral level practitioners with whom major responsibility and decision-making rest. In most states, functioning as a school psychologist within an institutional setting does not require a doctoral degree. Nationally, a great deal of debate exists about whether subdoctoral psychologists should be allowed to practice, but these arguments are beyond the scope of this chapter. For most multidisciplinary settings, the issue is moot because licensure laws regulating psychologists generally specify that practitioners must have a doctoral degree (and sufficient supervised practice) or be supervised by an individual who has a doctoral degree.

LOGICAL AND EMPIRICAL FOUNDATIONS UNDERLYING PSYCHOLOGICAL ASSESSMENT METHODOLOGIES

How is the value of a psychological test determined? What standards can be applied to the evaluation of tests? How is it known if a test is suitable for the purposes for which it is being used? Psychologists have developed several criteria by which to evaluate psychological tests, most of which, not surprisingly, reflect the empirical, scientific orientation of their training. This section examines the most important of these criteria by discussing the most important logical foundations of psychological assessment.

Assessment Is a Problem-Solving Process

One of the most important, but perhaps least known, assumptions of psychological assessment is that it is part of a larger problem-solving process. As indicated in Chapter 1, assessment is never an end in itself. The existence of a problem implies that there is a discrepancy between what is desired in a particular situation and what is actually occurring. Psychological assessment is designed to provide clues about the best method for ameliorating the problem. Properly carried out, assessment is a dynamic synthesis and evaluation of multiple sources of data relevant to the problem being examined. For many of the problems described in this text, optimally, assessment should include a comprehensive evaluation of not only the child and the child's behaviors, but also the environment in which the child is functioning. The present book, however, primarily addresses handicapping conditions, that is, conditions associated with characteristics of the learner. Consequently, because of that focus and because of space limitations, assessment of environments is not discussed. Instead, the interested reader is referred to Reynolds, Gutkin, Elliott, and Witt (1984), Witt (in press), or Witt, Elliott, Gresham, and Kramer (in press) for a detailed discussion of this topic.

Often assessment and testing are considered to be synonymous. In actuality, testing is only part of the assessment process and is only one particular method, among many others (e.g., interviews, observations), for obtaining data. Although this chapter has a primary focus on testing, it should be kept in mind that testing is only one element of assessment and assessment is only one element of the problem-solving process. An examination of one problem-solving model illustrates this important distinction.

Bergan (1977) developed a 4-stage model of problem solving that might be used to remedy academic problems, one of the prime purposes of assessment. The stages of this model are:

1. Problem identification
2. Problem analysis
3. Plan implementation
4. Problem evaluation

The first step in Bergan's model is to achieve a clear, objective definition of the problem. After the problem is defined, the goal is to analyze the factors that influence the problem. After a comprehensive assessment of the problem and factors influencing it, a treatment or intervention is developed and implemented. Finally, after a suitable time period, the intervention plan is evaluated to determine the extent of the problem resolution and plan effectiveness.

Assessment data are vital to the problem-solving process because Stages 1, 2, and 4 require the collection of data. Psychological tests of general ability, information-processing, academic achievement, and adaptive behavior, as this chapter shows, are often the most useful source of data to account for why a learning or development problem exists and to index its severity. Such data, when used as part of a problem-solving approach, accomplish the most important feature of Bergan's model: that assessment be linked to intervention. In other words, a comprehensive assessment should result in an intervention or plan to resolve the problem.

Assessment Data Should Be Objective

Assessment practices within psychology, paralleling the scientific method, have tended to emphasize the systematic collection of objective and verifiable data. This emphasis on objectivity has produced a preference for collecting assessment data with three important characteristics.

First, data should be quantifiable or potentially quantifiable. Thus, psychologists, in designing tests, search for ways to translate information about cognitive, social, behavioral, and perceptual functioning into numbers. For example, among many psychologists there is an obvious preference for saying that Sarah obtained a score of 125 on a test of anxiety (and saying what that means) over saying only that Sarah is "moderately anxious," leaving the meaning of the statement open to interpretation.

A second means for increasing objectivity is to link assessment data to external, usually quantifiable, criteria. Most frequently these criteria consist of a set of "norms" whereby the scores from a representative group of individuals are available for comparison. By using norms, one can say that Sarah is more hyperactive than 85% of children her age rather than say that Sarah is "very hyperactive."

A third element of objectivity is the degree to which assessment data are related to observable, and therefore verifiable, events. It is preferable to say, for example, that during a 10-minute observation interval, Sarah was out of her seat 14 times without permission rather than say only that Sarah is hyperactive. Any two individuals can easily be trained to agree on the number of times a child is out of her seat, but as researchers have repeatedly demonstrated, years of training may not result in any two people agreeing upon whether a child should be diagnosed as hyperactive (Witt et al., in press). In that sense, counting out-of-seat behavior is much more objective than diagnosing hyperactivity through clinical judgment. This is not to diminish the importance of clinical judgment for that will always be necessary (e.g., How many out-of-seat behaviors are needed before that behavior becomes a problem?). The point is to emphasize a preference for observable data.

When the three elements constituting objectivity are combined it becomes more obvious where psychological assessment strives to be on a continuum ranging from very objective to very subjective data. In examining the somewhat nebulous concept of motivation, for example, it is clear that psychologists are most comfortable with information that is quantified and tied to a particular norm group. For example, psychologists might quantify by using a pencil-and-paper measure of motivation that asks children to indicate whether a particular statement applies to them (e.g., "I take a lot of pride in doing a good job"). Children's scores can be transformed so that statements can be made about the degree to which a student is intrinsically motivated. Some psychologists may take this a step further and require that the data come from an observable, verifiable behavior measure. To evaluate motivation, and meet all three criteria, might require placing a child in a structured observational setting, presenting a prescribed series of tasks with specified directions and reinforcements, and simply counting the number of tasks completed. This number can then be compared to those from a normative group who performed under the same circumstances. This comparison allows one not only to state whether the child was motivated relative to other children but also under what specific conditions the child was motivated. Increases in objectivity often require a large amount of time and resources, and psychologists must evaluate whether this increase in precision is necessary. For some types of decisions, the subjective impression of someone who knows the child may suffice. For important decisions, the level of precision and objectivity should be increased.

Assessment Data Should Be Reliable

One of the most fundamental of all the assumptions underlying psychological assessment is that data should have a high degree of reliability. Reliability refers to the accuracy and precision of the measurement procedure (i.e., any given piece of assessment data should be consistent and reproducible). For example, if one weighs oneself on a bathroom scale three different times in a 15-second period and obtains readings of 140, 160, and 150, one has to question the reliability of the scale. Similarly, a psychological test is said to be reliable to the extent that the same score is obtained when testing the same person under similar circumstances.

For any individual, a test score can be divided into two parts. The first part, one hopes the major part, is called the hypothetical *true score*. On a test of mathematics, for example, a person's hypothetical true score represents his or her actual knowledge of mathematics. The score is hypothetical because there is really no way one can determine another's true knowledge of mathematics. The other part of an individual's score, the *error score,* is always present to some degree and prevents one from ever knowing a person's true score. The error score consists of all the factors, independent of a person's true score, that can cause scores to fluctuate. On a mathematics test, guessing, fatigue, and test anxiety can result in changes in a person's true score. Theoretically, to know a person's true score is impossible because every score obtained in assessing a child contains some degree of error. Even the best test may over- or underestimate a child's true ability.

This is an important piece of information if clinical decisions such as educational placement are being made on the basis of the obtained score. For example, in many states one component in labeling a child as mentally retarded is an IQ score of 69 or below. What if a child scores 69? Given that there is some degree of error in the test score, caution must be exercised in making the decision to label the child as retarded. Certainly error can work in a child's favor, in that his or her true IQ might be only 63. However, if the error worked against the child, the true IQ may be closer to 75. When problem-solving about a child's diagnosis, factors such as illness or motivation that could have affected test performance (i.e., inflated or deflated the error component) should be a topic for discussion. Test scores are not unalterable facts but are subject to a variety of factors that can make them unreliable. Recognizing the role that tests play in important life decisions, psychologists (through the American Psychological Association and other groups) have established standards requiring test publishers to report quantifiable indices of reliability and to describe the confidence intervals (number of score points plus or minus in which the true score is likely to fall; e.g., 69 ± 5) associated with their tests.

In some multidisciplinary settings, one must remain continually aware of the reliability of not only the components of the assessment process (e.g., individual tests) but of the reliability of the process itself. For example, in some settings it is customary to bring in a child for an entire day or two for a series of evaluations by a variety of specialists. Since assessment is conducted by strangers in an environment to which the child is unaccustomed, one might reasonably question the reliability of the assessment. Presumably, however, the test has been standardized under approximately the same conditions as it is being used. At any rate, the prudent specialist attempts to verify some of the inferences derived from this assessment data with independent sources of information.

Assessment Data Should Be Valid

As previously mentioned, reliability refers to how consistently and accurately a test measures something. Validity is the extent to which the test fulfills the function for which it is being used. That is, a test is valid if it measures what it is supposed to measure. Validity is, without question, the sine qua non of psychological tests. The validity of a test is dependent on yet separate from its reliability. Reliability is a necessary, but not sufficient, condition for validity: a test must be measuring a trait or a skill consistently to be considered a valid measure of what is being assessed. A test with high reliability, however, might not be a valid test. Reaction time, for example, can be measured very reliably but it may not be a valid measure of intelligence.

Cronbach (1970) asserts that the general question, "Is this test valid?" should not be asked, but instead, the question should be rephrased: "Is this a valid test for the purpose for which it is intended?" It is useful to consider Cronbach's assertion with respect to the different types of validity. Three of the most common types are content validity, criterion-related validity, and construct validity.

Content Validity   A test is said to have content validity to the extent that its content is an adequate sample of the attribute or trait being assessed. Content validity is established during test construction and is enhanced by selecting items that are representative of a specific skill or ability domain. If a test contains too few items, if important aspects of the domain being sampled are omitted, or if a test contains irrelevant subject matter, content validity suffers.

One would expect to be able to use the name of the test as a guide in selecting an instrument that is valid for one's purposes. The name of the test, however, is not always a good predictor of what the test actually measures. This problem can be illustrated by reference to the jingle fallacy, the jangle fallacy, and the jungle fallacy (Kelly, 1927; Messick, 1983). Test users fall victim to the jingle fallacy when they assume two tests with the same name are measuring similar traits or attributes. A case in point is the Illinois Test of Psycholinguistic Abilities (ITPA) (Kirk, McCarthy, & Kirk, 1968) which, because of its name, is assumed to measure something called psycholinguistic abilities or, more simply, language functioning. Nothing could be farther from the truth as John B. Carroll (1972) points out in his analysis of the ITPA:

> It requires some stretching of the meaning to call the ITPA a measure of "psycholinguistic abilities." The title is a misnomer, and users should be cautioned to look carefully at the true nature of the test, which might less misleadingly have been named the "Illinois Diagnostic Test of Cognitive Functioning." From the present title, a potential user might feel justified in expecting it to cover such language skills as reading, writing, and spelling. Actually, tests of these skills were deliberately excluded. (p. 442)

A companion to the jingle fallacy is the jangle fallacy which causes test consumers to assume incorrectly that two tests with different names are measuring different things. For example, close examination of the Devereux Child Behavior Rating Scale, which purports to be a measure of child behavior, and the Inferred Self-Concept Scale, which naturally enough is supposed to reflect self-concept, illustrates the jangle fallacy. Both instruments request that someone familiar with the child rate the child's behavior. In addition, both instruments contain a checklist of behaviors that the rater is to check if the behaviors apply to the child being evaluated. Even though they have different names, their content is very similar. The Inferred Self-Concept Scale appears to be more a measure of overt behavior than of self-concept.

The jungle fallacy is one to which many test developers fall victim. In the jungle fallacy, two tests that are supposed to measure different things are found to be highly correlated with each other (i.e., in the statistical sense). The correlation is taken as evidence that the two tests are measuring the same thing. The fallacy lies in not making the distinction between what is being measured and what the instruments are used to measure. Even though a test of creativity and a test of intelligence correlate highly, this should not be taken as evidence that they are both measuring intelligence or that they are both measuring creativity. Although either of these possibilities may be true, a third explanation is that both tests are measuring still another construct. For example, the two tests each may require the reading of lengthy questions and therefore may be measuring reading comprehension as much as anything else (i.e., the only people who do well on both tests are those who can read and comprehend very well). It would, therefore, be inaccurate to assume that a high correlation between the two tests is indicative of the two tests measuring the same thing. The jungle fallacy reminds one to draw a distinction between the test, the name of the test, and what the test is supposed to measure.

Criterion-Related Validity   A test is assumed to have criterion-related validity if it correlates highly with some other measure, usually some future or concurrent criterion. For example, it is important that tests given to medical school applicants be correlated with the criterion of "success in medical school" because predicting such success is the reason for giving the test. The criterion validity of such a test can be assessed by correlating the test scores of applicants for medical school with these same students' actual grades in medical school a year or two later.

Most intelligence tests are designed to have good criterion-related validity. With intelligence tests given to children, the most frequent goal or criterion is to predict success in school. Jensen (1980) reports correlations in the range of .50 to .70 between intelligence tests and school achievement.

In some cases, a more valid criterion measure is available at the time a particular test is taken, but administering the test is more efficient than measuring the criterion behavior directly. Furthermore, the criterion that is being predicted is often not available at the time a test is given; it is only available in the future. The Peabody Picture Vocabulary Test (PPVT) is sometimes administered as a screening device for purposes of determining intellectual functioning. Although the PPVT is not nearly as valid for this purpose as are other measures, such as the Wechsler Intelligence Scale for Children–Revised (WISC-R), its use is much more efficient in terms of time and cost. Depending upon the results of the PPVT, further testing with more elaborate measures may be warranted. The PPVT is an example of a test in which the criterion (i.e., a child's actual performance on a real intelligence test) is present at the time the test is given.

To what extent are tests capable of predicting future behavior? There are instances in which a very capable individual is misdiagnosed by a test and told he or she will never be a success in school. Accurate prediction of a future criterion continues to be one of the most problematic areas within test development, although empirically validated tests often substantially improve prediction when compared to clinical estimates based on little or no data.

Construct Validity   For a test to have construct validity it must be capable of measuring a hypothetical trait or construct. Tests are designed for measuring a number of such constructs including intelligence, motivation, anxiety, and self-concept. These traits or constructs are referred to as hypothetical because they do not represent observable behaviors. Intelligence, for example, is not something that can be seen or measured directly.

In assessing whether a test has construct validity, one must rely on the theory behind the construct. For example, psychological research has demonstrated repeatedly a curvilinear relation between anxiety and scores achieved by college students on exams. People with moderate levels of anxiety perform best on tests, people with extremely low levels of anxiety apparently are not motivated enough to perform well, and high levels of anxiety can interfere with test performance. New tests purporting to measure test anxiety can be employed similarly to determine whether this highly durable relation holds for them. Individuals with high, medium, and low levels of anxiety should perform in very prescribed ways on exams.

A major problem with a test lacking construct validity is that it may not be measuring the underlying trait. The PPVT, for example, yields an IQ score. Since the test only measures receptive vocabulary, it would not be surprising if a person who scored high on the PPVT did not perform in school in exactly the same way as a person with a high level of intelligence, as measured through a variety of tasks, is supposed to perform. This is because the construct of intelligence is being measured inadequately in the PPVT.

Norm-Referencing

In addition to objectivity, reliability, and validity, a fourth major foundation underlying psychological assessment practices is norm-referencing. The practice of norm-referencing involves the comparison of a score obtained for a particular child with some representative sample of children. Typically, this process yields a percentile, standardized score, grade-equivalent score, or other score that provides information pertaining to where the child stands relative to other children. Test manuals often facilitate test interpretation by providing a set of norms for use in comparing an individual's scores with a representative sample of people.

A good normative sample should meet two primary criteria. First, the sample should be reasonably comparable to the individuals being tested. This comparability or representativeness of the sample can be inferred by noting the number of people included from certain categories such as: sex, age, community size, geographic location, ethnic group, primary language, and socioeconomic status. Certainly, the manner in which a test of learning abilities is interpreted is affected if the norm group only consisted of "normal" children or only of children with learning disabilities.

In addition to being representative, the normative sample must also be recent. The decline in college board examination scores over the last decade provides an example of why it is necessary to update norms constantly. Changes in the population, due to, for example, more television watching and changes in school curricula, require that norms for all tests be updated regularly.

What are the consequences of using a test even if the normative sample is poorly constructed? Is using a bad test better than making decisions without any test information? As Salvia and Ysseldyke (1981) suggest, the answer is a resounding *no:*

> It is occasionally argued that inadequate norms are better than no norms at all. This argument is analogous to the argument that even a broken clock is correct twice a day. With 86,400 seconds in a day, remarking that a clock is right twice a day is an overly optimistic way of saying that the clock is wrong 99.99 percent of the time. Inadequate norms do not allow meaningful and accurate inferences about the population. If poor norms are used, misinterpretation follows. (p. 122)

A brief comment about psychologists' commitment to the previously mentioned factors of objectivity, reliability, validity, and norm-references is in order before proceeding to a discussion of specific assessment techniques. Test instruments are described among the techniques of occupational therapists, speech pathologists, special educators, and pediatricians in later chapters of this book. Nothing inherent in the use of standardized tests precludes their use by any professional group. However, all instruments should be evaluated by the same standards for reliability, validity, objectivity, and norm-referencing; and all professionals, regardless of discipline, require the same grounding in statistics and the logic of measurement in order to derive accurate results from testing. Because of psychology's empirical tradition and its role in test development, psychologists have long been seen as the testing experts. Whether that remains the case is unclear.

PSYCHOLOGISTS' ASSESSMENT TECHNIQUES

An enormous array of assessment methods has been developed to assist in the psychological evaluation of children. These methods range from the type that are highly formal with a great deal of research and development behind them (generally used by psychologists for important decisions) to the type that are informal and are developed on-the-spot by individual psychologists trying to understand a specific child. In this section, some of the best known and most frequently used assessment methods are described. Although tests are focused on almost exclusively, the use of tests represents only one aspect of the assessment part of the problem-solving process.

Assessment of Ability and Skill Deficits

Children who fail to learn in school are often referred to psychologists who may broadly classify failure as due to: 1) ability or skill deficits or 2) performance deficits. Children with an ability or skill deficit have not acquired, or cannot acquire, the academic skills being taught in school. On the other hand, children with performance deficits have already acquired a particular skill but because of behavioral, emotional, motivational, or social reasons do not display the skill. Thus, a 6-year-old with mental retardation who has not learned to write has a skill deficit with respect to printing the alphabet. Another child who has clearly learned to write the alphabet but chooses to play and do other things when requested to print the letters has a performance deficit. During the course of evaluations, psychologists typically include assessment of both skill and performance deficits, although many professionals incorrectly identify psychologists solely with ability (especially intellectual ability) assessment. This section reviews the most common methods of assessing skill or ability deficits, and the subsequent section discusses psychologists' roles in assessing performance deficits.

Intellectual Ability Measures   Probably the most common domain of assessment when evaluating children who are exhibiting learning problems is that of intellectual ability. The assessment of ability is premised on the supposition that it is necessary to know whether a child has the capacity to learn what is being expected of him or her. The goal is to ascertain the extent to which a child is capable of learning.

The assessment of intellectual ability is an essential element in the assessment of mental retardation, learning disabilities, and other disorders encountered within a multidisciplinary setting. As mentioned in Chapter 1, a major component of the diagnosis of mental retardation is a child's score on an intelligence test. In the diagnosis of learning disabilities, there is usually a need to establish a discrepancy between ability and achievement. Almost invariably an intelligence test is used as the measure of ability.

The practice of using intelligence tests to measure learning ability is so common among psychologists that the terms intelligence and learning ability are used almost interchangeably. But what is intelligence? The mere asking of this question implies correctly that no one answer exists. The problem, as noted earlier in this chapter, is that intelligence is a hypothetical construct. Unlike mathematics, reading, or other content areas, intelligence does not consist of a fixed compilation of facts or activities. Instead, it is typically considered to be a more global entity that affects functioning in many areas. Ideally, there would be an exact definition of intelligence and from that one could develop a test or series of tests that would measure it with a high degree of reliability and validity. Currently, a number of "intelligence" tests measure *something* with high reliability and validity; whether that something is intelligence is not known. The following sections briefly describe the most common approaches to the assessment of intelligence, with an overview of the most common exemplar within each approach.

General Intelligence Tests   In discussing the history of intelligence testing, Witt et al., (in press) point out that the first intelligence tests were devised by collecting groups of tasks thought or shown to reflect intellectual ability. Without question, the pioneering effort in this regard was the development of what is now called the Stanford-Binet Intelligence Scale. The current test can trace its origins to turn-of-the-century France when Alfred Binet became interested in complex mental processes. At the request of the Minister of Public Instruction, Binet, a French psychologist, developed a test that would assist schools in determining which students could not achieve in the regular classroom. Binet (along with Theodore Simon) published this test in 1905. The Binet-Simon Scale, revised in 1908, systematized the measurement of intelligence and formalized the concept of mental age. Louis Terman extended and revised the scale in 1916; because the work was completed at Stanford University, the scale was then called the Stanford-Binet. After using the test with large numbers of children, Binet was able to predict with great accuracy which individual tasks a normal child of a specific age could and could not accomplish successfully. He then ranked the tasks or items in order of difficulty and grouped them according to age levels.

For "normal" children, testing is initiated just below a child's age level. Children who fail at that level are given the next lowest level, and so on, until all of the tests (usually about six) at a given age level are passed. This level is called the person's basal age. After the basal is established, testing resumes until all of the tests at a given age level are failed. A person's mental age is established by giving credit for the basal age and for all tests passed beyond that point. A child who scores as well as the average 6-year-old has a mental age of 6 years.

Originally, the Intelligence Quotient (IQ) was determined by dividing mental age by chronological age and multiplying by 100. Thus, for a 6-year-old child who obtained a mental age of 6 years, the IQ would be 100—which is the average IQ. Similarly, a 5-year-old child who achieved a mental age of 8 years would have an IQ of 160. Because calculating IQ in this manner has some undesirable statistical side effects (see Sattler, 1982), the 1960 revision of the Stanford-Binet has abandoned the method while still retaining the age-scale ordering of tasks.

The Stanford-Binet is referred to as a general test of intelligence because, unlike most other intelligence tests that contain subscales reflecting specific subareas of intellectual functioning, the Stanford-Binet represents one large *general* scale. The goal of the developers of the Binet was to include tasks that were most highly associated with the construct of intelligence without apparent concern for whether each task was inherently meaningful and interpretable by itself. Intelligence tests developed more recently were constructed not only to yield a global measure of intelligence, but to provide diagnostic information about major subcomponents of intellectual functioning. Because it is difficult or impossible to obtain such diagnostic information from the Binet, it has been used less frequently in recent years, except with young children and adults with mental retardation.

Aside from the fact that the Binet does not lend itself to ipsative interpretation (i.e., the evaluation of intraindividual differences), other major problems exist. First, the test is dated, having been modified and revised only slightly in more than 40 years. A related problem is a tendency toward racial, ethnic, and sexual stereotyping within test items. Finally, the test is heavily loaded with verbal items (i.e., those requiring language) and may unfairly penalize children from different cultures or those with learning disabilities. For these reasons, use of the Binet is becoming quite limited.

Intelligence Tests with Subtests The most commonly used intelligence tests are those composed of a number of individual subtests. In contrast to instruments such as the Stanford-Binet, these tests yield interpretable scores for each of the subtests. Compared to the single global score derived from the Binet, it is possible to obtain an estimation of a child's functioning in 10–12 specific areas such as vocabulary, reasoning, perceptual-motor skill, and memory. Because individual subtest scores can also be combined to estimate a person's global intelligence, intelligence tests with subtests have all of the advantages of the general intelligence test plus the benefit of ipsative interpretation.

The most widely used example of an individually administered intelligence test with subtests is the Wechsler Intelligence Scale for Children–Revised (WISC-R). David Wechsler, a clinical psychologist, developed the test in order to find tasks that measure various functions and that could be used across various age levels. Originally published in 1949, the test's content was revised in 1974 and a thorough norm revision also occurred at that time.

The test can be administered by a qualified examiner in 60–90 minutes. It is designed to provide a global measure of intelligence that "avoids singling out any ability, however esteemed (e.g., abstract reasoning), as crucial or overwhelmingly important" (Wechsler, 1974). The test comprises 12 subtests, 6 of which form the Verbal scale and 6 of which form the Performance scale, as outlined in Table 2.1.

Verbal and Performance subtests are administered in alternating order. Mazes and Digit Span are considered supplemental tests and are generally not included in the calculation of IQ scores. The instrument yields an IQ score for the Performance scale, the Verbal scale, and the total test (termed the Full Scale IQ). Each of the IQ scores has a mean of 100 and a standard deviation of 15. Figure 2.1 represents a sample cover sheet from the WISC-R. Note that raw scores from the child's performance on each of the individual subtests are converted into scaled scores that have an average value of 10. The conversion process is completed by consulting age norms in the test manual. The scaled scores have a mean of 10 and a standard deviation of approximately 3. These scaled scores can be used to examine strengths and weaknesses or they can be summed to yield the individual IQ scores.

From a technical perspective, the WISC-R is a sound instrument. The test is quite reliable and numerous empirical investigations attest to the validity of the instrument for a variety of purposes. In fact, the WISC-R is the standard by which all new children's intelligence tests are evaluated. Although revised and restandardized in 1974, its organization and content remain essentially unchanged from the original WISC, published in 1949. How-

Table 2.1. Individual subtests for the Wechsler Intelligence Scale for Children–Revised (WISC-R)

Verbal Scale

1. *Information.* 30 questions requiring general knowledge and simple statements of fact (example: Where is Brazil?).
2. *Similarities.* 17 pairs of words that require the child to explain how the 2 items are similar (example: How are a mirror and a window alike?).
3. *Arithmetic.* 18 orally presented (timed) problems to which children must respond verbally without the aid of pencil and paper (example: If apples are priced at 2 for 25 cents, then how many can you buy for $1.00?).
4. *Vocabulary.* 32 words presented orally and requiring oral definitions (example: What is a garage?).
5. *Comprehension.* 17 problem situations requiring practical problem-solving ability (example: What should you do if someone steals your bicycle?).
6. *Digit Span.* Orally presented sequences of numbers requiring oral repetition (example: Please listen carefully and then say the following numbers: 5–1–6–9.).

Performance Scale

1. *Picture Completion.* 26 drawings of common objects in which children are requested to find an important part that is missing.
2. *Picture Arrangement.* 12 picture series similar to cut-up comic strips that the child is requested to place in correct order so that they make a sensible story.
3. *Block Design.* Picture of an abstract geometric design that the child is asked to replicate by using red and white blocks.
4. *Object Assembly.* Similar to a jigsaw puzzle in that the child is asked to assemble a number of puzzle pieces to make a common object, person, or animal.
5. *Coding.* Requires the child to copy symbols (e.g., vertical lines, circles) that are matched to numbers.
6. *Mazes.* 8 mazes requiring the child to find the most direct route out.

---

ever, much has been learned about cognitive abilities since 1949 and if the WISC-R is to continue to be a leader in the field, it will need to incorporate those findings (see Witt & Gresham, 1985).

Theory-Based Intelligence Measures   A major criticism leveled against both the Stanford-Binet and the WISC-R is the lack of any unifying theoretical underpinnings; the tests reflect a well-developed technology of mental measurement devoid of theory. There exist several relatively comprehensive theories of intelligence that are buttressed by a great deal of empirical research on factors such as memory and cognition. Although neither of these two tests was developed with research or theory in mind, this is not to imply that the tests are not valuable. If intelligence testing is to move forward, however, it is desirable to develop and utilize tests that incorporate a well-established theoretical base and are technically sound. The most recent and best exemplar of such tests is the Kaufman Assessment Battery for Children (K-ABC) developed by Kaufman and Kaufman (1983).

The K-ABC evolved out of the research and theorizing of neurology (Luria, 1966) and cognitive psychology (Das, Kirby, & Jarman, 1975) and

WISC-R

RECORD FORM

Wechsler Intelligence Scale
for Children—Revised

NAME _Sarah_ AGE _7_ SEX _F_

ADDRESS _123 Main St._

PARENT'S NAME _Mr. & Mrs Driftwood_

SCHOOL _Rover_ GRADE _2_

PLACE OF TESTING _School_ TESTED BY _Cavell_

REFERRED BY _Mrs Piehl_

WISC-R PROFILE

Clinicians who wish to draw a profile should first transfer the child's scaled scores to the row of boxes below. Then mark an X on the dot corresponding to the scaled score for each test, and draw a line connecting the X's.*

	Year	Month	Day
Date Tested	87	10	18
Date of Birth	80	3	16
Age	7	7	2

VERBAL TESTS — Information, Similarities, Arithmetic, Vocabulary, Comprehension, Digit Span

Scaled Score: 9, 11, 12, 17, 11, 10

PERFORMANCE TESTS — Picture Completion, Picture Arrangement, Block Design, Object Assembly, Coding, Mazes

Scaled Score: 10, 16, 12, 10, 5, 12

	Raw Score	Scaled Score
VERBAL TESTS		
Information	7	9
Similarities	9	11
Arithmetic	9	12
Vocabulary	30	17
Comprehension	12	11
(Digit Span)	(9)	(10)
Verbal Score		
PERFORMANCE TESTS		
Picture Completion	14	10
Picture Arrangement	30	16
Block Design	17	12
Object Assembly	18	10
Coding	21	5
(Mazes)	(19)	(12)
Performance Score		

	Scaled Score	IQ
Verbal Score	60	112
Performance Score	53	104
Full Scale Score	113	109

*Prorated from 4 tests, if necessary.

*See Chapter 4 in the manual for a discussion of the significance of differences between scores on the tests.

NOTES

Sarah was highly motivated and responded well to all test items

Was at ease and expressed herself well with adults.

Needed minimum of encouragement

Figure 2.1. Sample cover sheet. (From Wechsler, D. [1974]. *Wechsler Intelligence Scale for Children–Revised*. New York: Psychological Corporation. Copyright © 1974 by The Psychological Corporation. Reproduced by permission.)

has relied upon a dichotomy between Sequential and Simultaneous processing to establish a conceptual foundation for assessment. The K-ABC contains a Sequential processing scale that comprises a series of subtests that reflect a child's ability to "solve problems by mentally manipulating the stimuli in serial order, such as by reproducing an ordered series of hand movements performed by the examiner" (Kaufman, 1983, p. 206). Simultaneous processing "measures problem-solving skill whereby many stimuli have to be organized and integrated in parallel or simultaneous fashion" (Kaufman, 1983, p. 206). An example of a task requiring Simultaneous processing is the presentation of a partially complete "inkblot" drawing that a child is asked to envision mentally as complete (see Figure 2.2). In addition to the Sequential and Simultaneous processing scales, the K-ABC also contains an achievement scale that primarily reflects school achievement. The K-ABC contains 16 subtests, but at most only 13 are administered to a child. Descriptions of the subtests are included in Table 2.2.

Although the technical properties (e.g., reliability and validity) of the K-ABC are excellent, research pertaining to the clinical usefulness of the instrument is just beginning to appear. It will be some time before the true worth of the instrument is known. On the basis of previous research with simultaneous and sequential processing, it is likely that the K-ABC will be especially valuable in the assessment of children with learning disabilities. For example, Gordon (1983) reports results of a study in which an astounding 97% of children with learning disabilities scored higher on right hemisphere (i.e., simultaneous) tasks than on left hemisphere (i.e., sequential) tasks. Hooper and Hynd (1982) discovered that scores from the K-ABC were accurate in differentiating "normal" from dyslexic children 91% of the time. The fact that a research base already exists relative to the conceptual underpinnings of the K-ABC is a strong asset, but the information already accumulated is sure to pale in comparison to the research that will be generated by this newcomer to the testing field. Despite the existing research, which is strongly suppor-

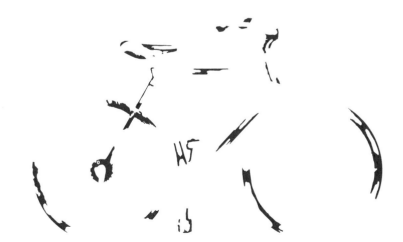

Figure 2.2. Gestalt closure; "inkblot drawing" of a bicycle. (From Kaufman, A. S., & Kaufman, N. L. [1983]. *Kaufman Assessment Battery for Children [K-ABC]—Sampler.* Circle Pines, MN: American Guidance Service. Reproduced by permission.)

Table 2.2. Individual subtests from the Kaufman Assessment Battery for Children (K-ABC)

Sequential Processing Scale

1. *Hand Movements.* Performing a series of hand movements in the same sequence as the examiner performed them.
2. *Number Recall.* Repeating a series of digits in the same sequence as the examiner said them.
3. *Word Order.* Touching a series of silhouettes of common objects in the same sequence as the examiner said the names of the objects. More difficult items include an interference task between the stimulus and response.

Simultaneous Processing Scale

1. *Magic Window.* Identifying a picture that the examiner exposed by slowly moving it behind a narrow window, making the picture only partially visible at any one time.
2. *Face Recognition.* Selecting from a group photograph the one or two faces that were exposed briefly on the preceding page.
3. *Gestalt Closure.* Naming an object or scene pictured in a partially completed "inkblot" drawing.
4. *Triangles.* Assembling several identical triangles into an abstract pattern to match a model.
5. *Matrix Analogies.* Selecting the meaningful picture or abstract design that best completes a visual analogy.
6. *Spatial Memory.* Recalling the placement of pictures on a page that was exposed briefly.
7. *Photo Series.* Placing photographs of an event in chronological order.

Achievement Scale

1. *Expressive Vocabulary.* Naming an object pictured in a photograph.
2. *Faces and Places.* Naming the well-known person, fictional character, or place pictured in a photograph or drawing.
3. *Arithmetic.* Demonstrating knowledge of numbers and mathematical concepts, counting and computational skills, and other school-related arithmetic abilities.
4. *Riddles.* Inferring the name of a concrete or abstract concept when given a list of its characteristics.
5. *Reading/Decoding.* Identifying letters and reading words.
6. *Reading/Understanding.* Demonstrating reading comprehension by following commands that are given in sentences.

tive, reviews of the K-ABC have identified a number of technical and theoretical problems with the instrument (Kieth, 1985).

Adaptive Behavior Measures Within the assessment part of a problem-solving sequence, children who fail to learn at school and who have a low score on an intelligence test (i.e., an IQ of 69 or below) are almost always administered a measure of adaptive behavior. That is, if a child scores in the mentally retarded range on an intelligence test, a psychologist will begin to examine the hypothesis that the child has mental retardation. Scoring in the retarded range on an intelligence test is necessary but not sufficient evidence that a child should be diagnosed as mentally retarded. In order to be so labeled, a child must also show evidence of significantly subaverage performance on a measure of adaptive behavior.

Prior to the establishment of guidelines by the American Association on Mental Deficiency (AAMD) (Grossman, 1983), mental retardation was defined almost exclusively in terms of a score on an intelligence test. Individuals who scored significantly below average were labeled as mentally retarded. With this unidimensional definition, abuses in categorizing children as mentally retarded occurred. This was particularly true for children from minority groups who, because of their language or culture, were penalized in their performance on an intelligence test. For example, in the case of *Guadalupe v. Tempe Elementary School District (1972)*, the plaintiff alleged that the school district was administering highly verbal intelligence tests to children who spoke little or no English and using the results as a primary criterion for placement in special classes for retarded learners. (These same children who were labeled as retarded in school behaved quite normally out of school in their home environment.) It was argued that such practices were inappropriate and resulted in a disproportionate number of minority children in the special classes. The court agreed and stipulated that the district must: 1) include an assessment of adaptive behavior outside of school when considering children for special classes, 2) refrain from using the results of intelligence tests as the primary basis for making educational placements, and 3) assess children in their primary language.

Today these stipulations seem logical and certainly difficult to argue against from the perspective of good professional practice. Following a rash of court cases similar in content and outcome to *Guadalupe* (see Reynolds et al., 1984, for a comprehensive review), lawmakers began drafting legislation that required the assessment of adaptive behavior. This culminated in the passage by the U.S. Congress of PL 94-142 (the Education for All Handicapped Children Act of 1975) that stipulated in part: ''Mentally retarded means significantly subaverage general intellectual functioning *existing concurrently with deficits in adaptive behavior* [emphasis added] and manifested during the developmental period, which adversely affects a child's educational performance'' (Federal Register, 1977, 42481).

Psychologists wishing to assess adaptive behavior have at their disposal well over 100 tests that purport to measure adaptive behavior skills. The selection of an adaptive behavior instrument that is appropriate for a given child in a specific situation requires careful study. The problem is that each of the various scales measures only certain components of adaptive behavior and is appropriate only for specific ages. Unlike tests in some other domains, there exists no general purpose adaptive behavior instrument that provides a comprehensive assessment of all children at all ages.

The potential test consumer must scrutinize prospective tests of adaptive behavior to determine whether they meet his or her intended purposes. For example, some instruments are designed solely for use in diagnostic decisions and provide virtually no information for instructional programming. Also, a few scales are so highly correlated with intelligence and in-school achievement that they are useless for assessing out-of-school adaptive behavior.

Of all the instruments available for the assessment of adaptive behavior, perhaps the most widely known and used is the AAMD Adaptive Behavior Scale (ABS) (Lambert & Windmiller, 1981). Its widespread use is due to three primary factors. First, the ABS is one of the oldest measures of adaptive behavior, with the present version representing a revision of the ABS that was originally published in 1974. Second, sponsorship by the American Association on Mental Deficiency (AAMD), an association closely identified with the development of definitions for both mental retardation and adaptive behavior, has added to the visibility of the ABS. Third, it is technically superior to other measures in terms of its standardization procedures and the degree to which it comprehensively assesses a broad range of competencies and skills.

The ABS is divided into two parts. Part One consists of 9 domains considered important to the development of personal independence and daily living. Part Two assesses a wide array of behaviors generally considered to be inappropriate and unacceptable. The behaviors assessed in Part One are those most commonly associated with textbook definitions of adaptive behavior (e.g., self-help skills or language). The personality and behavior disorders assessed in Part Two are not usually included on adaptive behavior instruments; this offers the professional a way to assess those behaviors that may actually interfere with successful adaptive functioning.

The items on the ABS have been categorized into five major factors of adaptive behavior functioning:

Personal self-sufficiency This cluster of items reflects the degree to which a child is able to handle his or her basic needs such as eating, drinking, and toileting.

Community self-sufficiency This factor assesses the extent to which a child can function appropriately in common, everyday situations such as traveling about the neighborhood, communicating with others, and performing economic activities.

Personal-social responsibility Items within this factor reflect relatively high-level social interaction skills including getting to school or a job on time, showing initiative in school or job settings, interacting cooperatively with others, and assuming responsibility for one's own actions.

Social adjustment This factor comprises items from Part Two of the ABS. The inappropriate behaviors assessed include those in which a child is interacting inappropriately with other individuals (e.g., the child is aggressive, lies, cheats, steals). Such behaviors are characteristic of children who act-out or have behavior disorders.

Personal adjustment Items included in this factor reflect three areas of inappropriate behavior: inappropriate mannerisms (e.g., stereotyped behaviors), inappropriate contact with others (e.g., excessive hugging, touching, kissing), and unacceptable vocal habits (e.g., echolalia, talking too loudly).

The first three factors are arranged in a developmental progression from least to most complex. Skills assessed by the first factor typically are developed early in life and are responsive to training. By contrast, the skills assessed by the second and third factors represent more complex learning which requires children to generalize skills learned in one situation to new settings. The last two factors are relatively independent of chronological age and instead represent inappropriate behaviors that can occur at almost any developmental stage.

Administration of the ABS is conducted by a third-party informant. That is, someone who knows the child well (e.g., a parent or caregiver) completes the items on the scale by reading them or having them read. Obviously a number of factors may influence an individual's perception (particularly if that individual is a parent) of how well a child functions. This introduces a source of error into the scale that must be taken into account when interpretations are derived from the data. The ABS, like most quality psychological instruments, presents norm-referenced quantitative scores on each of its factors. The scale also provides an innovative feature that allows for the calculation of each child's score compared to normal, educable, and trainable level children. This increases the objectivity of data that are often subjective when collected informally and helps assure more appropriate school placement decisions for children. Overall, the administration and full interpretation of the ABS can be a time-consuming process; however, the scope and depth of the data yielded by this process are impressive.

Standardized Individual Achievement Measures Within the realm of assessing skill or ability deficits it is occasionally necessary for psychologists, especially those employed in public school settings, to administer and interpret individual achievement tests. Although Chapter 3 is devoted to educational assessment, this section briefly describes how achievement testing meshes with other aspects of psychological evaluation. Psychologists typically have one of three purposes in mind when administering achievement tests and interpreting data.

First, achievement test data may be collected as part of an evaluation to determine whether a child should be classified as learning disabled. In the typical case of a child who is referred because of a failure to learn in school, learning disability and mental retardation are the two most likely reasons for such failure. If an intelligence test suggests that a child has normal intelligence, the hypothesis that a child has a learning disability must be examined. In the most general sense, a learning disability exists if there is a significant discrepancy between ability and achievement. For example, a child with normal intellectual ability but who is markedly deficient in one or more academic areas may be considered learning disabled. Hence, a major reason for the psychologist to consider administering an achievement test is to determine a child's achievement level.

A second goal for the administration of an achievement battery is to begin to determine the skills that the child can and cannot perform. This is essential if the evaluation conducted by a psychologist is to have any instructional relevance for a teacher. Although psychological evaluations are most often designed to answer diagnostic questions (e.g., Does this child have a learning disability?), if conducted properly they can also be quite helpful in providing instructional guidance to a teacher. Diagnostically, it is useful to know that a child is functioning at a second-grade level in math. However, a teacher must have much more specific information (e.g., Is the child capable of adding one digit numbers without regrouping?) if instructional interventions are to be planned. Because of their knowledge of learning hierarchies and of cognitive processes, psychologists are often in an ideal position to offer specific instructional recommendations that may complement those developed by an educational diagnostician.

A related reason for the involvement of psychologists in the assessment of academic achievement is that they can observe and interact with the child directly. The test scores that are derived from achievement testing do not convey the rich array of information available to the trained professional who actually interacts with a child during testing. Obviously there is a very great difference between a child who achieves at a third-grade level in an almost effortless fashion and another child who does so only through a painfully slow and laborious process.

Because of space limitations and because achievement tests are described in Chapter 3, they are not reviewed here. It is not uncommon for psychologists to use any of the norm-referenced tests (e.g., Woodcock Reading Mastery Tests) described in that chapter. In addition, criterion-referenced tests and informal assessment procedures are used when needed. For a more detailed description of psychologists' involvement in achievement testing, refer to Witt et al. (in press).

Neuropsychological Assessment Perhaps some of the most rapid, and yet most controversial, developments within the field of psychological assessment have occurred within the field of neuropsychology. The major contribution of neuropsychology to the assessment process is the provision of a theoretical or conceptual framework from which to view assessment data. Without a strong theoretical guide to test interpretation, psychologists must rely on past experience, illusory relationships, or trial-and-error procedures when a child with a relatively unusual pattern of test scores is assessed.

Neuropsychological testing techniques are useful in providing information to guide instructional planning for children with learning disabilities, and they can be very helpful in the evaluation of other categories of exceptional children. For children with more serious disorders (e.g., when there is clear evidence of central nervous system involvement), neuropsychological evaluation is becoming nearly routine. Neuropsychological assessment methodologies can be particularly helpful in ruling out specific neurological problems.

Although there is no one method of neuropsychological assessment and no standard battery of instruments that is used in every case, there are some common procedures and a cluster of instruments that have received a great deal of research attention and use. Dean (1982) provides a glimpse of what can be expected from a "typical" neuropsychological evaluation:

> Although emphasis and interpretation may differ, most evaluation procedures involve comprehensive batteries that assess intellectual, sensory-motor, and personality characteristics that relate to specific cortical functions. In assessing intellectual functioning, emphasis is placed on both expressive and receptive aspects of memory, learning, and cognition. Under the rubric of personality, aspects of both emotion (e.g., affect, anxiety, depression) and self-control (e.g., impulsivity, excitability, etc.) are assessed. The examination of sensory-motor systems focuses on the areas of perception, sensation, and motor integration. (p. 186)

The Luria-Nebraska Neuropsychological Test Battery is an example of a measure of neuropsychological assessment. This test battery was derived from Luria's (1966) view of neuropsychological systems that outlined three primary areas of the brain, each of which contained zones responsible for specific functions (e.g., integration of sensory information). The first major area, termed the arousal block, consists of the reticular formation and some related areas that play a role in the regulation of the energy level of the cortex. A second block, comprising the occipital, temporal, and parietal lobes, is thought to be responsible for the integration of sensory information. The third major area noted by Luria consists primarily of the frontal lobe that serves an important planning and organizing function.

Each area was viewed by Luria as a relatively integrated cluster. That is, each component has its own functional system, and problems within one area typically affect other functions within the same area. The system provides a qualitative rather than a quantitative analysis that permits a syndrome analysis, or "allows the clarification of a symptom's relationship to functional symptoms of the brain; thus, this process stimulates hypothesis building about the symptom's correspondence to a local brain lesion" (Luria, 1973, p. 46). According to Dean (in press), this syndrome analysis is important for two reasons. First, and most important, a careful syndrome analysis is useful in the understanding of both intact and disturbed functions. Second, within the

Luria system, lesions are seen as only rarely disturbing a single function to the exclusion of all others and this leads the psychologist who finds one disturbance to look further for other, related problems.

As mentioned above, the Luria system is very qualitative and stresses the importance of variability and flexibility in the administration of tests. The emphasis is on how the problems are solved rather than how many, and a primary goal is for the psychologist to discover what types of compensations are possible (Dean, in press). The orientation is toward clinical "feel" and away from strict quantification. Such systems often suffer from a lack of reliability and result in misdiagnosis. In an attempt to make the Luria system more of a science and less of an art, Golden, Hammeke, and Purisch (1978) developed the Luria-Nebraska Neuropsychological Test Battery that contains approximately 282 items and requires about 2 hours to administer. The instrument comprises 10 discrete subareas that correspond to the functional zones originally operationalized by Christensen (1975) (see Table 2.3).

Although this battery is based upon the Luria system, it has been criticized because its emphasis on quantification and standardization has resulted in a loss of some flexibility, a major hallmark of the Luria system. Another problem with the Luria-Nebraska is that to administer the battery one must be very familiar with Luria's theory. Thus, unlike many other tests, one must devote considerable study to mastering the conceptual underpinnings of the test. For a more complete discussion of the Luria-Nebraska and other neuropsychological assessment methodologies, especially as they relate to the evaluation of school-age children, refer to Dean (1982; in press).

Assessment of Performance Deficits

As mentioned previously, the problem of a failure to learn in school has been conceptualized into one of two categories: 1) skill or ability deficits, and 2) performance deficits. On the one hand, a skill or ability deficit is present when a child cannot perform a particular skill regardless of the circumstances (i.e., the child has not learned or cannot learn a particular behavior). A performance deficit, on the other hand, is present if a child has a particular skill but for one reason or another does not display it.

Diagnosticians in general, and perhaps pediatricians in particular, sometimes focus on physiological conditions (e.g., intactness of physical system, absence or presence of medical syndromes) to such an extent that characteristics in the learner's environment and his or her attitudes toward learning are overlooked as possible causes for failure. Psychologists with grounding in behavioral learning theory, especially those employed in school settings, can give balance to the evaluation of a child by examining the learning environment (Chapter 3 shows how the special educator can also participate in this evaluation). The psychologist as well as the child psychiatrist (Chapter 8) can assess personality, emotional, and attitudinal factors that help determine if a child's ability is likely to manifest in actual productivity.

Table 2.3. Summary of individual scales of the Luria-Nebraska Neuropsychological Battery

Individual Scale	Description	Items	Technical reference
Motor Functions	Assesses a number of motor skills for left and right sides of body. Unilateral and simultaneous simple and complex motor movement.	51	Golden et al., (1978)
Acoustico-Motor (Rhythm Scale)	Evaluates similarity of tones, reproduces tones orally and motorically. Rhythmic patterns generated from verbal description.	12	McKay & Golden, (1979)
Higher Cutaneous and Kinesthetic (Tactile Scale)	Without aid of vision requires identification of where touched, head and point of pin, direction of movement, geometric and alpha-numeric symbols traced on wrist, matching movements, and item identification.	22	Golden et al., (1982)
Spatial (Visual Functions)	Requires visual recognition of common objects, pictures with obscurity and disorganization. Matrices tasks and complex block count.	14	Golden (1981)
Receptive Speech Scale	Requires oral, written, and motoric response to spoken speech.	33	Golden (1981)
Expressive Speech Scale	Items involve orally repeated words, increasingly complex sentences; name, count, recite; offer missing words; and organize mixed-up sentence.	42	Golden (1981)
Writing Scale	Involves basic writing skills—spelling, copying words and letters from cards and memory. Writing words and letters from dictation and spontaneously.	13	Golden et al., (1978)
Reading Scale	Range includes reading letter sounds, syllables, words, sentences, and a short story.	13	Golden et al., (1978)
Arithmetic Scale	Involves simple number identification, writing and reading series of numbers; simple skills to more complex skills.	22	Golden et al., (1981)
Memory Scale	Requires learning word list, picture memory, rhythmic pattern, hand positions, sentences, story, and paired associate task.	13	Golden et al., (1982)
Intellectual Scale	Involves sequencing pictures, identifying abstract theme of pictures, identifying picture absurdities, proverbs, definitions, opposites, analogies, and word problems.	34	Golden & Berg (1983)

From Dean, R. S. (in press). Perspectives on the future of neuropsychological assessment. In B. S. Plake and J. C. Witt (Eds.), *The future of neuropsychological assessment*. Hillsdale, NJ: Lawrence Erlbaum Associates. Reprinted by permission.

Some children exhibit behaviors and characteristics that interfere with a teacher's ability to teach, their own ability to learn, or the opportunity for their classmates to profit from academic instruction. It is quite common, for example, to find children who are capable of performing assigned work who, instead, choose to talk with classmates or go to the pencil sharpener several times per hour. Such performance deficits range in severity from mild acting-out behaviors to very severe behavior disorders (see Chapter 8).

This section briefly describes the general processes and methods used by psychologists to assess performance deficits. Although the discussion of performance deficits follows the discussion of skill and ability deficits, it should not be assumed that assessment of deficits necessarily follows that order in actual practice. Typically, a psychologist utilizes information from initial interviews and initial observations to determine whether a performance deficit or a skill or ability deficit is the most likely cause of the problem. Regardless of which area is assessed first, it is quite common to include an assessment of skill or ability and performance deficits in a thorough evaluation of a child who is doing poorly in school.

In the following discussion of various methodologies for the assessment of performance deficits, two broad types of assessment are discussed: personality assessment and behavior assessment.

Personality Measures   Personality assessment is based on the assumption that individuals have certain traits or characteristics that are relatively stable over time. For example, any observer of human nature soon realizes that some people are more anxious, motivated, happy, or paranoid than others. Personality tests are designed to assess the degree to which these various human characteristics are present within a specific individual. Koppitz (1982) suggests that personality assessment can serve at least four functions in the evaluation of children who have difficulty learning at school. Such testing can: 1) assist in determining a child's behavior and learning styles; 2) aid in discovering a child's motives, attitudes, and modes of adjustment to work; 3) provide valuable information about a child's self-concept and capacity to relate to others; and 4) determine whether a child shows evidence of anxiety, serious emotional disturbance, thought disorders, or other problems that can have serious detrimental effects on learning and that may require direct intervention.

Objective Personality Measures   Children taking a typical objective personality test are required to respond to typewritten questions. The test items are selected empirically and the actual content of the items is almost irrelevant. For example, a test item may state "I cry easily when my feelings are hurt." From an empirical standpoint, it is relatively unimportant whether children who answer *true* to such an item actually cry more easily than children who answer *false*. If one direction (i.e., affirmative or negative) of answering this item is shown to be related to anxiety, then in some ways the most important fact is that children who answer in the scored direction display greater anxiety and have behavior problems that are more severe than children who respond in the opposite way. Certainly content validity is important in a test; however, it is the empirically derived, actuarial implications that most interest a psychologist.

An example of an objective personality test may help to illustrate the type of data derived from this form of assessment. One of the newer personality instruments gaining relatively widespread acceptance in the evaluation of children and adolescents is the Personality Inventory for Children (PIC) (Lachar, 1982; Wirt, Lachar, Kleindinst, & Seat, 1977, 1984). The 1977 PIC contains 12 scales: achievement, intellectual screening, development, somatic concern, depression, family relations, delinquency, withdrawal, anxiety, psychosis, hyperactivity, and social skills. Subsequent item analysis resulted in the development of a multipart administration booklet in which the first 131 items constitute four broad band screening or summary measures derived through factor analysis: Undisciplined/Poor Self-Control, Social Incompetence, Internalization/Somatic Symptoms, and Cognitive Development (Lachar, Gdowski, & Snyder, 1982). In addition, the first 280 items provide shortened versions of the original profile scales, and the first 420 items provide 20 full length scales and a "critical item" list.

The PIC appears to be modeled after the Minnesota Multiphasic Personality Inventory (MMPI), which is designed for adults, but differs from that instrument in one major respect. With most adult personality inventories, the person being evaluated does all of the responding. Responses to the PIC are made by a third party such as the child's parent or someone who knows the child well. Thus, a potential source of error is introduced in this and many other child scales simply because responses are descriptions of someone else's behavior rather than self-descriptions.

To counteract this problem, there are some safeguards built into most tests. The PIC, for example, has three profile validity scales (i.e., Lie, Frequency, and Defensiveness) that are designed to signal respondent defensiveness or exaggeration. The bottom line is whether the instrument is capable of correctly classifying children; the PIC has received empirical support in a series of studies that demonstrate classification potential (Lachar, 1982; Lachar, Kline, & Boersman, in press; Wirt et al., 1984). Thus, the PIC has been shown to distinguish between children meeting the *DSM-III* criteria of attention deficit disorder with hyperactivity and children with other forms of behavioral noncompliance (Fabres, 1985), and also, data exist on the effectiveness of the PIC in classifying children for special education (Lachar, Kline, & Boersman, in press).

In summary, a primary value of objective personality inventories is that they allow comparison of a particular child relative to a group norm, thus reducing some of the professional's subjectivity when using less structured assessment methods such as the clinical interview. The quantitative features of such objective measures also allow empirical studies of reliability and validity. Ultimately, the objective, quantifiable, easily researched aspects of objective personality tests make them valuable sources of data in the comprehensive assessment of children who are experiencing difficulty in school.

Projective Measures   Projective testing was originally based on the psychoanalytic theory developed by Freud in which overt behavior is thought to be a manifestation of underlying needs, motives, and conflicts. These determinants of personality are considered to be unconscious and are therefore difficult to assess directly. Hence, by presenting ambiguous stimuli (e.g., inkblots) to individuals, there is a greater likelihood they will respond in ways that reveal their motivations and true personality with far less interference from the conscious mind. Because the stimuli are ambiguous and there are no restrictions placed upon the individual's response options, it is assumed that a much clearer picture is obtained of an individual's internal state. However, this advantage is partially offset because of the extreme subjectivity of the method. This subjectivity often results in disagreement concerning the scoring and interpretation of an individual's responses. For any particular response, various psychologists would be likely to give varying interpretations concerning its meaning and importance (Reynolds et al., 1984).

A wide array of projective techniques have been developed and these can be categorized into one of three basic types depending on the type of stimulus presented and the method of response. In the first category are tests such as the Rorschach Inkblot and the Thematic Apperception Test (TAT) that call for an oral response to an ambiguous visual stimulus. The second category is composed of completion methods, whereby a child is asked to finish a sentence or a short story when provided an ambiguous beginning by the psychologist. Tests in this area include a number of relatively standard stories (e.g., The Madeleine Thomas Stories) as well as a wide variety of sentence completion measures. The third category comprises projective art, in which children are provided with the necessary materials to complete a piece of art (usually a drawing) but are provided with relatively minimal instruction. Typically the child is requested to draw a picture of a person, himself or herself, his or her family, or geometric figures. Detailed scoring systems (usually quantitative) are available for almost all of the major projective tests. However, individual clinicians may choose not to utilize these systems, preferring instead to use their own clinical judgment concerning the meaning and significance of particular responses. (Koppitz [1982] provides a detailed description of most of the projective instruments available for use with school-age children.)

The area of projective assessment has a very long but controversial history. The controversy stems from the subjective nature of the instruments and the lack of evidence for their validity versus fierce testimonial and anecdotal evidence of their utility in specific cases by devoted clinicians (Reynolds et al., 1984). Practically speaking, many psychologists include projective measures when completing a comprehensive evaluation; however, these instruments are less likely to meet the standards of objectivity, reliability, validity, and norm-referencing than most other instruments noted in this chapter.

Behavior Assessment   Behavior assessment is perhaps the most rapidly growing area of assessment. Although there is no single model of child behavior assessment, all such models emphasize the importance of environmental events on behavior, emphasize direct observation of behavior in natural settings, and use ongoing assessment data to plan and evaluate intervention programs.

Distinctions from Personality Assessment   Unlike personality assessment, which focuses on traits and characteristics assumed to reside within a child (e.g., anxiety, depression), the major assumption of behavior assessment is that *behavior* should be the focus of assessment. Furthermore, behavior is viewed primarily as a function of environmental events (e.g., antecedents and consequences), and certain organismic variables (e.g., past learning history, levels of arousal, cultural background). Adjustment problems are considered to be behaviors that are excessive (i.e., behaviors such as fighting that are performed too frequently), deficient (i.e., behaviors such as homework completion that may be performed too infrequently), or situationally inappropriate (i.e., behaviors such as yelling that are appropriate in some situations like ballgames but are not appropriate in many other situations).

Traditional personality assessment assumes that a person's behavior is a function of psychological inner states (e.g., drives, needs, defenses) and overt behavior is seen as a characteristic or manifestation of the global underlying trait. Behavior assessment makes no such assumptions regarding underlying personality traits, particularly as a causative factor in the emergence of problem behavior. In fact, adherents of behavior assessment typically do not acknowledge the existence of "personality traits," at least not as they are discussed within a traditional assessment model. Although proponents of behavior assessment may use global terms to describe or summarize specific behavior patterns (e.g., noncompliance), there is no underlying assumption that specific behaviors are caused by the label or trait used to describe the behavior. In short, labels for a class of behaviors are merely descriptive in a behavior assessment model, whereas they are sometimes viewed as causative within a traditional personality assessment framework.

Behavior assessment seeks causes of behavior in the current environment or situations in which the behavior occurs. A critical aspect of behavior assessment is not only the assessment of behavior per se, but also the assessment of settings, situations, and other environmental variables present when focal behaviors are exhibited. A thorough behavior assessment should provide an evaluation of behavior and the antecedent and consequent conditions surrounding it.

Processes, Methods, and Goals   The primary goal of behavior assessment is to identify the problematic behaviors and the environmental factors that are contributing to the problem. Within most settings, behavior assessment is used to determine the features of an individual and his or her environment that maintain behavior. In a simple yet typical case, assessment may suggest that a problem behavior such as excessive and inappropriate talking is resulting in a failure to complete assignments. A great deal of peer attention and a lack of negative consequences from the teacher appear to be contributing to the problem. From this simple analysis, one could begin to design an intervention program to decrease talking and to increase assignment completion.

Several unique features of behavior assessment make it very useful in the assessment of learning and behavior problems. First, behavior assessment is individualized and can be specifically tailored to a given problem. Second, it is by design linked closely to any intervention plan that may be designed and implemented. Third, behavior assessment is continuous in nature for it is utilized not only in problem identification but in the monitoring and final evaluation of a given problem as well.

Psychologists utilize a wide array of techniques within a behavior assessment framework. One of the most important methods is direct behavior observation, which involves systematically observing children within the setting where problems occur. Often, this requires going into a child's classroom and noting the frequency of off-task behaviors and the conditions that may be maintaining the inappropriate responses (e.g., poor teaching, peer attention). Interviews and behavior rating scales provide alternative methods for obtaining information about a child's behavior. Using these methods, information can be obtained indirectly through interviews with individuals who interact with the child (e.g., teachers) and by asking teachers and others to complete rating scales that ask questions about the presence and severity of various problem behaviors. Data of this type may prove invaluable in determining if the child has a skill or ability deficit that requires intervention or circumvention, or a performance deficit that modification in the teaching environment can overcome.

THE PROCESS OF ASSESSMENT:
INDICATIONS FOR REFERRAL TO A PSYCHOLOGIST

As pointed out in the foregoing discussion, psychological testing is simply one method of gathering assessment information. The role of testing and other information-gathering techniques used by psychologists is most clearly understood when viewed in the context of the process of assessment. Certainly, characteristics of this process are to be found in any diagnostic situation (e.g., pediatrics, special education, speech/language pathology). However, given the often inexact nature of psychological assessment, a coherent, empirically based process can greatly minimize the degree to which assessment decisions are based on incomplete, inaccurate, or biased information.

Two separate models can be used to illustrate the process of psychological assessment (Reynolds et al., 1984). First, the process of assessment can be conceptualized as an instance of problem solving. Most models of problem solving outline a sequence of steps that, if adequately performed, enhance the probability of deriving an effective solution. Effective problem solving requires that one adequately identify and analyze the problem situation, generate alternative hypotheses for its resolution, systematically choose the most promising solution, and then evaluate the results of that choice (Bergan, 1977; D'Zurilla & Goldfried, 1971). Analogous to the stages of problem solving are the steps that psychologists follow as they conduct an assessment. Initially, information is obtained from multiple sources in order that problems may be identified and their contributing factors analyzed. Second, psychologists generate hypotheses that may explain the often disconnected appearance of incoming data. Third, based on their assessment, psychologists are frequently asked to make decisions concerning screening, classification, prognosis, intervention planning, placement, and program evaluation. Finally, comprehensive psychological assessment should include follow-up evaluations in order to confirm the accuracy of previous hypotheses or examine the results of previous decisions.

Use of the second heuristic model is based on the fact that the process of psychological assessment reflects an attempt to understand, predict, and devise ways of changing complex human behavior. One model for understanding human behavior that is currently well received by psychologists is Bandura's (1978) model of reciprocal determinism. This model, based on the principles of social learning theory, conceptualizes human behavior as the result of continuous reciprocal interactions between an individual's internal thoughts and feelings, behavior, and environment. This model seeks to understand the functional, as opposed to the causal, relationships between what an individual brings to a given situation (e.g., genetic makeup, developmental background, cognitive skills, beliefs, attitudes), his or her overt behaviors in that situation (i.e., what is expressed behaviorally, verbally, and emotionally), and what environmental stimuli are present before, during, and after the behavior occurs (e.g., cues for responding, current situational tasks, others' reactions). For various children with problems, each with a unique combination of strengths and weaknesses, the degree of influence from each of these three areas will, of course, vary. Still, this model forces one to search for variables that, if altered, may substantially change the quantity and quality of important behaviors.

The preceding sections of this chapter reviewed some of the data-gathering techniques used by psychologists. The application of these techniques to help solve the problems unique to each case referral is the aim of psychological assessment. Using multiple sources of information gathered by objective, reliable, and valid means, psychologists attempt to identify and functionally analyze problem behaviors, devise programs to remedy those behaviors, and evaluate the efficacy of the programs chosen. Furthermore, given a reciprocal determinism model of human behavior, the process of psychological assessment does not focus on any single source of behavioral influence. Rather, the child's organismic factors, behaviors, and environment all merit systematic scrutiny.

Ultimately, the value of any assessment is reflected in the degree to which it effectively guides intervention and instruction. Assessments that fail to inform the actions of persons responsible for the child (i.e., parents, teachers, other professionals) are, at best, academic exercises. Examples of behavior that are influenced by psychological assessment include parental attitudes pertaining to a child's diagnosis and prognosis, further evaluations by other agencies, and specific treatment recommendations. Thus, one way in which other professionals can evaluate reports received from psychologists is to assess the extent to which their behavior vis-à-vis the child is guided by the assessment. Vague, esoteric ramblings that culminate in only a diagnostic label or in vacuous or unrealistic recommendations are of little use. Conversely, assessments that provide specific information about relevant behaviors and the circumstances affecting those behaviors are considerably more useful to parents, other professionals, and the child.

As a way of illustrating the process of psychological assessment in response to case referrals involving developmental and learning problems, the assessment of two very general and very common indications for referral are discussed in this section. An important point to note is that psychologists, like many child care professionals, tend to use those assessment methods that they view as cost effective. The amount and quality of information provided by any one assessment technique are weighed against the time and cost their usage requires (Barkley, 1981). Of course, much variability exists among psychologists owing to differences in time constraints, perceptions of the quality of information provided by particular assessment methods, and perceptions psychologists have of their role in the assessment of various disorders (e.g., adjunctive diagnostician vs. primary treatment planner). Nevertheless, competent psychological assessment requires the use of methods that are supported by empirical research findings and that provide practical information to persons charged with a child's care and treatment. Therefore, the assessment methods that this section describes were chosen to reflect the compromise clinicians must make each day between practical constraints and empirical research regarding optimal assessment. It should also be recognized that many of the tasks may be accomplished by another professional previously assessing the child, in which case some of these tasks may be eliminated or reduced in complexity for the psychologist. In an established team setting, some of these duties may be accomplished routinely by individuals other than the psychologist.

Delayed General Cognitive Development

As with other childhood disorders, psychological referrals involving delayed general cognitive development result from a discordance between the expectations of significant adults and the behaviors a child exhibits. For cases involving severe delay, the referrals typically occur during infancy or preschool. Children who are already in school and whose cognitive deficits were not identified previously usually demonstrate less severe delay and are most often referred for academic problems (Taylor & Warren, 1984). Therefore, the following discussion focuses on the assessment of delayed general cognitive development among infant and preschool populations.

A referral of a child for developmental delay may result from several factors. Parents may feel that their child has failed to mature at the same rate as other children with whom they are familiar. Pediatricians may routinely refer children whose medical problems are often associated with developmental delay (e.g., failure to thrive, fetal alcohol syndrome). Speech/language pathologists may refer children for evaluation when the child's limited verbal productivity confounds their own assessment. Referrals may also be initiated by public health nurses, social workers, preschool teachers, or others who have frequent contact with children.

The general methods by which a psychologist evaluates a child's general cognitive development include: 1) interviews with parents, 2) reviews of pertinent records compiled by other agencies, 3) psychometric tests of the child's cognitive-developmental skills, 4) measures of adaptive behavior, and 5) direct observation of naturally occurring child behavior. If the child has been attending day care or preschool, teacher interviews and direct observation of the child's school behavior may also be used.

Parent Interviews Parent interviews are a necessary starting point for psychologists conducting virtually any assessment of children. During the initial meeting with parents, several important points are discussed. If the child had been referred by his or her parents, then the psychologist may begin the interview by requesting the parents to elaborate on the referral statement. If the child was directly referred by another professional, then the psychologist begins by elaborating on the referral statement. In the latter case, interviewing the parents is facilitated by an honest, straightforward explanation from the referring agent as to why their child is to be seen by a psychologist. This point is especially valid in cases in which parents may feel they are being accused of neglecting or abusing their child (e.g., failure to thrive cases).

A second topic to be covered in the parent interview is a description of the assessment plan, including tasks required of the parents (e.g., additional interviews), tests to be administered, and any communication with other persons or agencies familiar with the child. The specific purposes of the assessment are also outlined along with some mention of how the assessment may benefit the family. Having informed the parents of what they can expect from participating in the assessment process, the psychologist then obtains written consent from them prior to continuing the assessment. Parental consent allowing the psychologist to communicate with and obtain records from other agencies is also obtained at this time.

Information obtained from parent interviews generally comes from three areas. First, parents are asked to recall relevant events in their child's developmental history. Areas of inquiry include medical, family, social, and academic (if applicable) history as well as information pertaining to important developmental milestones. Issues regarding medical history include any prenatal, perinatal, or postnatal problems, growth parameters, previous illnesses or accidents and treatments thereof, family medical history, and any previously assigned medical diagnoses. Family history entails information pertaining to the parents' marital, educational, and occupational history; significant events surrounding sibling development; and any major changes in the home environment. The social history, depending on the age of the child, includes such aspects as the quality of interactions between parent and child during infancy (e.g., when held or fed), and descriptions of past sibling or peer interactions (e.g., prosocial, aggressive, withdrawn). Academic history includes the amount of time the child has been enrolled in day care or preschool and any noticeable progress made as a result. Parents are also asked to estimate the age at which their child achieved certain developmental milestones in areas such as crawling, walking, speaking, self-feeding, and toileting behaviors.

The second type of information gained from parent interviews relates to the child's current level of functioning. One method of gathering this information involves asking parents to list and give examples of their child's strengths and weaknesses in each of the topic areas previously covered in the developmental history. Strengths include the prosocial behaviors the child consistently performs and which meet or exceed parental expectations. Weaknesses include behaviors that make for difficult child-rearing, occur too infrequently (e.g., sharing) or excessively (e.g., aggression), or threaten the welfare of the child or others. In addition, parents are asked to describe any behaviors their child exhibits that they view as bizarre or unusual.

A third type of information to be gleaned from parent interviews is more specifically concerned with parent behaviors and the home environment. The relevance of assessing these particular areas in cases of general cognitive delay is underscored by Sattler's (1982) review of studies in which children from homes characterized by overly punitive parenting techniques and minimal stimulation tended to show decreases in IQ during the preschool years. Parent behaviors to be assessed include general parenting style (e.g., consistent and encouraging, punitive, or neglectful), parental expectations (e.g., realistic, pessimistic, or overly optimistic), and specific parenting techniques applied to previously noted problem situations. Assessment of the home environment entails estimates of the degree of appropriate stimulation for the child as well as information related to overall living conditions. Estimates of appropriate stimulation include, for example, frequency and quality of interactions with others and the number and type of toys available to the child. Psychologists who assess living conditions focus on factors such as socioeconomic conditions, number of persons living in the home, and social support resources available to the family (e.g., extended family, various service organizations).

Guiding the psychologist throughout the parent interview is an awareness of the normal process of human development and the amount of variability in this developmental process that is still considered to be within normal limits. Also, indications of significant deviations in the child's development should prompt the interviewer to investigate further and generate hypotheses regarding possible contributing and remediable factors. For example, reports of substantial growth delay unexplained by medical factors might warrant inquiries into the child's nutritional history and patterns of mother-child interactions. Reports of hospitalizations may prompt questions about possible central nervous system (CNS) damage due to trauma, infection, or toxins. Accounts of bizarre behavior (e.g., self-mutilation) suggest that certain syndromes involving developmental delay (e.g., autism) be investigated. Refer to Mash and Terdal (1981) for further discussion regarding parent interviews.

Review of Records   Once parental consent has been obtained, records from other agencies familiar with the child can be used as a source of valuable assessment information. Indeed, given the number of factors associated with delayed general cognitive development that are of a biological nature (either genetic or environmental), the importance of carefully reviewing medical and health care records cannot be overemphasized (Repp & Deitz, 1983). Although much difficulty currently exists in determining the precise etiology of many cases of cognitive developmental delay, recognition of factors that place the child at risk may result in the delivery of needed preventive measures.

Psychometric Tests of Cognitive-Developmental Level   Norm-referenced scales have been developed to assess a child's cognitive-developmental skills. The age of the child is a primary influence on the psychologist's decision of which instrument to use. Sattler (1982), noting the important qualitative changes that occur during the first years of a child's life, suggests that developmental scales used to assess children under 18 months of age primarily measure sensorimotor functions. As cognitive functioning and verbal abilities begin to emerge, Sattler states that "the assessment of functions connoting intelligence" becomes possible (1982, p. 57). Sattler's (1982) observations are supported by research findings that suggest that scores from infant developmental scales do not obtain adequate correlations with later IQ scores until the age of 18 months. Thus, while psychologists have means available for assessing developmental progress at different ages, the nature and relative value of the scores produced varies with the age of the child. Sattler (1982) also points out, however, that the developmental and mental quotients of infants and children with severe developmental disabilities are more stable and predictive of later IQs than are similar measurements involving cases of mild delay or superior test performance.

Children between the ages of 2 months and 2½ years referred for psychological evaluation of developmental delay are frequently administered the Bayley Scales of Infant Development (Bayley, 1969). The Bayley scales, described as the best available measure of infant development (Sattler, 1982), are individually administered and require approximately 1 hour to complete. Two scores are provided by the Bayley scales, an index of Mental Development and an index of Psychomotor Development. Also available for use with the Bayley scales is the Infant Behavior Record. This observational record allows for systematic assessment of behaviors exhibited during the examination that are qualitative in nature (e.g., cooperativeness, endurance, tension) and that may have affected test performance. The Mental and Psychomotor Developmental indices are expressed as standard scores (with a mean of 100 and a standard deviation of 16) identical to the way IQs are expressed. Their primary value is in documenting a child's current level of developmental functioning so that subsequent evaluations have a basis for comparison.

The McCarthy Scales of Children's Abilities (McCarthy, 1972) are frequently used by psychologists to assess the general cognitive functioning of children between the ages of 2½ and 8½ years. These scales require about 1 hour to administer and yield a General Cognitive Index (GCI) that is quite comparable to an IQ score.

The Stanford-Binet Intelligence Scale (Terman & Merrill, 1960) is also commonly used to assess general cognitive development, as is the Wechsler Preschool and Primary Scale of Intelligence (WPPSI; Wechsler, 1967). Both of these scales provide IQ scores: the Stanford-Binet for children as young as 2 years old, the WPPSI for children aged 4 to 6½ years.

In cases of general cognitive delay, intelligence tests are used to determine whether a diagnosis of mental retardation is warranted. As mentioned in Chapter 1, the AAMD defines mental retardation partly on the basis of "significantly subaverage intellectual functioning" (Grossman, 1983, p. 1). Significantly subaverage, in turn, has been operationally defined as an IQ score that is below 70. Scores from intelligence tests are also used to determine the severity of mental retardation (i.e., mild, moderate, severe, profound), a determination that often influences placement and programming planning. Because of the potentially negative consequences of diagnosing a child as mentally retarded (e.g., the stigma of being labeled, lowered parent and teacher expectations), choosing, administering, and interpreting tests of intellectual functioning requires both competence and caution.

Adaptive Behavior Scales For children whose developmental or intelligence scale scores indicate substantial delay or for whom the parent's report indicates potential problems with adaptive functioning, psychological assessment often includes a measure of adaptive behavior. The existence of deficits in adaptive behavior is an additional criterion for classification of mental retardation (Grossman, 1983). Therefore, objective and reliable measurement of this important area is needed as well. Fortunately, well-constructed, standardized instruments are available. These scales assess which adaptive behaviors are currently present in the child's repertoire. However, because many of these instruments utilize an interview format rather than direct observation of the child's behavior, the quality of information obtained depends on the accuracy of the parents' (or other informants') report.

Direct Observation of Naturally Occurring Child Behavior Direct observation of child behavior in natural settings is one method by which psychologists can investigate potential inaccuracies in parent report information. Moreover, observations conducted in the home and at day care or preschool settings offer an opportunity to view behaviors when they are less constrained by the artificiality of test or interview situations.

In cases of delayed general cognitive development, direct observation focuses on the age appropriateness of the child's behaviors as well as the stimulus events influencing the occurrence of the behaviors. Once again, an awareness of the normal process of child development serves as a standard by which the observer evaluates the developmental level of the behaviors. Particular attention is given to behaviors that are age appropriate, behaviors representative of much younger children, and behaviors inappropriate for children of any age. Natural observations may also suggest age-appropriate skills that are noticeably absent from the child's repertoire. In day care or preschool settings, direct comparison with the child's peers is also possible and often informative.

Observations of stimulus events (e.g., parent and teacher instructions and reactions) that influence the child's behavior provide information about the modifiability of that behavior. In addition, the effectiveness of instructions and responses that are delivered to the child by adults can be evaluated. Home and school observations also allow the psychologist to ascertain whether adult behaviors and expectations are appropriate given the developmental level of the child. The frequency and quality of parent- and teacher-child interactions are noted along with the overall level of environmental stimulation to which the child is exposed. The extent to which other family members either contribute to or impede the developmental progress of the child is also worthy of examination.

When observation of child behavior in natural settings is not possible, unobtrusive observation (e.g., via one-way mirror or videotape) of role play behavior in the clinic is often a reasonable alternative. Role play tasks should represent realistic situations involving both unstructured (e.g., child and mother playing together) and structured (e.g., mother instructing child to put toys away) scenes.

Summary Information gained from the assessment methods just described should provide an adequate start for most cases involving delayed general cognitive development. However, depending on the age of the child and the degree of developmental delay, important decisions regarding classification and placement may have to be postponed until later evaluations confirm initial assessment findings. For example, an infant whose standard scores from the Bayley scales are equivalent to IQs in the mentally retarded range may not warrant a diagnosis of mental retardation. In such a situation, a diagnosis of mental retardation requires additional testing over time as well as indications of significant deficits in adaptive behavior (see Chapter 1). As discussed earlier, technical limitations in the assessment of infant and preschool cognitive-developmental functioning (e.g., lack of reliable instruments for young children) necessitate caution when considering a diagnosis of mental retardation. Of course, few assessment results and recommendations are seen as absolutely precise and final. Caveats and qualifications surrounding the assessment process should be made explicit when assessment findings are communicated to parents and others. Further, specific recommendations concerning the nature and schedule of program evaluation and assessment reevaluations should also be included in the psychological report.

Academic Failure

Psychologists have a long history of involvement in the assessment and remediation of academic failure. Given that societal and legal demands for the academic achievement of all students has become quite intense (e.g., PL 94-142), psychology's role in educational matters seems to have intensified similarly.

Psychologists receiving a referral of academic failure are often faced with a formidable task. The reciprocal interactions between a child's genetic/internal factors, overt behaviors, and environmental context can be quite complex in cases involving poor school performance. Behaviors required of students within the school setting include basic academic skills such as reading, spelling, and arithmetic as well as those behaviors that foster additional skill acquisition and minimize obstacles to learning. Skills involving information storage and retrieval, selective attention, control of impulsivity, cooperativeness, and dealing with authority are just a few of the behaviors that promote continued school success. Teacher, classroom, and administrative variables also affect a child's academic performance. Achievement in school is further influenced by family variables such as parental expectations of and reactions to school performance (Reynolds et al., 1984).

The methods by which psychologists evaluate referrals for academic failure typically include: 1) parent, teacher, and child interviews; 2) reviews of school and other relevant records; 3) psychometric tests of intellectual functioning; 4) academic achievement tests; and 5) direct observation of classroom behavior, including examination of the productivity and accuracy of the student's work.

Parent, Teacher, and Child Interviews Parent interviews conducted by psychologists to assess academic problems proceed in much the same manner as those described for developmental delay. The focus of the interview is, of course, more on academic than developmental issues. Still, general information pertaining to developmental history, current child functioning, and family interaction is gathered during the interview so that any existing school problems can be viewed in their proper historical and social contexts.

Important questions to be asked of parents concern their child's general academic history (e.g., grades passed/failed, number of school changes) and the nature and history of current school problems. In addition, parental attempts to rectify the problems and the child's responses to such attempts should be explored. Barkley (1981) cites the importance of assessing the extent to which parents work with their child on homework. For families in which the parents have unsuccessfully tried to remedy their child's poor academic achievement, feelings of failure and frustration can lead to harsh conflicts or avoidance behaviors that interfere with intervention efforts. Other areas of inquiry include the parents' level of education, significant events in the academic history of parents and siblings, and whether the child has been recently evaluated for visual and hearing problems.

Teacher interviews should provide answers to questions concerning the nature of the child's academic strengths and weaknesses, the situational or task demands that are especially difficult for the child, and previous efforts by the teacher to assist the child. Teachers' impressions of factors that contribute to the child's poor academic performance or that have produced positive results can also prove to be valuable assessment information. For example, specific class activities, methods of instruction, and proven incentives that influence school work might be identified. At the least, brief consideration should be given to teachers' perceptions of classmates' reactions to the target child's academic failure or the presence of any nonacademic behavior problems that exist.

Child interviews offer an opportunity to ascertain the child's view of which subjects are considered interesting or easy and which can be a source of frustration. Incentives in the home and school for which the child would be willing to work can also be generated by the child. In addition, child interviews can facilitate later test administration by fostering rapport between the child and the examiner.

Review of Records   Systematic review of a child's cumulative school folder is vital to the comprehensive assessment of academic failure. The review usually begins by documenting general information such as grades passed and failed, number of schools attended, and the general level of academic functioning achieved. Patterns of successful and deficient performance in various academic areas should also be investigated. Scores from annual, group-administered achievement tests, and quarterly, semester, or final course grades represent potential sources of assessment data gathered across time. Consistent difficulty across time within certain academic areas should, of course, be thoroughly investigated during testing. School records may also contain important information regarding persistent discipline problems, an inordinate number of school absences, or the results of previous psychoeducational evaluations.

Tests of Intellectual Functioning   Individually administered tests of intellectual functioning are fairly predictive of school achievement. Therefore, scores from these measures provide a rough guide of what may be expected in terms of a child's academic performance. Of course, cases involving severe intellectual deficits are usually identified prior to school entry. Cases of mild mental retardation, however, may not be identified until certain school tasks prove to be too demanding and the child's teacher makes the needed referral. Intelligence scale scores are used to classify these students so that proper special education services can be provided.

Some children referred by teachers because of academic failure do not, however, demonstrate impaired performance on tests of intellectual functioning. These children may still be eligible for special services, but first must meet criteria for categories such as learning disabled, behavior disordered, or emotionally disturbed. In such cases, "normal" or "near normal" intelligence test scores have failed to accurately predict academic achievement. For children with behavior disorders or emotional disturbance, external or behavioral factors that have interfered with school success (e.g., constant fighting, truancy, elective mutism, depression) are often easily identified. For children considered to have learning disabilities, though, a determination of why academic success is not forthcoming can be very difficult. Under the present legal definitions, classifying a child as learning disabled usually involves several exclusionary steps (see Chapter 1). One exclusionary step is the measurement of the child's intelligence level and a determination of whether the child has or does not have mental retardation.

The Wechsler Intelligence Scale for Children–Revised (WISC-R; Wechsler, 1974) is often used by psychologists to perform this function. Some research findings suggest that children with learning disabilities have distinctive patterns of results on the WISC-R. For example, Verbal IQ may be lower than Performance IQ, or scores on a certain group of subtests (e.g., Arithmetic, Coding, Information, and Digit Span—the ACID pattern) may be far lower than other subtest scores. Unfortunately, such research findings have not proven useful to the clinician (Barkley, 1981; Sattler, 1982). For one thing, such findings are based on IQ scores from a large group of identified learning disabled students, any number of whom may have test profiles discrepant with the group's average. Thus, for the purpose of assessing an individual student, WISC-R patterns have little diagnostic value. Second, current explanations for the appearance of certain learning disabled WISC-R profiles are mainly speculative and rarely influence intervention planning.

Nevertheless, in order to classify a child as learning disabled, current school problems must not be determined to be the result of mental retardation (PL 94-142); thus, the role of intelligence testing in the assessment of most cases of school failure is a significant but limited one. The identification of children who are clearly at risk for later school success due to intellectual deficits is certainly aided by intelligence testing. Also, for students whose IQ scores do not indicate intellectual impairment, test results and informal observations of the student's test behavior may provide the psychologist with hypotheses about specific deficit areas. However, additional interpretations of intelligence test results not supported by empirical research have little utility in the assessment and remediation of academic failure.

Academic Achievement Tests Individually administered tests of academic achievement provide psychologists with an independent and current assessment of a student's academic skills. Usually, test results parallel information obtained from other sources. Occasionally, though, discrepancies arise and the psychologist must reconcile differing estimations of the student's academic level. Achievement tests are also useful in identifying particular areas of academic strength and weakness. Areas in which the student appears to be deficient can be further evaluated by using achievement tests designed to measure the component skills (e.g., word attack, reading comprehension) of a single academic area such as reading.

Academic achievement tests are often used to make decisions regarding educational placement. These tests can be very useful in identifying the subject areas that are most problematic for the student and in making comparisons of the student's performance with age- or grade-based norms. Norm-referenced tests of academic achievement are, unfortunately, inadequate in formulating ways of remedying academic deficiencies. In order to identify academic behaviors that can serve as useful targets of remediation adequately, the psychologist must assess specific skills by entering the educational environment and directly observing the student's behavior and the circumstances that influence that behavior.

Direct Observation of Classroom Behavior The sine qua non of competent psychological assessment for school failure is the direct observation of a student's behavior in the classroom setting. The importance of classroom observation is based on the premise that the behaviors a student must perform in order to acquire academic skills do not take place in a social vacuum. Instead, the behaviors are at least partially determined by factors existing only in the particular classroom situation. Furthermore, the remediation of poor achievement usually requires the identification of environmental variables that can be manipulated in order to foster more desirable behaviors.

The classroom behaviors that psychologists elect to observe should be easily quantifiable and potentially meaningful targets for change. Although some individuals may choose to assess the percentage of time in which a child appears to be "on-task" (e.g., eyes on own paper, seated at own desk), research has shown that school work productivity (i.e., amount of work completed) and accuracy (i.e., proportion done correctly) are more appropriate target behaviors (Barkley, 1981). Samples of the student's work should be collected and used to establish a baseline measure of these behaviors. Since permanent products of a student's work are relatively easy to collect, teachers may be willing to perform this function over several days in order to examine the consistency of the behavior. Samples of the student's work can be examined for often repeated errors suggestive of the student's failure to learn certain prerequisite concepts or skills. In fact, an analysis of the specific components involved in a particular academic task is a very useful way of establishing appropriate target behaviors (see Elliott & Piersel, 1982).

Besides identifying and measuring relevant child behaviors, classroom observation involves assessment of the environmental stimuli that influence the behaviors. Actual classroom variables might include the number of students in the class, the arrangement of the desks, and the time of day in which the class is held. Teacher variables include expectations for the identified student, methods of disciplining the class, and methods of assessing and rewarding successful completion of school work. Instructional variables include the level of instruction (at or below grade), the manner in which the material is presented, the types of classroom activities used, and the nature and difficulty of class assignments and tests.

Attention should also be given to the interactional behaviors occurring between the teacher and the child as well as between the child and the other students. For example, how does the teacher respond to the child's inappropriate behavior or failure to complete assigned work? What is the reaction of other students to the child's academic shortcomings or disruptive behavior?

Summary   The assessment of academic failure requires a considerable amount of "detective" work. Given the multitude of factors and behaviors that can determine academic failure, comprehensive assessment requires the use of multiple sources of information gathered through a variety of means. The assessment methods described in this chapter provide information useful in making placement decisions, devising strategies for remedying academic problems, and providing methods for evaluating remedial programs. Of course, the presence of additional behavior problems that are nonacademic in nature requires additional assessment approaches. Refer to Mash and Terdal (1981) for discussions regarding the assessment of additional behavior problems.

REFERENCES

Bandura, A. (1978). The self-system in reciprocal determinism. *American Psychologist, 33,* 344–358.

Barkley, R. A. (1981). Learning disabilities. In E. J. Mash & L. G. Terdal (Eds.), *Behavioral assessment of childhood disorders* (pp. 441–482). New York: Guilford Press.

Bayley, N. (1969). *Bayley Scales of Infant Development: Birth to two years.* New York: Psychological Corporation.

Bergan, J. R. (1977). *Behavioral consultation.* Columbus, Ohio: Charles E. Merrill.

Carroll, J. B. (1972). Review of the Illinois Test of Psycholinguistic Abilities. In O.K. Buros (Ed.), *The seventh mental measurements yearbook* (pp. 1012–1014). Highland Park, NJ: Gryphon Press.

Christensen, A. L. (1975). *Luria's neuropsychological investigation.* New York: Spectrum Publications.

Cronbach, L. J. (1970). *Essentials of psychological testing* (3rd ed.). New York: Harper & Row.

Das, J. P., Kirby, J. R., & Jarman, R. F. (1975). Simultaneous and successive syntheses: An alternative model for cognitive abilities. *Psychological Bulletin, 82,* 87–103.

Dean, R. S. (1982). Neuropsychological assessment. In T. R. Kratochwill (Ed.), *Advances in school psychology* (Vol. 2, pp. 171–218). Hillsdale, NJ: Lawrence Erlbaum Associates

Dean, R. S. (in press). Perspectives on the future of neuropsychological assessment. In B. S. Plake & J. C. Witt (Eds.), *The future of neuropsychological assessment.* Hillsdale, NJ: Lawrence Erlbaum Associates.

D'Zurilla, T. J., & Goldfried, M. R. (1971). Problem solving and behavior modification. *Journal of Abnormal Psychology, 78,* 107–126.

Elliott, S. N., & Piersel, W. C. (1982). Direct assessment of reading skills: An approach which links assessment to intervention. *School Psychology Review, 11,* 267–280.

Fabres, G. B. (1985). The Personality Inventory for Children (PIC) and hyperactivity: Clinical utility and problems of generalizability. *Journal of Pediatric Psychology, 10,* 141–149.

Federal Register, 42 (42474–42518), August 23, 1977.

Golden, C. J. (1981). A standardized version of Luria's neuropsychological testing: A quantitative and qualitative qpproach to neuropsychological education. In J. B. Filskov & T. J. Boll (Eds.), *Handbook of clinical neuropsychology* (pp. 416–512). New York: John Wiley & Sons.

Golden, C. J. (1982). *Diagnosis and rehabilitation in clinical neuropsychology.* Springfield, IL: Charles C Thomas.

Golden, C. J., & Berg, R. A. (1983). Interpretation of the Luria-Nebraska Neuropsychological Battery by inter-item intercorrelation: Intellectual processes. *Clinical Neuropsychology, 5,* 23–28.

Golden, C. J., Hammeke, T. A., & Purisch, A. D. (1978). Diagnostic validity of a neuropsychological battery derived from Luria's neuropsychological tests. *Journal of Consulting and Clinical Psychology, 46,* 1258–1265.

Gordon, H. W. (1983). Dyslexia. In R. E. Tarter & G. Goldstein (Eds.), *Neuropsychology of childhood.* New York: Plenum.

Grossman, H. (Ed.). (1983). *Classification in mental retardation.* Washington, DC: American Association on Mental Deficiency.

Guadalupe v. Tempe Elementary School District 71-435, District Court for Arizona (1972, January).

Hooper, S. R., & Hynd, G. W. (1982). *The differential diagnosis of developmental dyslexia with the Kaufman Assessment Battery for Children.* Paper presented at the meeting of the National Academy of Neuropsychologists, Atlanta.

Jensen, A. R. (1980). *Bias in mental testing.* New York: Free Press.

Kaufman, A. S. (1983). Some questions and answers about the Kaufman Assessment Battery for Children (K-ABC). *Journal of Psychoeducational Assessment, 1,* 205–218.

Kaufman, A. S., & Kaufman, N. (1983). *The Kaufman Assessment Battery for Children.* Circle Pines, MN: American Guidance Service.

Kelly, T. L. (1927). *The interpretation of educational measurements.* Yonkers-on-Hudson, NY: World Book.

Kieth, T. Z. (1985). Questioning the K-ABC: What does it measure? *School Psychology Review, 14,* 9–20.

Kirk, S. A., McCarthy, J. J., & Kirk, W. D. (1968). *Illinois Test of Psycholinguistic Abilities.* Urbana: University of Illinois Press.

Koppitz, E. M. (1982). Personality assessment in the schools. In C. R. Reynolds & T. B. Gutkin (Eds.), *Handbook of school psychology.* New York: John Wiley & Sons.

Lachar, D. (1982). *Personality Inventory for Children (PIC) revised format manual supplement.* Los Angeles: Western Psychological Services.

Lachar, D., Gdowski, C. L., & Snyder, D. K. (1982). Broad-band dimensions of psychopathology: Factor scales for the Personality Inventory for Children. *Journal of Consulting and Clinical Psychology, 50,* 634–642.

Lachar, D., Kline, R. B., & Boersman, D. C. (in press). The Personality Inventory for Children: Approaches to actuarial interpretation in clinic and school settings. In H. M. Knoff (Ed.), *The psychological assessment of child and adolescent personality.* New York: Guilford Press.

Lambert, N., & Windmiller, M. (1981). *AAMD Adaptive Behavior Scale, School Edition.* Monterey, CA: CTR/McGraw-Hill.

Luria, A. R. (1966). *Higher cortical functions in man.* New York: Basic Books.

Luria, A. R. (1973). *The working brain.* London: Penguin Press.

Mash, E. J., & Terdal, L. G. (1981). Behavioral assessment of childhood disturbance. In E. J. Mash & L. G. Terdal (Eds.), *Behavioral assessment of childhood disorders* (pp. 3–76). New York: Guilford Press.

McCarthy, D. A. (1972). *Manual for the McCarthy Scales of Children's Abilities.* New York: Psychological Corporation.

McKay, S., & Golden, C. J. (1979). Empirical derivation of neuropsychological scales for the lateralization of brain damage using the Luria-Nebraska Neuropsychological Test Battery. *Clinical Neuropsychology, 1,* 1–5.

Messick, S. (1983). Assessment of children. In P. Mussen (Ed.), *Manual of child psychology* (4th ed.). New York: John Wiley & Sons.

Raimy, V. (Ed.). (1950). *Training in clinical psychology.* Englewood Cliffs, NJ: Prentice-Hall.

Repp, A. C., & Deitz, D. E. D. (1983). Mental retardation. In T. H. Ollendick & M. Hersen (Eds.), *Handbook of child psychopathology* (pp. 97–122). New York: Plenum.

Reynolds, C. R., Gutkin, T. B., Elliott, S. N., & Witt, J. C. (1984). *School psychology: Essentials of theory and practice.* New York: John Wiley & Sons.

Salvia, J., & Ysseldyke, J. E. (1981). *Assessment in special and remedial education.* Boston: Houghton Mifflin.

Sattler, J. M. (1982). *Assessment of children's intelligence and special abilities* (2nd ed.). Boston: Allyn & Bacon.

Taylor, R. L., & Warren, S. A. (1984). Educational and psychological assessment of children with learning disorders. *Pediatric Clinics of North America, 31,* 281–296.

Terman, L. M., & Merrill, M. A. (1960). *Stanford-Binet Intelligence Scale.* Newton, MA: Houghton Mifflin.

Wechsler, D. (1967). *Manual for the Wechsler Preschool and Primary Scale of Intelligence.* New York: Psychological Corporation.

Wechsler, D. (1974). *Manual for the Wechsler Intelligence Scale for Children–Revised.* New York: Psychological Corporation.

Wirt, R. D., Lachar, D., Kleindinst, J. K., & Seat, P. D. (1977). *Multidimensional description of child personality: A manual for the Personality Inventory for Children.* Los Angeles: Western Psychological Services.

Wirt, R. D., Lachar, D., Kleindinst, J. K., & Seat, P. D. (1984). *Multidimensional description of child personality: A manual for the Personality Inventory for Children.* Los Angeles: Western Psychological Services.

Witt, J. C. (in press). Assessment of educational environments. In T. B. Gutkin & C. R. Reynolds (Eds.), *Handbook of school psychology: Vol. 2.* New York: John Wiley & Sons.

Witt, J. C., Elliott, S. N., Gresham, F. M., & Kramer, J. J. (in press). *Assessment of children's learning and behavior problems.* Boston: Little, Brown.

Witt, J. C., & Gresham, F. M. (1985). Review of the Wechsler Intelligence Scale for Children. In J. V. Mitchell (Ed.), *The ninth mental measurements yearbook* (pp. 1716–1719). Lincoln, NE: Buros Institute of Mental Measurements.

Chapter 3

Special Education Assessment

~~/

Michael J. Hannafin

The importance of the special education assessment cannot be overstated. More than other team members, such as the psychologist and physician who are concerned with broader classification and diagnosis, the assessment techniques of the special educator are woven with the nature of the intervention. The conditions assessed by the special educator, and the focus of the assessment, may have far-reaching implications for the student as well as the assessment team. If the intervention is to be tied to the findings of the special education assessment, then it is important that the special education assessment is philosophically consistent with the other members of the assessment team and the academic setting.

Special education assessment can be a complicated process. The sheer number of formal and informal tests available and the associated range of skills to be assessed can be formidable. Indeed, several comprehensive textbooks exist that review the myriad of tests used to assess the skills of students with handicaps (see Salvia & Ysseldyke, 1981; Witt, Elliott, Gresham, & Kramer, 1986).

Despite the availability of textbooks on tests and interpretation, little is available concerning the nature of special education assessment. For instance, what type of information is needed and why particular techniques are applied are at least as important as which techniques are to be employed and how they will be administered and interpreted. Since tests are developed and revised continuously, it is necessary to comprehend the nature and functions of assessment to be able to select appropriate techniques. The purpose of this chapter is to describe the nature and functions of special education assessment.

CHARACTERISTICS UNIQUE TO SPECIAL EDUCATION ASSESSMENT

Unlike the kinds of sophisticated and formal technical assessment techniques described in other chapters of this text, the special education assessment techniques and procedures include far greater emphasis on nonstandardized tests and informal techniques. Principally, this is due to the fundamentally different purposes that assessment serves at this level. Special education assessment is more for prescription than for description; more for remediation than for classification; more for skill specification than for identification of broad academic domains. In short, the techniques used for special education assessment, while incorporating many of the formal assessment techniques of other team members, have evolved to emphasize instructional utility to a greater degree than most.

What this means, typically, is that the perspective adopted during assessment is tied closely to academic performance settings, such as those found in everyday classrooms. The special educator attempts to identify the specific ways in which the academic achievement of a given student deviates from the performance of the typical student. At issue is neither how much of a deviation is found nor identification of the etiology of the deficiency. At issue is the specific locus of student performance deficiencies, and the implications for the design of instructional interventions.

Assessing Academic Performance: Functional Differences

In many school settings, academic performance and achievement are assessed by school psychologists as well as by special education diagnosticians. For psychologists, however, assessment is conducted for fundamentally different purposes: diagnosis and classification. It is rarely the function of the school psychologist's achievement testing to identify the specific sources of performance deficiency, except as a general subject area, or in some cases global skill domains. For the psychologist, achievement is defined using terms such as grade level, percentile scores, and other standardized test scores that provide indices of individual performance compared to a broader normative population. Since diagnosis and classification focus on whether a student is "handicapped" according to given criteria, standardized achievement tests provide reliable and valid techniques for evaluating the relative performance of a student in comparatively global rather than specific terms.

In practice, however, global achievement has little instructional value when defined as grade level, percentile, or standard scores. The scores merely provide a single indicator of untold specific knowledge. They account for the amount of learning, large or small, but not the skills learned. They provide broad normative estimates of the performance of a particular student versus the general student population, but nothing upon which to base instruction or remediation.

For the special education diagnostician, assessment of academic performance and achievement assumes a very different meaning. The goal of assessment for these diagnosticians is at a level designed to improve the teaching-learning process directly on an individual student basis. The focus is on the learning of well-defined skills and information by individual students. The techniques used take into account the specific information to be learned, the abilities and capabilities of the learners as determined among team members, and both formal and informal methods for evaluating the academic performance status of students. From the special educator's viewpoint, assessment procedures and techniques are needed to identify specific performance deficiencies, to permit the prescription of instructional plans based upon identified deficiencies, to provide sufficient focus and detail to permit the identification or development of appropriate instructional materials, and to provide the basis for remedial, compensatory, or supplementary instruction. These functions are fulfilled through the special education assessment, provided in consort with a comprehensive, multidisciplinary assessment team.

A Typical Referral Example

A fourth-grade teacher becomes concerned due to the slow, and apparently deteriorating, performance of Jessica. The teacher reports that Jessica was never a "top student," and that she appears to have "slipped through the cracks" to reach the fourth grade. The teacher observes very low reading and math performance, frequent periods of crying, fighting on the playground, and withdrawal from participation in the classroom.

In most cases, such a student is initially referred to the psychologist for an evaluation of her emotional condition, and possibly her intellectual and achievement status. The psychologist determines that Jessica is a child with intellectual development in the educable mentally handicapped range and determines her emotional outbursts to be related to her academic frustration in the classroom. Her overall achievement in reading and math is roughly at the first-grade level. Jessica is eligible for special education assistance, but assessment thus far still does not answer what will be taught. The achievement tests administered have established in a general way that a deficiency exists, but have not identified the special skills requiring additional instruction. Which skills must be developed and which have already been learned?

The answers to these questions are typically provided through special education assessment. The special education diagnostician administers a battery of tests and conducts a series of observations sufficient to define the specific instructional targets and priorities for students. As this chapter progresses, the types and nature of special education assessment are described.

TRAINING AND COMPETENCY REQUIREMENTS FOR SPECIAL EDUCATORS

Virtually every state in the United States and every country in the English-speaking world has developed certification procedures and standards for special educators. In addition, advocacy groups such as the Council for Exceptional Children (CEC) and the Association for Retarded Citizens (ARC) publish competency requirements for teachers of students with learning disabilities or mental retardation. The entry level academic training for special education certification is usually at the bachelor's degree level, with advanced training at either master's or doctoral degree level. The focus of typical certification and competency requirements, however, is usually on the skills necessary for effective teaching, and the emphasis is not heavily oriented toward assessment.

Generally speaking, certification standards include formal coursework in learning theory, introductory tests and measurement, methods courses in teaching exceptional children, and courses in specific exceptionalities such as the psychology of the child with emotional disturbance. Applied experience, provided through prior experience, internships, or student teaching is also required. The breadth of training required for certification can be very helpful in understanding the practical problems and constraints involved in special education instruction.

The absence of a concentration in assessment, however, can be troublesome, since certification requirements rarely specify proficiency in specific tests and techniques. The following section addresses the major assessment tools and concepts appropriate for the special educator, and provides an estimation of the degree of knowledge needed at each level.

OVERVIEW OF THE ASSESSMENT PROCESS

The primary functions of special education assessment in multidisciplinary teams are synthesis, diagnosis, and prescription. These functions require the ability to collect, sort, and analyze input from other team members regarding global aspects of the learner and identified capabilities and disabilities in order to develop relevant, workable, and appropraite instructional solutions. This means that the special educator must be familiar with the diagnostic techniques of other team members as well as the administration and interpretation of specific educational tests. The following is a description of the kinds of general concepts and specific tools needed by an individual conducting special education assessment for students with learning disabilities or mental handicaps.

Basic Concepts and Areas of Information

The special education diagnostician must have a basic knowledge of tests and measurement in general. The following are general concepts important to such an understanding.

Reliability and Validity   At a conceptual level, it is important that special education diagnosticians comprehend reliability and validity. In essence, reliability pertains to the consistency of assessment techniques and validity to their legitimacy. These concepts are described fully in a variety of sources (see Chapter 2; Cronbach, 1970; Thorndike & Hagen, 1969), and are not repeated here. Specific applications of these concepts, however, are described throughout this chapter.

Test Construction   Knowledge of test construction, which is essential both to users of commercial assessment devices and to developers of custom-made tests, is also important. For example, the strengths and weaknesses of different item types, such as multiple choice versus short completion items, are important to both test selection and development. Other factors such as test length, test item complexity, and test clarity must be understood before the special educator can select or develop appropriate tools.

Types of Tests   Finally, perhaps the most important general measurement information required is the difference between norm-referenced standardized tests and criterion-referenced assessment. Standardized tests are designed to differentiate student performance by comparing an individual student to a "typical" population. In effect, they provide a relative indication of an individual student's performance. Criterion-referenced assessment is more skill-specific, comparing student performance in specific areas to a standard or criterion for effective performance. The standard is usually based on the importance of the skill assessed: more important skills have more rigorous standards, less important skills have less rigorous standards. Decisions as to which type of assessment to use are made continually, and should be based on firm knowledge of what each type of assessment does effectively, the nature or purpose of the assessment, and the amount of specific detail required. These issues are addressed throughout this chapter.

Other Important Areas of Knowledge

Several aspects of assessment related to the comprehensive assessment of students, and to special education in particular, are also notable. The following are areas of which the special education diagnostician should be aware, but which generally do not require advanced proficiency.

Intelligence Testing   Since intellectual competence is a more or less routine part of learning disability and mental retardation assessments, special educators should be very familiar with the construct of intelligence, and be knowledgeable of the principal intelligence tests used. However, they are not usually expected to possess the operational competency necessary to actually administer and carry out primary interpretation of such tests. To a large extent, student performance on IQ measures dictates the classification of a handicapping condition. More important, the kinds of specific skills to be assessed for special education may be broadened, or restricted, depending on the intellectual ability of a particular student. Whereas operational competence in intellectual assessment is rarely required, conceptual knowledge is often very valuable.

Formal and Informal Assessment Individuals should also be well versed in the differences between formal and informal assessment techniques. Most of the tests used in education are classified as formal in that administration techniques are prescribed, as are scoring and interpretation guidelines. However, the assessment repertoire of the special educator should include informal assessment techniques as well, such as classroom observations, background data collection, and analysis of work samples. This type of assessment is characterized by a greater emphasis on professional judgment, informal analysis, and anecdotal information. Both formal and informal techniques can be very useful, provided that the strengths and limitations are understood.

Background Influences Special education diagnosticians also need to be aware of the social and cultural influences that may affect academic performance. This is especially true when assessing students from backgrounds that are markedly different from the "norm" on which test items and norms have been developed. In some cases, the student being evaluated is atypical of the local student population. His or her score on a test may reflect difficulties due to cultural differences, rather than intellectual or perceptual problems. Awareness of social and cultural influences in the assessment process, especially those most unique to the immediate region, is particularly important in extreme cases.

Types of Assessment Tools

The areas in which advanced training and competency are required are those that provide the special educator with his or her primary diagnostic tools. In some cases, the tools involve the use of specific tests; in others, they require the ability to develop assessment items and procedures to match referral needs. The kinds of assessment measures necessary for special education assessment that are introduced in this section are described more fully later in this chapter.

Standardized Diagnostic Achievement Tests A number of standardized diagnostic achievement tests exist, including: the Key Math Diagnostic Arithmetic Test (Connolly, Nachtman, & Pritchett, 1971), the Woodcock Reading Mastery Tests (Woodcock, 1973), the Assessment of Basic Competencies (Somwaru, 1981), the Diagnostic Skills Battery (Anderhalter, 1980), and the Diagnostic Reading Scales (Spache, 1963). Standardized diagnostic achievement tests provide information regarding a student's performance in given skill domains, usually nested within a specific subject matter area such as reading or mathematics. Proficiency with tests of this type is useful because it enables the special educator to examine a broader area of known deficiency in order to identify specific strengths and weaknesses. They provide a more refined analysis of the global scores provided by typical achievement tests. Instead of the grade-equivalent for a particular subject provided by standardized achievement tests, diagnostic achievement tests reveal a more detailed breakdown of the skills related to the subject tested. Rather than simply identifying that a student is reading at a third-grade level, the diagnostic test can isolate such areas as letter recognition, word attack, and word comprehension that collectively enable a student to read. However, they do not generally provide enough specificity to permit the development of individual instructional prescriptions.

Criterion-Referenced Tests Special education diagnosticians should be very familiar with criterion-based assessment techniques. Two examples of such measures are the Criterion Test of Basic Skills (Lundell & Evans, 1976) and the Brigance Diagnostic Inventory of Basic Skills (Brigance, 1976). In criterion-based assessment, test items and procedures correspond directly to defined objectives. For example, instead of either the broad grade-equivalent yielded by a standardized achievement test or the word attack scale of a diagnostic achievement test, a criterion-referenced test assesses a skill such as a student's ability to read words with a specific vowel combination such as "ou." The skill is assessed for "ou" words and requires a given percentage of accuracy. The performance of students is assessed relative to specific prescribed outcomes, and according to the criteria for acceptable performance. This type of assessment can be readily translated into instructional prescriptions since the tasks tested and the skills targeted for instruction are identical. Such procedures are the cornerstone of special education assessment.

Perceptual Assessment A variety of perceptually oriented assessment techniques are also widely used, such as The Marianne Frostig Developmental Test of Visual Perception (Frostig, Maslow, Lefever, & Witlesey, 1966), the Southern California Sensory Integration Tests (Ayers, 1972), and the Motor-Free Test of Visual Perception (Calarusso & Hammill, 1972). The basic philosophical approach of such techniques is that correct perception of stimuli is requisite to effective learning. Such procedures isolate a particular perceptual capability such as visual discrimination among symbols, and require that the student perform a particular task to demonstrate perceptual integrity. Many proponents of perceptually oriented assessment advocate remediation of the perceptual deficiency per se, rather than a focus on the "symptoms" of the deficiency, although attempts to remedy perceptual processes are not without controversy (see Chapter 1).

Diagnosis to Prescription

In most schools, the special educator's primary function is the development and implementation of a well-defined individualized education program (IEP). This requires the synthesis of relevant data into a working plan for addressing the individual learning problems of the student. An abbreviated sample IEP is shown in Figure 3.1. Important skill requirements for the diagnostician include the ability to identify those features of a comprehensive assessment that have direct relevance for instructional planning and to convert the findings into a manageable and appropriate instructional plan. This process typically involves a balancing of the strengths and limitations of each learner, the development of instructional objectives around which teaching efforts will revolve, and the identification of instructional materials appropriate for the objectives established. To complete these tasks effectively, the special educator's base of experience should extend well beyond training in formal assessment, and include field experience in the development and implementation of individualized education programs.

Progress Evaluation

Related to the development of IEPs is the application of formal and informal assessment techniques to monitor and evaluate student progress. The focus of the IEP, established by the instructional objectives, provides the basis for the

---

Bellvue Area School District
Individualized Education Program

Student Name: Juan Ortiz   Date Plan Established: 9/15/85
Teacher Name: Johnson   Scheduled Review Date: 12/1/85

OBJECTIVES:

Reading: To pronounce correctly 1 syllable words containing "ou" vowel combinations with at least 95% accuracy.

Math: To compute sums for single digit addition problems with at least 90% accuracy.

Teacher Signature: _____
Parent Signature: _____
Date of Signature: _____

Figure 3.1. A sample IEP form.

precise type of progress assessment to be conducted. While standardized assessment techniques are occasionally used, it is more likely that criterion-based assessment techniques that focus directly on the specific skills addressed in the IEP will be used. Earlier, an example of criterion-referenced assessment to identify competence in reading words with an "ou" vowel combination was provided. If a student were unable to perform, presumably the instruction provided should focus on this skill. In order to determine whether or not the instruction has been successful, the same skill is usually retested. In effect, the diagnostic tool becomes the progress evaluation tool. In order to conduct appropriate evaluations of student progress after entry into special education programs, therefore, competency in criterion-based assessment is essential.

COMPONENTS OF SPECIAL EDUCATION ASSESSMENT

As noted previously, the special educator assumes primary responsibility for assessing the academic classroom performance of the student, including problems that require a precise description of the status of academic and related skills. Whereas this may appear to be an enormous assessment responsibility, this is seldom true in practice.

As part of a multidisciplinary team, the types of assessment activities of the special educator are necessarily limited. The scope of the assessment is typically constrained by already identified, but more broadly defined, problems. Many children with severe handicaps have biomedical conditions identified, others have behavioral syndromes or symptoms, and most are assigned broad labels such as learning disabled or mentally retarded by the time they are referred to the special educator. For example, a student may be identified as having a learning disability, a reading deficiency, and an expressive language problem, all resulting in classroom performance that is significantly below expectations. This student may be referred for special education assessment to identify more precisely the deficient skills.

There are two principal classes of special education assessments used: those that address performance outputs and those that address the processes of learning. This section provides an overview of each.

Assessment Focusing on Observable Performance

This class of assessment includes the observable products of the student's effort, with the emphasis on either achievement at appropriate levels or attainment of specific skills or competencies. Standards such as developmental milestones or curriculum objectives can provide the expected performance yardstick against which student performance is compared. Deficiencies are usually defined as the difference between expected and observed performance. In general, the causes of the deficiencies are not the focal point of the assessment; instead, the emphasis is on detecting deficient skills for purposes of establishing meaningful instructional objectives.

Consider the following example of an evaluation of observable performance. John, a third-grade student, is referred for evaluation due to problems associated with reading. The teacher notes that John does not apply phonetic reading skills very well, and as a result both reading fluency and comprehension are very poor. Of initial concern in the assessment is the identification of the phonics skills that are mastered, and those that are not. In addition, the assessment might include the application of phonetic skills in an oral reading task. The results of a series of criterion-referenced tests show the student to be deficient in producing the short vowel sounds for "a," "i," and "e," often confusing the sounds among the three letters. Since this is a fundamental skill, the problem is manifested across a variety of words, resulting in the poor fluency and comprehension cited by the teacher.

In effect, each component of the assessment addresses a performance output, in this case the oral production of vowel sounds for given letters. Little is assumed as to the internal reasons for the observed deficiencies. An initial objective for remediation, as a result, might be to teach the student to produce correct sounds for each of the deficient vowels, both in isolation and in context.

Assessment Focusing on Learning Processes

Unlike observable performance assessment, assessment of learning processes focuses on the presumed perceptual skills required to learn effectively, and the degree to which such processes are considered intact or deficient. The underlying assumption is that accurate initial encoding and subsequent retrieval and decoding into responses is requisite to effective learning. Ineffective learning may be related more to impaired or inaccurate perception or processing of information than to difficulties pertaining to particular instructional content.

For example, special education assessment might focus on the specific visual and auditory processing skills considered necessary to perform the task of reading. First, the student is required to discriminate visually and demonstrate the detection of differences among certain visual symbols. Often, the letters "b" and "d" or "p" and "q" are not discriminated effectively due to their configuration similarities. Difficulty noted in the observable act of reading words that include these letters might be associated with the encoding process itself.

Next, the student is tested to determine if auditory discriminations can be made consistently. If the student has difficulty reading words that include either "b" or "d," this may be manifested by frequent "b for d" or "d for b" substitutions by the student when reading the words. If, however, the student effectively differentiates each sound when heard, then the problem might be considered to be primarily a visual discrimination deficiency.

Combined Performance-Process Assessments

Assessments combining process and performance are perhaps the most common among special educators. Diagnosticians frequently consider both specific performance indicators, such as achievement or academic skill development, and perceptual competence, such as visual or auditory discrimination. In some cases, combined assessment is done to exclude severe perceptual processing deficiencies as a cause of academic problems. Minor processing deficiencies, when paired with significant academic problems, are not usually considered the focal point of either diagnosis or prescription. More often than not, combined assessments are used to identify areas of extreme perceptual deficiency, indicating processing problems so influential as to make academic skill remediation efforts futile.

Assessment Orientation

The orientation of assessment frequently affects the type of instructional interventions to be employed. Deficiencies of a perceptual nature are often addressed by perceptually based instruction, with the "symptoms" of the disorder generally de-emphasized in favor of the presumed perceptual roots of the performance deficiencies. In the preceding example, perceptually oriented instruction designed to make the student more sensitive to the subtle differences in sounds might be recommended. The emphasis on remediation generally follows the perceptual orientation of the assessment.

Conversely, deficiencies of a performance nature are usually addressed via performance-based instruction. In the preceding example, John might receive extensive practice, using a variety of instructional techniques, on producing the correct sounds for the letters "a," "i," and "e." The focus of the instruction is tied directly to the nature of the assessment, in that the remediation focuses directly on the specific performance output deficiencies identified through assessment.

TECHNIQUES AND TOOLS OF ASSESSMENT

The basic functions of special education assessment are reinforced throughout this chapter. The principal functions of assessment are to localize the source or sources of academic deficiency, and to plan remedial, compensatory, or supplementary instruction. These two functions are highly interrelated; the nature and content of the assessment prescribe the nature and content of subsequent instruction. This relationship is important to recognize because assessment procedures for the special educator are fundamentally different from those of other team members. Although the method of applying assessment data to instruction is not the focus of this chapter, in practice, the assessment-prescription functions are virtually inseparable.

Instructional Analysis

The methods used to assess the academic performance of children with learning disabilities or mental retardation include consideration of a variety of factors. Several prominent instructional theorists have advocated the implementation of instructional analysis procedures (Dick & Carey, 1985; Gagné, 1985). Instructional analysis is a formal process used to evaluate learner characteristics, situational or contextual factors, and specific learning task considerations systematically. The various levels of instructional analysis are shown in Figure 3.2. The following are brief descriptions of the levels of instructional analysis.

Learner analysis Learner analysis is a process whereby relevant characteristics of the student, such as age, grade level, motivational factors, entry level skills, known abilities and disabilities, and physical limitations are evaluated for influence on classroom performance. Information derived from both previous and current assessments is considered. Each characteristic potentially influences student performance; the task of learner analysis is to identify which characteristics actually exert influence.

Consider the referral of an inner-city, ninth-grade student, Juan, for academic deficiencies. It is obvious to all that Juan's academic performance is

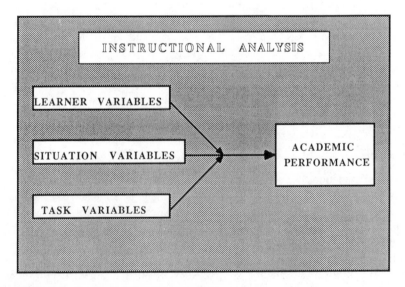

Figure 3.2. Levels of instructional analysis.

deficient, but it is necessary to identify those influences that contribute to poor performance before meaningful remediation can be provided. Through learner analysis, it is discovered that Juan requires instructional procedures that are more motivating than traditional workbook approaches, preferably with content perceived as relevant to his employment goal: automotive mechanics. Further, while his performance on standardized achievement tests indicates math and reading skills typical of a third-grader, an in-depth analysis indicates that he has little difficulty with functional mathematics skills such as using money and telling time, and is able to read and comprehend automotive and sports magazines effectively. The information was obtained by closely analyzing the attributes of the learner and examining those factors likely to exert influence on academic performance. As a result, the diagnosis is richer in prescriptive value.

Situation analysis Several factors in the classroom or other learning setting may influence academic performance. The goal of situation analysis is to identify which factors actually influence student achievement, either positively or negatively. Situation variables include considerations such as class size, specific instructional materials, classroom procedures, opportunity for individualized instruction, clarity of directions, and the general organizational structure of the classroom.

Consider the role of situation analysis in the preceding example. Juan attends class in an economically disadvantaged school with poor teacher morale, old and worn-out instructional materials, large class sizes, and inconsistent student attendance. The school has a very high dropout rate, and several of Juan's friends already have dropped out, or intend to. For all but the exceptionally bright, self-motivated students, the situation is not likely to promote effective learning. Of interest in situation analysis is the identification of factors likely to influence deficient performance negatively, and those factors, if any, that are likely to support learning. What is clear in this example is that the present situation may be significantly influencing the resulting performance deficiencies. By identifying those factors likely to exert such influence, the opportunity to prescribe solutions that account for them is improved.

Task analysis Perhaps the most widely used method of instructional analysis is that of task analysis—the systematic analysis of the procedures or steps needed to perform a given skill. Task analysis provides information regarding the sequence of steps, or in some cases the information requirements, requisite to learning the concepts, skills, or procedures taught in the classroom. There are three basic types of task analysis: sequential analysis, hierarchical analysis, and information-processing analysis.

Sequential analysis Also referred to as procedural analysis, this is the process of organizing the observable steps involved in completing a task into a sequentially, or chronologically, ordered progression. In effect, sequential analysis identifies each of the behaviors that are necessary to produce effective responses. This analysis, in turn, permits the special educator to assess student competence at each step, to locate the precise steps that the student is unable to perform, and to prescribe instruction focusing specifically on the deficient steps.

For a child with severe mental retardation, for example, the simple tasks involved in personal grooming often need to be analyzed sequentially to isolate the specific components of the task that are missing or applied ineffectively. A sequential analysis of teeth brushing includes steps ranging from the initial visual location of the toothbrush and toothpaste to the final step of postbrushing cleansing and maintenance. Each step of the process can potentially constitute an instructional objective, if the child is unable to perform the step effectively. The identification of the specific steps of a sequential task, then, permits assessment of each step, the identification of problem steps, and eventual remediation for the deficient steps.

Hierarchical Analysis In general, hierarchical analysis refers to the process of identifying the information that an individual needs to be able to perform specific tasks. The types of information included in hierarchical analysis are: basic vocabulary, the capacity to make necessary discriminations, knowledge of relevant rules, the ability to apply rules in appropriate contexts, and the ability to determine which types of rules should be applied in given situations, such as those encountered in problem-solving situations (cf. Gagné, 1985). The simple observable act of purchasing a candy bar, for instance, requires discriminating among different sized coins and among bill denominations, identifying the correct value of available currency, identifying the cost of the candy bar, comparing the cost to available funds, and so on. The act of purchasing the candy bar is actually the only observable step in the process; the other steps are mental, requiring information and skills that enable effective performance. Such an analysis typically identifies prerequisite information, without which performance of a more advanced skill is presumably impossible.

Consider again the example of the child with severe retardation. Even if the diagnostician is certain of the child's inability to brush his teeth well, the question of whether or not the child has the necessary prerequisite skills and information may be at issue. How much basic information must be taught before remediation of the steps involved can occur? Is it necessary, for example, that the child recognize, and be able to differentiate between the toothbrush and toothpaste? Is comprehension of the concept of time necessary in order to brush in the morning and at night? Can some of the presumed prerequisites be eliminated, or can compensatory skills (such as substituting light and dark for 7 A.M. and 9 P.M.) be used to account for the child's inability to learn certain concepts and skills? A hierarchical analysis thereby identifies the information needed in order to perform a task, permitting the diagnostician to "inventory" the available information and prescribe instruction for deficiencies.

Information-Processing Analysis   The relationship between external events and presumed internal responses is analyzed in information-processing analysis, with the result illustrating the relationship between thought and action (Gagné, 1985). Such an analysis provides a kind of "response decision map" that represents the mental decision-making presumed to occur in order to produce a desired response. This may be used to diagnose specific points where appropriate options have not been considered, or have been considered ineffectively; that diagnosis, in turn, can then be used as a focus of remediation.

When teaching students with learning disabilities or mild mental retardation to drive an automobile, it is necessary not only to know the correct sequences, but also to understand the nature of the decision points themselves. Upon approaching a traffic control signal, the student must follow a series of mental steps, including: instantaneously recognizing the sign, knowing the meaning of the sign, and evaluating whether the sign should elicit a response in order to perform appropriately. Information-processing analysis provides a method for articulating the decision options necessary for effective responses. This enables the special educator to comprehend more precisely why performance flaws are detected.

Summary   Instructional analysis, at the different levels, provides a comprehensive perspective of the student. The goal of instructional analysis is to identify the characteristics of the learner, learning environment, and learning tasks that influence the academic success or failure of the student, and to account for such influences systematically in the prescription of instructional plans.

The depth of instructional analysis varies according to the nature of the problem. In cases where severe performance deficiencies have been identified, typical of certain mental retardation referrals, the level and depth of the analyses correspondingly increase.

Unlike "normal" learning sequences, in which the steps, information needed to perform, and mental decision-making are accomplished seemingly effortlessly, severe inabilities to perform are characterized by the inability to piece together correct responses. Such students tend to lack the response "automaticity" (Gagné, 1985) of their "normal" counterparts. The instructional analysis process identifies the necessary components of effective responses that may be absent, present, or ineffective.

Regardless of the assessment effort that precedes special education referral and the findings of other assessment team professionals, the special educator must conduct an instructional analysis before meaningful and focused instruction can be provided. In this sense, it may be considered the final and most detailed assessment of the learner with a handicap, incorporating but transcending preceding assessments.

Standardized Tests

Typically, standardized tests are those that have prescribed procedures for test administration, scoring, and interpretation. Such tests are usually norm-referenced, providing information regarding how a particular student's performance compares with the other students. Thus, they share certain features with the psychological tests discussed in Chapter 2. While standardized tests can be found in both group and individually administered formats, the one-to-one individually administered tests are used almost exclusively during special education assessment due to the precision of the data obtained and the need to make observations during the assessment.

There are two general classes of standardized achievement tests that have the most bearing on special education assessment: global achievement and diagnostic achievement. Since the assessment of overall global achievement is typically conducted by a school psychologist, this discussion addresses standardized diagnostic achievement tests and their utility in the assessment of children for special education.

Standardized diagnostic achievement tests are typically used to isolate the type of skill, within an identified area of achievement deficiency, in which the deficiencies are most severe. Standardized diagnostic achievement tests generally provide a breakdown of a subject area into major skill classifications (e.g., word recognition, word attack) with norm-referenced scores available for each classification. Students are administered such tests to identify which, if any, of the major skill classifications are most deficient. Assuming that skill deficiencies are localized, the focus of the subsequent assessment can be directed toward specific skills.

Perhaps two of the best known and most widely used tests are the Key Math Diagnostic Arithmetic Test (Connolly et al., 1971) and the Woodcock Reading Mastery Tests (Woodcock, 1973). Both are similar in appearance, test format, administration, and scoring procedures. The types of information yielded, apart from the obvious differences in content orientation, are also similar.

Key Math Diagnostic Arithmetic Test The Key Math is a standardized diagnostic test that measures student achievement across a series of relatively narrow math skills. The test comprises math facts and concepts that are applicable for use with preschoolers to beginning high school students. The test is administered individually, and guidelines are provided for establishing starting points as well as the number of errors causing termination of the test.

Three math-related subscales are included: Content, Operations, and Applications. (The Key Math subscales and a few skill domains are shown in

Figure 3.3.) Each subscale represents a skill domain considered important in the teaching and learning of mathematics. For each subscale, student performance is assessed in more specific categories, such as addition, division, and measurement. The Content subscale tests the student's knowledge of the concepts of measurement, from the fundamental to the more advanced; the Operations subscale focuses on basic mathematical operations, which range in difficulty from simple one-digit addition to complex long division; and the Applications subscale measures the student's ability to apply mathematical knowledge to solve problems. Student scores are converted to norm-referenced grade-equivalents in each math category. In effect, the Key Math is a norm-referenced test of achievement that also offers sufficient detail to provide diagnostic information about the domains and categories of math skill development.

From a diagnostic perspective, the Key Math is used to identify the relative development of different math domains compared to established norms. It is also useful to identify the relative strengths and weaknesses of a particular student in the various math domains. It is possible to develop a math performance profile for the student, which defines performance domains within mathematics and provides some specificity to the source of observed deficiencies.

The Key Math does not, however, identify the specific skills that are deficient. The identification of deficiencies is restricted primarily to categories such as multiplication; the test does not isolate the specific aspects of multiplication that result in the deficiency. While the Key Math provides information that a student is achieving below established norms in multiplication, it does not identify whether the deficiency is with multiplication of single digits, factors of three or four, or any other specific sources. As a

Content	Operations	Applications
Measurement	Addition	Time
Counting	Subtraction	Money
	Multiplication	
	Division	

Figure 3.3.   Scales and subscales of the Key Math Diagnostic Arithmetic Test (Connolly, Nachtman, & Pritchett, 1971).

general rule, the domain identified via tests such as the Key Math defines where more specific assessment via criterion-referenced tests is needed.

Woodcock Reading Mastery Tests The Woodcock tests are typical of the standardized diagnostic reading tests used in special education assessment. In format and administration, they are similar to the Key Math. The Woodcock tests are administered individually using a combination of reading and multiple choice responding; they contain reading skill domains considered applicable from about first grade through high school.

The Woodcock Reading Mastery Tests consist of five subscales (Letter Identification, Word Identification, Word Attack, Word Comprehension, Passage Comprehension) and a Total Reading index. The subscales are thought to represent the major skill domains required for effective reading. The Letter Identification subscale requires the simple identification of numerals and letters (upper and lower case) in various font styles. The Passage-Comprehension subscale is administered by having students respond to fact and inference questions after reading short paragraphs. The Word Comprehension subscale requires the student to provide a missing word in order to establish a meaningful relationship among sets of analogies. The Word Attack subscale requires the application of phonetic reading skills to nonsense words. Based upon the student's pronunciation of the nonsense words, inferences can be made regarding the student's knowledge and application of the rules of effective decoding. The Word Identification subscale tests the student's ability to decode familiar words—words pronounced either through the application of decoding rules or through "sight" recognition. The combination of the Word Attack, Word Identification, and Word Comprehension subscales (see Figure 3.4) provides diagnostic information as to the sophistication of decoding skills and the development of word meaning. Each of the subscales yields three grade-equivalents that indicate the level at which the student

Word Attack	Word Identification	Word Comprehension		
scurb	horse	meat:eat	::	milk: ?
puz	mirror	car:drive	::	bike: ?
plaiter	elbow	eye:see	::	nose: ?
clance	baby	knife:cut	::	fork: ?

Figure 3.4. Representative test items similar to those found on three subscales of the Woodcock Reading Mastery Tests (Woodcock, 1973).

might be able to read easily, with average difficulty, or only with substantial difficulty.

As with most standardized diagnostic achievement tests, the Woodcock Reading Mastery Tests provide a profile of student performance that can be used to gauge performance compared to other students or relative to other aspects of his or her own performance. In both cases, the special educator uses standardized, norm-referenced scores to determine student proficiency in the skill domains provided on the test. The Woodcock provides a profile of student performance in each of the five skill domains, which aids the diagnostician in further specifying areas of deficiency.

Most standardized diagnostic achievement tests, however, provide little information as to the specific nature of performance deficiencies. Achievement deficiencies may be established in domains such as word attack (or phonetic decoding), but one cannot establish which specific skills require remediation and which are already mastered. The information yielded is too broadly defined to permit ready prescription of instructional plans.

Perhaps the greatest utility of standardized diagnostic achievement tests is their capacity to locate which areas or domains of student performance require more detailed assessment and which do not. Typically, the special education diagnostician receives a referral for further assessment of already identified achievement deficiencies. Tests such as the Key Math and the Woodcock Reading Mastery Tests effectively narrow the range for intensive skill assessment. They identify the skill domains in which deficiencies are most apparent, and allow the diagnostician to systematically select intensive skill assessments for only those areas needed.

Consider the following example of a referral for special education assessment. Anna is a fifth-grade student who has been referred for assessment due to reading deficiencies. Through psychological assessment, it is learned that Anna is above average intellectually, but is only achieving at roughly the second-grade level. Perhaps a learning disability diagnosis has already been made, but the special educator is asked to define skill deficiencies more precisely and to develop a plan for remedial instruction. The special education assessment might consist of the administration of a standardized diagnostic reading test to identify the domain or domains that are deficient, followed by assessment with a more specific criterion-referenced test to assess reading skills more precisely.

Criterion-Referenced Assessment

Criterion-referenced tests differ from achievement tests in a very fundamental way. Instead of providing global achievement estimates or relative performance across a series of skill domains, criterion-referenced tests focus on student performance of specific, well-defined skills. Usually, skills are assessed relative to defined academic objectives, with some standard or criterion for acceptable performance provided for each defined skill. Figures 3.5 and 3.6 illustrate the specific nature of the instructional objectives identified and tested during a typical criterion-based assessment.

Criterion-referenced tests typically isolate the specific components, rather than the general areas, of deficient performance. There tends to be little norm-referencing of the skills—only the ability or inability to perform specific tasks to defined criterion levels is noted.

Standardized tests are designed to maximize the performance differences among students. Such tests sample representative groups of skills, and identify which students perform well overall, and which do not. Criterion-referenced test items, however, are uniform within each defined skill with regard to item difficulty and content. A criterion-referenced test might include 5 one-syllable words, each requiring the application of the same ''silent e'' spelling rule at least 80% of the time. The skill assessed and the level of difficulty are both uniform. If the student answers 4 of 5 correctly, the prescribed criterion level for the skill has been met. Criterion-referenced tests tend to have very high internal consistency within skills, since each item is representative of the same defined skills. The emphasis is not on discriminating among learners; instead, the purpose is to identify precisely which skills have been learned and which have not.

At this level, the focus of assessment is different as well. Unlike standardized achievement tests, students are not designated as performing at a particular grade level, or at a given percentile level. Instead, students are assessed relative to the adopted performance standard for each given skill, such as the 80% accuracy standard required for the previous example. The

WHO	WHAT	TO WHAT DEGREE
The student	will select the correctly spelled "ou" word from among 5 choices	with at least 80% accuracy
The student	will compute the products for 5x0 through 5x10	a minimum of 19 out of 20 times, within 5 minutes
The student	will insert the correct article (a/an) into an incomplete sentence	a minimum of 80% of the time

Figure 3.5. Sample instructional objectives.

Objective # 1:

DIRECTIONS: *Select the correctly spelled word.*

1) foul   2) boul   3) cloun   4) toun   5) goun

NOTE: *Similar items are presented 5 times.*

Objective # 2:

5x6= ____   5x9= ____   5x1= ____   5x0= ____

NOTE: *This type of item is repeated 20 times.*

Objective # 3:
DIRECTIONS: *Complete each sentence with the correct article (a/an).*

1)   The boy owns ___ dog named "Boo."
2)   ___ apple a day keeps the doctor away.
3)   There are ten dimes in ___ dollar.

NOTE: *This type of item is repeated 10 times.*

Figure 3.6. Sample criterion-referenced assessment items (for instructional objectives in Figure 3.5).

skills themselves may be estimated as being taught at given grade levels, but the focus of the assessment is not normative in nature.

Criterion-referenced tests are exceptionally valuable in moving from the diagnostic to the prescriptive function of special education assessment. Essentially, an inability to meet performance standards for specific skills of a criterion-referenced test implies that instruction for that specific skill may be necessary. In general, the diagnostician attempts to develop a profile of competencies across specific skills, to determine the deficient skills that are either most important or most amenable to intervention, and to prescribe an instructional plan designed to ameliorate the measured deficiencies.

Commercially Available Criterion-Referenced Tests   A number of criterion-referenced tests are available commercially. In general, such tests include more or less generic academic skills—those that are most likely to occur across curricula at various schools. Commercially available criterion-referenced tests are most commonly used in basic skill areas such as mathematics, reading, and language. This assures applicability across school districts in that the criterion-referenced tests are almost certain to be relevant to at least a portion of each local curriculum.

The Criterion Test of Basic Skills (CTBS) (Lundell & Evans, 1976) is an example of a criterion-referenced test, available commercially, that is of a generic curriculum nature. This test focuses principally on mathematics and reading skills, for the most part at the elementary level. The math section of the CTBS contains several levels of addition, subtraction, multiplication, and division, as well as specific manipulations of fractions and decimals. Skill complexity ranges from very simple, such as single digit addition, to more complex problems, such as long division of three and four digit numbers with remainders. Sample reading skills assessed range from identifying letters to reading vowel combinations, to interpreting vowel combinations in words.

It is important to note the difference in the levels of specificity provided by criterion-referenced tests as contrasted with other assessments. The typical overall achievement test provides a global measure of achievement in a subject area, providing between-student comparisons. Diagnostic achievement tests provide a more detailed breakdown of performance with a subject area, and offer both between-student norm-referenced information and within-student relative performance profiles. Neither typically provides information that can be acted upon directly for purposes of designing instructional plans. Criterion-referenced tests focus on whether student performance on specified skills has reached defined standards. Criterion-referenced tests also provide individual student performance profiles, from which the relative competency of each student can be identified and used to determine specific instructional priorities. This prescriptive utility makes criterion-referenced assessment an essential tool of special education assessment.

Custom-Made Criterion-Referenced Tests Many criterion-referenced tests are developed by trained diagnosticians for their own use, but are not available commercially. Such tests are often necessary when the specific skills of interest are not assessed by commercially available tests, or when the level of specificity required is not provided in available tests. This is not uncommon in assessment of severely mentally retarded persons, whose capacity to perform routine everyday tasks is in question. Since the range of possible skills for such applications is so broad, but the market for distribution so limited, it is often necessary to develop a criterion-referenced test to assess specific skills.

Curriculum-Referenced Assessment A special type of criterion-referenced testing that combines specificity with locally established instructional priorities is curriculum-referenced assessment. This type of assessment essentially embeds the specificity of criterion-referenced assessment within established instructional systems. The skills as well as the context of typical instruction in the school system are considered simultaneously.

Most school districts have adopted or developed comprehensive curriculum objectives, such as those shown in Figure 3.7, that outline the scope and sequence of instruction. Typically, such objectives are available for most basic academic disciplines, and across virtually every grade level. In most cases, tests designed to assess progress toward the specific curriculum objectives are also available.

Curriculum-referenced assessment, therefore, examines the academic skills that are identified as important by a given school system. Carefully prescribed local objectives such as those shown in Figure 3.7 have enormous importance for special educators, particularly when attempting to mainstream learners with handicaps into the regular instructional environment. By comparing the student's skills directly to curriculum-referenced objectives, it is possible to identify the magnitude of learning deficiencies, to pinpoint the skills to be taught next, and to locate opportunities to align special education instruction with mainstream instruction (Hannafin & Barrett, 1983; cf. Niedermeier & Yelon, 1981). In effect, this permits the diagnostician not only to assess specific skills, but also to conduct the assessment with the assurance of relevance to local school priorities.

Student performance must be examined within the context of local institutional priorities if planning and intervention are to be accurate and meaningful. While comparisons to national norms or other broader criteria can be

OBJECTIVES	GRADE LEVEL		
	I	M	R
The student will be able to:			
1. Compute the sums of simple addition problems.	K	1	2-3
2. Identify the number of concrete objects associated with each addend as well as the total sum.	K	2	3-4
3. Identify sets of objects with the same number of elements as each addend.	1	2	3

Figure 3.7. Sample curriculum objectives. (I = introduced, M = mastered, R = reviewed)

useful during assessment, learner competence relative to locally prescribed standards is critical. The on-site special educator is indispensable in assessing such factors.

Referent-Based Testing   Referent-based assessment is conducted in the actual setting in which skill application is to occur (Davis, Alexander, & Yelon, 1974). In some cases, this is within a classroom. In many cases in special education, however, the performance context is necessarily external to the classroom. For example, many educable mentally retarded and learning disabled high school students are taught functional applications of math, reading, and language skills. Such students are taught in the classroom how to apply skills in the supermarket, on job applications, and in other everyday situations. Referent-based assessment focuses on the application of the learned skills in their appropriate performance contexts.

Referent-based assessment is valuable as a measure of skill transfer to the intended context. In many ways, it is a special case of criterion-referenced testing, focusing on specific skills performed at acceptable levels. The principal quality of referent-based assessment is its emphasis on meaningful performance contexts, those that represent the most appropriate applications of the skills taught.

An Illustrative Case   Jason, a 10th-grade student in a middle-class school system, is referred for assessment of severe math and reading performance deficiencies. Initial standardized testing conducted by the school psychologist reveals that Jason is of normal intelligence, but is achieving at the fourth-grade level in reading. As a consequence, he is failing, or doing poorly in, history, science, literature, and virtually all classes for which reading is an integral skill. Jason does not have a behavior problem, he interacts well with his peers, and his teachers indicate a willingness to retain him in their classes *if* he can receive some supplementary assistance.

With a referral such as this, several questions require consideration. First, what are the specific sources of reading deficiency? This question can be answered effectively through the use of a criterion-referenced reading test. Next, what kind or type of criterion-referenced tests are to be administered to ensure that the skills that are truly important for classroom success have been mastered? Several commercially available tests might be considered, or the diagnostician might construct a test to measure reading skills; but the nature of the referral suggests that assessment techniques that are closely aligned with existing curriculum objectives might be the best option.

Of special interest is Jason's performance on the specific reading competencies required by the school system and his ability to perform in each of the deficient subjects. What is sought is an articulation of the specific reading deficiencies, for possible remediation, as well as the skills specific to each subject that will require supplementary assistance for Jason to remain in mainstream education. Finally, after the initial instructional prescriptions are developed, a referent-based assessment is conducted to determine the extent to which supplementary special education instruction has transferred to the specific problems experienced in the regular classroom.

Summary Criterion-referenced tests have several desirable features. First, and perhaps most important, they provide highly specific diagnostic information without which precise remedial special education cannot occur. This assessment technique provides information so precise that it can be translated directly into an instructional prescription, with a high degree of confidence in the target areas selected for instruction.

Second, criterion-referenced tests provide a higher degree of external validity for skill assessment than norm-referenced achievement tests. They address not general areas of performance, but specific skills; they focus on comparisons not to a student norm, but to the specific skills by which "competence" is defined. While norm-referenced achievement tests provide information as to general academic areas, or in some cases the performance domains within academic disciplines, they do not identify specific skill deficiencies. Unlike norm-referenced achievement or domain-oriented tests, where difficulties can only be generally identified, criterion-referenced tests require little or no inference as to the source of deficiency. Criterion-referenced tests isolate performance on the skill or skills of concern. The diagnostician need not guess about a deficiency—the source of deficiency can be identified directly.

Finally, criterion-referenced tests provide an accurate means for monitoring and evaluating the progress of students in special education programs. Since the purpose of special education placement is to improve certain skills, it is necessary to have a reliable and valid procedure by which to measure student progress. Since they provide a more or less one-to-one relationship between assessment and instruction, criterion-referenced tests are ideally suited to the evaluation function of the special educator. They are often used either to validate the learning of specific pieces of information, such as particular automotive road signs, or to evaluate competency in the more conceptual areas, such as the classification of chemicals as dangerous or not dangerous.

The limitations of criterion-referenced tests are related principally to availability. As noted, there is an enormous range of skills for which specific assessment is needed, but for which measures are not available. This places the burden of development on the diagnostician, a task that can be both formidable and time-consuming, and requires proficiency in the measurement concepts described earlier.

Assuming tests are to be developed, a good deal of time is often required for the creation of procedures and tests that have limited applicability. In addition, to provide the level of detail necessary to offer precise teaching prescriptions, it is often necessary to conduct highly detailed instructional analyses of several skill areas. This is a time-consuming proposition, and the procedures developed for the assessment are usable for very few additional students. The cost of true precision in skill assessment can be steep; the benefits, however, are most worthwhile.

Observational Assessment

Most of the assessment techniques reviewed thus far are conducted in more or less sheltered settings, away from the actual context in which problems are observed. This is very useful in determining optimal performance since the situation can be highly controlled and student effort can be monitored easily. However, it is often necessary to obtain first-hand insights into the nature of the student's typical behavior and performance. This must be obtained by a careful examination of the student in the setting in which problems have been reported.

Certain methods are often used to observe students' performance of particular tasks or their behavior in general. There are two basic classes of observation: obtrusive and unobtrusive.

Obtrusive Observations   Obtrusive observations generally involve the observer as an obvious recorder of information on student performance. This type of observation is typical of the kind of assessment done during a driver's license examination, when the observer is a visible part of a setting in which observation would not normally take place. Obtrusive observation cues the student to perform in an exemplary fashion, and generally provides the observer with an estimate of optimal performance.

Unobtrusive Observations   Observational assessments that focus on typical rather than optimal performance often provide a valuable indication of the student in a more normalized environment. The unobtrusive observer is not identified as an observer per se, and gathers information on particular students without the creation of an artificial assessment environment.

Structured and Unstructured Methods   Observational assessments are conducted in a variety of ways. Structured methods of observation commonly involve the careful monitoring of a student during the performance of a defined task. Usually, the task is defined in detail via a sequential task analysis. The procedures of the task provide the basis for recording observations. The observer notes each aspect of the defined task that the student demonstrates. Deficiencies in performance are usually attributable to the aspects of performance that are not demonstrated.

Structured methods are very useful for identifying specific deficiencies within tasks that can be well defined. More often than not, such tasks are procedural in nature; that is, they require the execution of a defined series of steps. For instance, the preparation of food according to recipes can be observed and evaluated fairly readily. The student's performance can be observed and evaluated in terms of his or her adherence to the steps and requirements of the recipe. The nature of the observation enables the observer to identify specifically which steps in the task the student did not complete. Similarly, structured observation can be useful for diagnosing the deficient grooming habits of students with severe mental retardation. Virtually any task that can be specified clearly can be analyzed using structured observation techniques.

In some cases, the nature of a problem is not well defined. It may be useful to observe simply "to see what happens." Less structured methods are often useful for less well-defined problems. This permits a greater range, but seriously hampers the focus of the observation. In instances where a performance problem has not been well defined and where further assessment direction cannot be determined effectively, less structured methods of observation may be necessary.

An Illustrative Case Lindsay, a sixth-grade student, is referred for evaluation due to poor classroom performance. The teacher describes Lindsay as very verbal and apparently very intelligent, but says she is doing very poor classroom work, turning in incomplete assignments, not following directions, and making careless errors. The school psychologist confirms that Lindsay is above average intellectually and that she performs at roughly a ninth-grade level on all sections of the standardized achievement test.

Why is there such a striking difference between performance on the individually administered tests and daily classroom performance? Perhaps the best way to further refine the problem specification is to observe Lindsay's typical classroom performance. It is possible that she is especially distractible, has a low tolerance for disruption, tends to act-out, or simply races through class assignments carelessly, perhaps because they are not challenging. It is also conceivable that the situation itself is not generally conducive to learning, characterized by poor student control or a lack of clarity as to what is expected of students. Unstructured observation may permit the diagnostician to begin to identify the initially unclear source of a problem.

Structured observation, however, might be very useful in the assessment of Lindsay's problem-solving or skill application, in an instance where the exemplar steps to the solution are patterned and prescribed. The steps involved in computational math, for example, can be observed to identify where problems arise.

Choosing the Appropriate Assessment Techniques

The options available for special education assessment provide a variety of tools and techniques that can be used to assess skills under varied circumstances. Assessment techniques range from formal to informal, structured to unstructured, standardized to nonstandardized, output to process, and norm-referenced to criterion-referenced. Thus, the process of special education assessment can be as broadly or narrowly defined as each referral dictates.

Clearly, the different assessment options are more useful for some aspects of testing than others, and for some given circumstances than others. Indeed, some types of assessment are inappropriate under certain conditions in which the types of capabilities the assessment techniques can test provide little or no useful information. How, then, does the diagnostician determine appropriate assessment techniques for special education referrals?

First, one must note the fundamentally different purpose of assessment assumed by the special educator as contrasted with other team members. Unlike medical diagnosis and some aspects of psychological assessment, the goal is neither the assignment of labels such as learning disabled or mentally retarded, nor the identification of behavioral syndromes or biomedical conditions. These considerations often have too little bearing on instruction to be of concern to special educators. Instead, the special educator focuses almost exclusively on assessment designed to facilitate remediation (the first purpose of assessment identified in Chapter 1) through the creation of academic prescriptions. This process ultimately poses the question: Which assessment procedures best enable the special educator to develop IEPs, or otherwise prescribe instructional interventions?

From the foregoing discussions of the various assessment options, it is clear that some form of criterion-referenced assessment is necessary to specify deficient skills sufficiently and to monitor and evaluate student progress in special education programs. The specification of target skills for special education instruction is a cornerstone of the individualized instruction provided through academic programs for students with mental retardation or learning disabilities.

To facilitate mainstreaming as well as to unify special education programs within an existing curriculum, it might also be useful to base the assessment on the curriculum objectives of the school system. Not only is the opportunity to parallel special and regular education curricula made easier, but criterion-referenced assessments based on curriculum objectives also provide an immediately meaningful context for the interpretation of assessment data to students, parents, and teachers. Such assessments provide both specific information about the skill deficiencies and a contextual reference to the mainstream educational system. The assessment provides a more accurate measure of the magnitude and location of student performance deficiencies. This is essential information for special education programs that are mainstreamed with regular programs.

In order to determine which specific criterion-referenced tests are potentially useful, it may be necessary first to gather more information than was provided at the time of reference. In some cases, when only minimal information is known about the performance deficiencies of the student, it is often necessary to administer more global measures, such as norm-referenced achievement tests. After the academic disciplines in which global achievement deficiencies exist have been identified via norm-referenced achievement measures, a standardized diagnostic achievement test might be appropriate. Such tests assist in successively narrowing the locus of deficiency, and are very useful as an aid to choosing specific criterion-referenced tests.

Consideration should also be given to the philosophical orientations of both the assessment team and the special education programs served by the assessment team. While most special education programs are oriented toward academic performance, some adhere to perceptually oriented theories that essentially endorse the modality preference approach, as opposed to the behavior analysis approach, described in Chapter 2. If assessment is to have functional utility, as special education assessment must, then it is important to provide the kinds of information, process and/or performance output, that will be most useful in planning for the particular instructional context.

In conclusion, the assessment techniques used by the diagnostician must be appropriate to the nature of the referral, the amount of specificity provided at the time of referral, and the instructional context to be served through assessment. It is reasonable to assume that each of the assessment techniques described in this chapter can be used appropriately in different circumstances. Still, there remains the basic purpose of special education assessment as the ultimate litmus test: If assessment is to serve both diagnostic and prescriptive functions, then information that is specific enough to develop meaningful instructional plans must be obtained. The wealth of techniques available to the diagnostician may be useful, but ultimately the superior information yielded through criterion-referenced assessment mandates that assessment concentrate on techniques in that area.

THE ROLE OF THE SPECIAL EDUCATOR IN MULTIDISCIPLINARY ASSESSMENT

Unlike diagnosticians who are called on to identify the presence of a handicapping condition or to describe its etiology, the special educator often becomes involved after an initial identification or classification has been made. Also in contrast to other diagnosticians, the special educator is usually not an independent practitioner to be called upon on a per case basis, but is associated with the school or school district in which the student is identified. Consequently, it is often possible to gain important insights as to the effects of school, teacher, and curriculum variables on observed problems and possible solutions. In many cases, the special educator will provide not only assessment but also instruction to the student. For these reasons, other professionals seldom question the importance of the participation of special educators in multidisciplinary assessment teams.

For instance, once the student has been identified and placed in a special education program, the special educator conducts frequent, almost continuous, assessment. Special educators perform a considerable amount of maintenance and monitoring assessment for students already participating in special education programs. This usually involves the administration of criterion-referenced tests to evaluate progress, establish new instructional objectives, or comply with locally or federally imposed guidelines for formal reporting and accounting.

Though few decisions about the inclusion of the special educator as an assessment team member need be made, special educators should be included routinely for any of the following purposes: identification of prerequisite skills, specification of problems with current performance, development of individualized education programs (IEPs), evaluation of student progress in special education programs, or revision of IEP objectives.

Identification of Prerequisite Skills

When problems with performance are observed, it is initially necessary to identify the source of the deficiency. The inability to perform a given task may be related to deficiencies in the specific skills requisite to effective performance, or to a lack of basic information needed to comprehend the task. For example, deficiencies observed for simple subtraction may have little to do with task comprehension, but may be moderated by such prerequisite skills as number-object associations or the inability to discriminate between given numerals. Assessment of prerequisite skills provides information necessary to plan instruction related to the source of performance deficiency; the special educator should complete such an assessment.

Problems with Current Performance

In many cases, special education assessment focuses on the inability of a student to apply general skills such as following directions, or to perform specific academic tasks such as writing correct sentences. Referral may be made for such problems, requiring the special educator to conduct observations, administer specific tests, and otherwise determine the status of student performance. Typically, referral in such cases comes through a psychologist who has already established general parameters of performance.

Development of IEPs

During initial assessment, development of IEPs is probably the most common, but important, function of the special education diagnostician. When students are placed in special education programs, detailed education programs that prescribe the specific objectives of the placement must be developed. The special educator's assessment generally provides the basis for such a plan, which includes precise statements of strengths and weaknesses as well as a delineation of the specific instructional priorities for the student.

Evaluation of Progress and Revision of IEPs

While comprehensive multidisciplinary assessments are required periodically, the re-evaluation cycle of the special educator is virtually continuous. After initial placement in special education, routine re-evaluations of the student are mandated. Re-evaluation is required for several reasons: to insure that progress is being made toward instructional priorities; to avoid "dead ending" a student in ineffective programs; to develop new and more appropriate instructional priorities in a timely manner; and to meet local, state, and federal requirements for program accounting. Since such evaluations are routinely conducted for all special education students, the majority of the special educator's diagnostic efforts are applied toward this purpose.

REFERENCES

Anderhalter, O. F. (1980). *Diagnostic Skills Battery.* Bensenville, IL: Scholastic Testing Services.

Ayers, A. J. (1972). *Southern California Sensory Integration Tests.* Los Angeles: Western Psychological Services.

Brigance, A. H. (1976). *Brigance Diagnostic Inventory of Basic Skills.* North Billerica, IL: Curriculum Associates.

Calarusso, R. P., & Hammill, D. D. (1972). *Motor-free Test of Visual Perception.* Novato, CA: Academic Therapy Publications.

Connolly, A. J., Nachtman, W., & Pritchett, E. M. (1971). *Key Math Diagnostic Arithmetic Test.* Circle Pines, MN: American Guidance Service.

Cronbach, L. J. (1970). *Essentials of psychological testing* (3rd ed.). New York: Harper & Row.

Davis, R. H., Alexander, L. T., & Yelon, S. L. (1974). *Learning systems design: An approach to the improvement of instruction.* New York: McGraw-Hill.

Dick, W., & Carey, L. (1985). *The systematic design of instruction* (2nd ed.). Glenview, IL: Scott, Foresman.

Frostig, M., Maslow, P., Lefever, D. W., & Witlesey, J. R. B. (1964). *The Marianne Frostig Developmental Test of Visual Perception.* Palo Alto, CA: Consulting Psychologist.

Gagné, R. M. (1985). *The conditions of learning* (5th ed.). New York: Holt, Rinehart & Winston.

Hannafin, M. J., & Barrett, B. K. (1983). Preparing for educational change: Systematizing support curriculum. *American Education, 19* (4), 32–37.

Lundell, W. B., & Evans, J. (1976). *Criterion Test of Basic Skills.* Novato, CA: Academic Therapy Publications.

Niedermeier, E., & Yelon, S. (1981). Los Angeles aligns instruction with essential skills. *Educational Leadership, 38,* 618–620.

Salvia, J., & Ysseldyke, J. E. (1981). *Assessment in special and remedial education* (2nd ed.). Boston: Houghton Mifflin.

Somwaru, J. P. (1981). *Assessment of basic competencies.* Bensenville, IL: Scholastic Testing Services.

Spache, G. D. (1963). *Diagnostic Reading Scales.* Monterey, CA: California Test Bureau.

Thorndike, R. L., & Hagen, E. (1969). *Measurement and evaluation in psychology and education.* (3rd ed.). New York: John Wiley & Sons.

Witt, J. C., Elliott, S. N., Gresham, F. M., & Kramer, J. J. (1986). *Assessment of children's learning and behavior problems.* Boston: Little, Brown.

Woodcock, R. W. (1973). *Woodcock Reading Mastery Test Manual.* Circle Pines, MN: American Guidance Service.

Chapter 4

Audiological Assessment

Deborah Hayes

Approximately 10% of all children suffer some degree of hearing impairment between birth and age 11 years (Northern & Downs, 1984). For the normally developing child, this hearing loss has important effects on speech and language development (Sak & Ruben, 1982). For the child with other handicaps, the additional handicap of hearing loss has profound effects on overall social, emotional, and educational development. Unfortunately, it is this child who is most likely to develop the additional handicap of hearing loss. Many medical/developmental conditions that result in other childhood handicaps also result in childhood hearing loss. It is essential that the child with handicaps receive early, aggressive audiological assessment and management.

Any child can be successfully tested. The optimal time for audiological assessment is as soon as the child is identified as being at risk for hearing impairment. In many neonatal intensive care units (NICU) for example, children are tested immediately prior to discharge. If the child is identified as having hearing impairment, rehabilitative steps may be instituted as early as age 1 month. The appropriate person to assess hearing sensitivity in infants and young children is a certified audiologist. Such an individual is specifically trained to diagnose the degree and configuration of hearing loss, and to provide rehabilitative services.

TRAINING OF AUDIOLOGISTS

The *Dictionary of Occupational Titles* (United States Department of Labor, 1977), recognizes audiologists as professional persons whose services are rendered as independent professionals.

> **AUDIOLOGIST** (profess. and kin.) 076.101-010. Specializes in diagnostic evaluation of hearing, prevention, habilitative and rehabilitative services for auditory problems, and research related to hearing and attendant disorders: Determines range, nature, and degree of hearing function related to patient's auditory efficiency (communication needs), using electroacoustic instrumentation. . . Coordinates audiometric results with other diagnostic data, such as educational, medical, social and behavioral information.

The audiologist's role in the habilitative/rehabilitative process is defined as follows: ". . . plans, directs, conducts, or participates in conservation, habilitative and rehabilitative programs including hearing aid selection and orientation, counseling, guidance, auditory training, speech reading, language habilitation, and speech conservation" (United States Department of Labor, 1977).

In order to be able to provide such comprehensive services, the audiologist receives extensive training in psychoacoustics, electronic instrumentation, auditory development and pathology, speech and language development, aural rehabilitation, hearing measurement, and electrophysiological measurement techniques, and completes a variety of related coursework. In addition, during his or her training program, the audiologist participates in 300 hours of supervised practicum in a variety of clinical settings. The minimum training level for an audiologist is a postbaccalaurate master of science (M.S.) or master of arts (M.A.) degree. Audiologists may also be trained at the doctoral (Ph.D.) level.

In addition to minimum training at an M.S. or M.A. degree level, audiologists are also certified by a national organization, the American Speech-Language-Hearing Association (ASHA). In order to hold an ASHA Certificate of Clinical Competence in Audiology (C.C.C.-A), the individual must meet three basic requirements: 1) obtain a master's degree in audiology from an accredited training program, or from a program that meets equivalent accreditation standards; 2) complete a postgraduate 9-month supervised clinical fellowship experience; and 3) pass a nationally standardized examination. In 1985, there are approximately 6,500 accredited audiologists in the United States.

Thirty-five states require licensure of audiologists. These states are listed in Table 4.1. In most states, requirements for licensure are equivalent to ASHA standards for certification.

Audiologists are employed in a variety of settings including hospitals, private physicians' offices, public schools and institutions, university clinics, and their own private practices. These settings may be accredited by a board

Table 4.1. States requiring licensure of audiologists

Alabama	Maine	Ohio
Arkansas	Maryland	Oklahoma
California	Massachusetts	Oregon
Connecticut	Mississippi	Pennsylvania
Delaware	Missouri	Rhode Island
Florida	Montana	South Carolina
Georgia	Nebraska	Tennessee
Hawaii	Nevada	Texas
Indiana	New Mexico	Utah
Iowa	New York	Virginia
Kentucky	North Carolina	Wyoming
Louisiana	North Dakota	

of ASHA, the Professional Services Board (PSB). To obtain PSB certification, the setting must meet strict criteria for administration, staffing, clinical practices and procedures, recordkeeping, equipment, and facilities. This certification is granted for 5-year periods and is renewable upon annual documentation and a site visit by peer reviewers at the end of the 5-year period. As of 1985, there are approximately 190 PSB-accredited audiology programs providing professional services in the United States and Canada.

CATEGORIES OF AUDITORY DYSFUNCTION

Auditory dysfunction is typically related to the site of the disorder within the auditory system. The peripheral auditory system is described in three sections: the outer ear consists of the auricle (pinna) and external auditory canal; the middle ear includes the tympanic membrane, tympanic cavity, and ossicles; and the inner ear consists of the cochlea (Figure 4.1). More central elements of the auditory system include the auditory or eighth cranial nerve, and the brain stem and temporal lobe (Figure 4.2). Disorders at each site produce a specific pattern of auditory dysfunction, influence auditory processing, and affect aural rehabilitation in a distinct manner.

External and/or Middle Ear Sites

A disorder of the external and/or middle ear produces a conductive hearing loss. The principle characteristic of a conductive hearing loss is threshold elevation for air-conducted sounds. Under normal operating conditions, the external-middle ear system acts as an impedance matching transformer (i.e., a device that maximizes the transfer of energy between systems of differing resistance). This system transforms low impedance air-borne sound pressure waves into relatively higher impedance fluid-borne pressure waves. This is accomplished by a variety of specific transformer mechanisms, the primary of which is the mechanical advantage provided by the difference between the effective areas of the tympanic membrane (TM) and the stapes footplate (Möller, 1970).

A disorder that alters the optimal transformer characteristics of the external-middle ear system creates an energy loss for air-conducted sound. Bone-conducted sounds, that is, sounds that are presented by direct vibration of the skull, are unaffected. This results in a peculiar audiometric characteristic termed the *air-bone gap*. Thus, the signature of auditory dysfunction of the external-middle ear is an audiogram characterized by loss of sensitivity for air-conducted signals, but normal sensitivity for bone-conducted signals.

In general, disorders of the external-middle ear system result in a mild to moderate conductive hearing loss. These disorders are typically treated by medical and/or surgical intervention. When such treatment is not possible, hearing aids are recommended. Patients with conductive hearing loss receive maximum benefit from amplification because, essentially, conductive hearing loss produces loss in sensitivity but does not affect signal clarity. Simple amplification overcomes the loss in sensitivity; thus, the patient with conductive hearing loss obtains almost normal results with the use of hearing aids. Children with medically or surgically untreatable conductive hearing loss should be provided with amplification as soon as possible.

Cochlear and/or Eighth Cranial Nerve Sites

Dysfunction of the cochlea or eighth cranial nerve results in a sensorineural hearing loss. The principal manifestation of sensorineural hearing loss is elevation in threshold (i.e., the lowest level at which sound can be detected 50% of the time) for both air-conducted and bone-conducted signals. Under

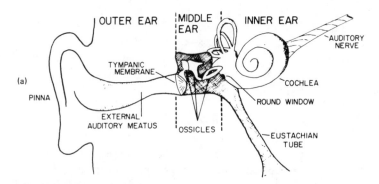

Figure 4.1. Schematic diagram of the peripheral auditory system showing the outer ear, the middle ear, and the inner ear. (pinna = auricle; external auditory meatus = external auditory canal; middle ear = typanic cavity) (From Green, D. M. [1976]. *An introduction to hearing*. Hillsdale, N.J: Lawrence Erlbaum Associates. Reproduced by permission.)

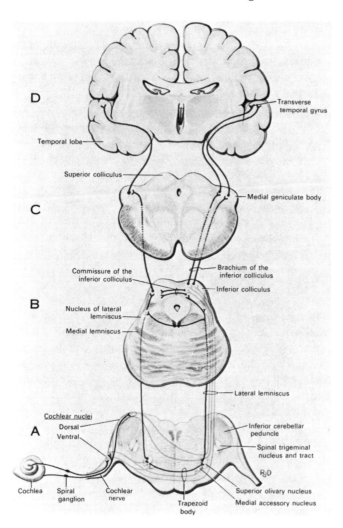

Figure 4.2. Schematic diagram of the central auditory system showing neural projections from the cochlea to the temporal lobe. (cochlear nerve = auditory or eighth cranial nerve; A, B, and C, = brain stem) (From Carpenter, M. B. [1972]. *Core text of neuroanatomy*. Baltimore: Williams & Wilkins. Copyright © 1972. Reproduced by permission.)

normal operating conditions, the cochlea acts as an electromechanical transducer, transducing mechanical deformation of sensory structures (hair cells) into electrical energy that is transmitted along the nerve fiber toward the brain. The eighth cranial nerve transmits the neural code to higher auditory structures in the brain stem. In the case of cochlear and/or eighth cranial nerve dysfunction, there is no loss in energy transformation, but rather a disorder in transduction/coding. This disorder affects signals delivered by both air conduction and bone conduction. The signature audiogram of an individual with this disorder shows threshold elevation without the air-bone gap characteristic of the conductive disorder.

Cochlear and eighth cranial nerve disorders may result in any degree of sensorineural hearing loss, ranging from very mild to profound. In general, these losses cannot be treated by medical or surgical means. Depending on the degree of loss, hearing aids are the principle approach to rehabilitation. Sensorineural hearing loss produces not only loss in sensitivity but also loss in speech clarity. In contrast to the patient with conductive hearing loss, the patient with sensorineural hearing loss receives more limited benefit from amplification. Nevertheless, all children with sufficient sensorineural loss should be fitted with hearing aids as soon as possible. Usually, even the child with profound loss will receive some benefit from amplification.

Brain Stem and/or Temporal Lobe Sites

Disorders at the brain stem or temporal lobe are considered central auditory disorders. In such disorders, the effect on auditory behavior is not typically demonstrated by elevation in threshold sensitivity, but rather by inability to process complex speech messages. The primary function of the central auditory system is to decode the neural code and to respond in a meaningful manner to the acoustic/auditory message. In most cases, because the central auditory system is highly redundant, a specific site of dysfunction in the brain stem or temporal lobe is not revealed by routine audiometric measures. Instead, specialized test conditions are necessary to demonstrate breakdown in central auditory processing.

Persons with central auditory disorders usually do not complain of auditory symptoms. The high redundancy of the auditory system results in only limited breakdown in auditory processing under normal circumstances. However, in complex listening conditions, these individuals may complain of difficulties in understanding speech. The most effective management for persons with such disorders is to control the listening environment and to avoid noisy or excessively distracting communication situations.

Evaluation of central auditory dysfunction in children has met with only limited success. Most test materials are nonspecific in that they contain items pertaining to nonauditory areas such as attention, memory, and linguistic competence. In addition, variability among children with apparent central auditory processing dysfunction is substantial, and tests that are sensitive to one group of children with hearing impairment may be inappropriate for another group. Results of central auditory evaluation in children should be interpreted with extreme caution.

AUDITORY DISORDERS IN CHILDREN

Conductive Hearing Loss

Conductive hearing loss is the most common childhood auditory disorder. Otitis media with effusion (OME) (i.e., middle ear infections with fluid accumulation) affects more than 10% of preschool and school-age children (Northern & Downs, 1984). This disease results in mild to moderate, fluctuant, bilateral conductive hearing loss. Recurrent OME can result in significant speech and language delays (Sak & Ruben, 1982). Although hearing loss may be only mild, even minimal auditory deprivation during the critical language learning years (birth through age 3 years) has a pronounced effect on speech and language development. Recurrent OME should receive rapid and aggressive medical management.

Other causes of conductive hearing loss in children include congenital atresia (failure to develop) or stenosis (narrowing) of the external canal. These disorders are usually identified at birth. Surgical management is not always possible for these children, or may be delayed for growth/development reasons. These children should be fitted with hearing aids as soon as possible.

Sensorineural Hearing Loss

Sensorineural hearing loss in children may be present at birth (congenital) or acquired. Approximately 50% of childhood sensorineural hearing loss is related to genetic factors. Table 4.2 shows some of the more important causes of sensorineural hearing loss in children (Gerkin, 1984; Northern & Downs, 1984; Paparella, 1980).

The table lists etiologies under two major categories of hearing loss; congenital and acquired. In each category, hearing loss is further defined as genetic or nongenetic. Under congenital, genetic etiologies, for example, the table shows that hearing loss may occur alone (inner ear aplasia), or in conjunction with other abnormalities (e.g., Waardenburg's syndrome). Chromosomal abnormalities may also result in congenital sensorineural hearing loss.

Nongenetic etiologies of congenital sensorineural hearing loss include prenatal infection (e.g., cytomegalovirus, rubella), ototoxicity (e.g., drug toxicity), and anoxia (lack of oxygen) at birth. The Joint Commission on Newborn Hearing, established in 1969 by representatives from pediatrics, otolaryngology (ear, nose, and throat), and audiology, recommends identifying infants at risk for congenital deafness by using the *High Risk Register For Deafness* (Gerkin, 1984). The *Register* is a checklist of prenatal conditions known to affect hearing and is an economical approach for identifying infants at risk for hearing impairment. Children identified as being at risk by the *High Risk Register* should be tested by an audiologist before age 3 months.

Table 4.2. Classification of sensorineural hearing loss in children

---

I. Congenital sensorineural hearing loss
  A. Genetic etiologies
    1. Hearing loss occurring alone—inner ear aplasia (Michel, Mondini)
    2. Hearing loss associated with other abnormalities (syndromes)
      a. Waardenburg's syndrome (deafness may be delayed)
      b. Albinism
    3. Chromosomal abnormalities
      a. Trisomy 13–15
      b. Trisomy 18
  B. Nongenetic etiologies
    1. Hearing loss occurring alone
      a. Ototoxic poisoning (streptomycin, quinine, etc.)
    2. Hearing loss associated with other abnormalities
      a. Congenital perinatal infections: TORCH (toxoplasmosis, syphilis, rubella, cytomegalovirus, herpes simplex)
      b. Prematurity
      c. Anoxia at birth
II. Acquired sensorineural hearing loss
  A. Genetic etiologies
    1. Hearing loss occurring alone—familial progressive sensorineural deafness
    2. Hearing loss associated with other abnormalities (syndromes)
      a. Alport's syndrome
      b. Hurler's syndrome (gargoylism)
      c. Klippel-Feil syndrome
      d. Neurofibromatosis
      e. Crouzon's syndrome
  B. Nongenetic etiologies
    1. Inflammatory diseases
      a. Bacterial (labyrinthitis, meningitis, and otitis media)
      b. Viral (measles, mumps, influenza, labyrinthitis, etc.)
      c. Spirochetal (congenital and acquired syphilis)
    2. Ototoxic poisoning (cis platinum)
    3. Neoplastic disorders (tumors)—acoustic neuroma (brain stem glioma)
    4. Traumatic injury (temporal bone fractures)
    5. Metabolic disorders (hypothyroidism, allergies, etc.)
    6. Vascular insufficiency (sudden deafness)

Source: Adapted from Gerkin (1984), Northern and Downs (1984), and Paparella (1980).

Acquired childhood sensorineural hearing loss may also be related to genetic factors (e.g., familial progressive sensorineural hearing loss) or to nongenetic etiologies. Meningitis (CNS infection) is one of the leading nongenetic causes of childhood deafness.

In both genetic and acquired sensorineural hearing loss, a number of etiologies produce multiple handicapping conditions. Successful rehabilitation of childhood hearing impairment is often dependent on the presence and degree of other handicaps.

ASSESSMENT OF THE INFANT AND YOUNG CHILD

A primary goal of audiological assessment is to determine the presence and degree of hearing impairment. Ideally, this information is gained for each ear and for a variety of frequencies (pitches) encompassing the speech range. For each ear, the threshold (lowest intensity yielding 50% detection) is obtained for pure tones at octave intervals ranging from 125 Hertz (cycles per second; Hz) to 8,000 Hz. Thresholds are usually obtained for signals delivered by air conduction through earphones, and by bone conduction through a bone vibrator. Threshold sensitivity at each frequency is then plotted on a pure tone audiogram. The pure tone audiogram is obtained in a controlled, noise-attenuated environment (i.e., a sound-treated room). Instrumentation for generating the test signals must meet national standards for calibration and stability.

Figure 4.3 shows a typical pure tone audiogram form. The frequency scale, ranging from low (125 and 250 Hz) to high (4,000 and 8,000 Hz), is plotted on the abscissa; the intensity scale, ranging from very faint (0 decibels, or dB) to extremely loud (80+ dB), is plotted on the ordinate. Intensity is recorded in dB hearing level (HL); that is, in decibels relative to the threshold (0 dB HL) for normally hearing young adult listeners. Table 4.3 defines the dB level associated with normal hearing, and with mild, moderate, severe, and profound hearing impairment.

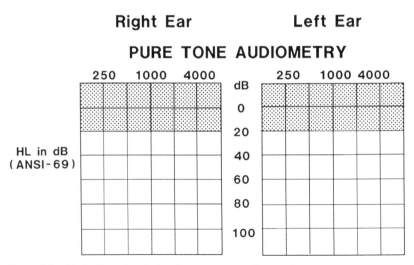

Figure 4.3. Typical form for plotting the pure tone audiogram. Frequency in Hertz (Hz) is plotted on the abscissa; intensity in decibels (dB) hearing level (HL) is plotted on the ordinate. (ANSI-69: American National Standards Institute 1969 standard for audiometric normal hearing.) (Form developed by Jerger, S., & Jerger, J., personal communication.)

Table 4.3. Decibel level, in HL, associated with normal hearing, and with mild, moderate, severe, and profound hearing impairment

Category	dB HL
Normal hearing	0–19
Mild hearing loss	20–39
Moderate hearing loss	40–59
Severe hearing loss	60–79
Profound hearing loss	≥ 80

It is not difficult to obtain a pure tone audiogram from a cooperative adult patient. The audiologist simply describes the test condition and defines the response behavior. It is much more difficult to obtain this information from an infant or young child; for these patients, the audiologist must employ a variety of test techniques appropriate to the child's age, level of development, and attention. In general, a test battery approach consisting of both behavioral and physiological measures is employed to obtain a complete picture of the child's hearing sensitivity.

Behavior Measures

In assessing a child's behavior response to sound, the audiologist selects test techniques that are appropriate to the child's age and level of development. For the child less than 24–30 months of age, most behavior measures are obtained in the sound field (i.e., testing via loudspeakers in a sound-treated room) rather than under earphones. In this case, the audiologist plots a sound field audiogram of the child's minimal response level to calibrated tonal or noise stimuli. Unlike the pure tone audiogram, the sound field audiogram represents only overall responses to sound from the child's better hearing ear (if there is a difference between ears) since individual ear measures cannot be obtained without earphones. For the older child, who will accept earphones, individual ear sensitivity to pure tone signals and speech is measured.

There are two general categories of behavior measures of hearing sensitivity in children. The first category, behavior observation audiometry, is an unconditioned test procedure. The second category consists of tests (three of which are described below) in which conditioning procedures are employed.

Behavior Observation Audiometry (BOA) Behavior observation audiometry involves controlled observation of the child's response to sound. Typically, the child is held or seated in the sound-treated room. Calibrated speech and tonal or noise stimuli are presented from loudspeakers located at a specific distance from the child's head. The audiologist observes the child's unconditioned response to these test signals. The expected nature of responses depends on the child's age, level of development, and state. Such responses include arousal from light sleep, startle reflex, eye-blink or eye-widening, cessation of ongoing activity, or other startle-like behaviors. BOA is most often employed in the evaluation of infants age 6 months or younger, or of children with severe developmental delays. The sound field audiogram generated by BOA does not represent threshold sensitivity, but rather shows the child's minimum overt responses to sound. Based on the child's age and developmental level, the audiologist interprets these minimum response levels as consistent with normal hearing or as suggestive of hearing impairment.

Visual Reinforcement Audiometry (VRA) Visual reinforcement audiometry is a conditioned procedure employed in the evaluation of children age 6 months to approximately 30 months (Liden & Kankkonen, 1961). During the conditioning procedure, an animated toy, mounted on top of a loudspeaker, is lighted simultaneously with the presentation of the sound stimulus. The desired response is a head-turn to the sound source and animated toy. Once the conditioned bond has been established, testing commences. Calibrated speech, noise, and tonal signals are presented at a variety of frequency and decibel levels. An appropriate response is reinforced with the animated toy. That is, if the child turns to the source of the sound within an appropriate time interval following stimulus presentation, the toy is illuminated and activated. The audiologist notes the lowest decibel level at each frequency that elicits a response, and plots the sound field audiogram. VRA can also be used with children who will accept earphones. In this case, the audiologist can obtain ear-specific information and plot a pure tone audiogram.

Tangible Reinforcement Operant Conditioning Audiometry (TROCA) Originally described as a technique useful with children and adults who are difficult to test, TROCA uses systematic reinforcement for appropriate responses to sound stimuli (Lloyd, Spradlin, & Reid, 1968). The child is conditioned to press a response button each time a test signal is presented. A correct response is reinforced with an edible item. TROCA may be used with children age 36 months and older to generate either a sound field audiogram or a pure tone audiogram.

Conditioned Play Audiometry In conditioned play audiometry, the child is conditioned to respond to test signals with an appropriate play activity such as stacking rings on a peg or dropping clothespins in a bottle. The audiologist structures the child's play to prevent positive responses that are extraneous or false. This technique is successful in children age 30 to 36 months and older. Through conditioned play audiometry, it is often possible to generate a complete pure tone audiogram. For the child who refuses to wear earphones, conditioned play audiometry may be used to obtain a sound field audiogram.

Summary Whatever behavioral technique is used, the audiologist observes responses to both tonal or noise signals and speech. Children who can be tested by a conditioned procedure should respond to speech and to tones or noise at close to actual threshold levels. Since speech is a wide band signal (i.e., composed of multiple frequencies), the child's response represents his or her "best" hearing (lowest tonal threshold). Significant discrepancy in response levels for speech as opposed to tones or noise (i.e., responses to speech are lower than responses to tones or noise by more than 15 dB) is not consistent with peripheral sensitivity loss. This pattern of behavior suggests either central auditory dysfunction, deviant auditory behavior, or functional (nonorganic) hearing loss.

Physiological Techniques

Physiological measures serve two important purposes in pediatric audiological assessment. First, they permit a cross-check of behavioral test results (Jerger & Hayes, 1976). Second, they permit objective evaluation of specific aspects of auditory function. The two primary physiological measures used in pediatric assessment are acoustic immittance measures and auditory evoked potentials.

Acoustic Immittance Measures   The terms "acoustic immittance measures" and "impedance audiometry" are used interchangeably to describe a series of procedures employed to assess middle ear and cochlear function. The immittance battery consists of three measures: 1) tympanometry, a measure of mobility of the middle ear system; 2) static compliance, a measure of impedance of the middle ear system; and 3) acoustic reflex measures, a measure of both middle ear function and cochlear–eighth cranial nerve/brain stem integrity.

Acoustic immittance measures are performed by way of a small probe tube that is sealed in the external ear canal. A constant sound pressure is delivered through the probe. Reflection of the sound pressure from the tympanic membrane is measured under various conditions. Alterations in the physics of the middle ear system caused by pathological conditions affect the acoustic immittance measures in predictable and meaningful ways. From the battery of measures (i.e., tympanogram, static compliance, and acoustic reflex), the audiologist can predict the presence of middle ear dysfunction. In addition, in the case of normal middle ear function, acoustic reflex thresholds provide prediction of sensorineural hearing loss (Jerger, Burney, Mauldin, & Crump, 1974).

Auditory Evoked Potentials   Investigators have recorded changes in the electroencephalogram (EEG) in response to sound for more than 40 years (Davis, 1939). Clinically useful recordings of auditory evoked potentials, however, were not possible until the introduction of electronic averaging techniques in the early 1950s. Auditory evoked potentials are typically classified by their latency (i.e., time interval from stimulus to response) into three major components: the early response, or auditory brain stem response (ABR; 0 to 10 milliseconds, or msec); the middle latency response (MLR; 20 to 100 msec); and the late response, or vertex potential (100 to 300 msec). Of these three responses, the ABR provides the most important predictive information.

The auditory brain stem response is a series of five vertex positive waves recorded from averaged EEG activity within 10 milliseconds following acoustic click stimulation. These waves are usually labeled by Roman numerals I–V, following the convention suggested by early investigators (Jewett & Williston, 1971). These sub-microvolt responses to click stimuli are thought to represent electrical activity of the eighth cranial nerve (wave I) and the various auditory nuclei or nerve centers (waves II through V) of the brain stem. Of the five waveforms, wave V is the most pronounced in humans. Figure 4.4 shows a representative click-elicited ABR recorded from a sleeping 3-year-old child with normal hearing.

The ABR has several powerful clinical applications. One of the most important applications is the prediction of hearing level in infants and young children. In infants at risk for hearing loss, ABR audiometry can often provide a reliable estimate of hearing level before it is possible for behavioral or acoustic immittance techniques to yield entirely adequate results. In young children who can cooperate for more conventional testing, the ABR can provide a valuable cross-check of traditional test results.

The ABR is recorded between pairs of electrodes on the child's scalp. The ongoing EEG is amplified, filtered, and averaged. Typically, responses to 2,000 click stimuli are averaged to define a given response. Click stimuli are most effective in eliciting a response from the mid- to high-frequency region of the cochlea. For this reason, the threshold of the ABR (lowest click intensity level that yields a response) predicts hearing level in the 1,000 to

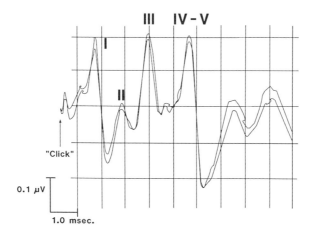

Figure 4.4.   Representative click-elicited auditory brain stem response from a 3-year-old girl with normal hearing. Clicks were presented at 80 dB HL. Waves I (eighth cranial nerve) and II through V (brain stem auditory nuclei) are labeled.

4,000 Hz region of the pure tone audiogram. Children of more than 6–8 months of age are usually sedated for ABR audiometry. For this reason, the test is used primarily as a cross-check of behavioral audiometry or acoustic immittance measures when a hearing loss is suspected, or when no other test technique is effective in yielding a prediction of hearing sensitivity.

The Test Battery

Most clinicians employ a cross-check technique when selecting a test battery for pediatric audiological assessment. That is, whatever technique is selected for testing a child's hearing, results are confirmed by an independent cross-check. In most instances, behavioral test results can be cross-checked by acoustic immittance measures. In other cases, behavioral audiometry yields only minimal information about a child's hearing sensitivity. In these cases, acoustic immittance measures in combination with ABR audiometry can provide clinically useful predictions.

INDICATIONS FOR REFERRAL TO AN AUDIOLOGIST: ILLUSTRATIVE CASES

The following cases illustrate application of behavioral and physiological techniques in pediatric evaluation. These cases exemplify some of the more common causes of childhood hearing impairment, and represent cases encountered by other professionals that call for the involvement of an audiologist. Each case demonstrates the importance of both behavioral and physiological measures in the audiological evaluation of children.

Case 1: Chronic Otitis Media with Effusion (OME)

J.M. is a 6-year-old boy who developed his first episode of OME before age 1 year. His mother estimates that he had 6–10 episodes of OME before age 2 years. He has received ongoing medical/surgical management for middle ear disorder.

Figure 4.5 shows J.M.'s pretreatment and posttreatment audiogram obtained by conditioned play audiometry. Prior to treatment for his most recent episode of OME, J.M. demonstrates a mild conductive bilateral hearing loss. Thresholds for air-conducted pure tones are depressed, ranging from 20–30 dB HL in each ear. Thresholds for bone-conducted pure tones are normal, ranging from 0–10 dB HL. This difference in threshold between air-conducted and bone-conducted pure tones is the hallmark of conductive hearing loss.

Acoustic immittance measures were consistent with middle ear dysfunction. For both ears, tympanograms, static compliance measures, and the acoustic reflex were abnormal. Thus, both behavioral audiometry and acoustic immittance measures were consistent with middle ear disorder and the resulting conductive hearing loss.

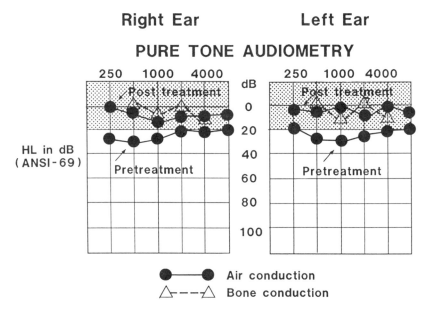

Figure 4.5. Pre- and posttreatment behavioral audiogram from a 6-year-old boy with recurrent otitis media with effusion. This audiogram was obtained by conditioned play audiometry. Pretreatment audiogram shows mild bilateral conductive hearing loss. Following treatment (insertion of pressure equalizing tubes in the tympanic membrane) the pure tone audiogram is normal. (ANSI-69: American National Standards Institute 1969 standard for audiometric normal hearing.)

Medical/surgical management involved placement of pressure equalizing (PE) tubes through each eardrum. The posttreatment audiogram (Figure 4.5) reveals normal hearing bilaterally, indicating that the placement of the PE tubes was a success.

Summary   Otitis media with effusion is the most common cause of childhood hearing loss. Although such hearing loss is amenable to medical/surgical improvement, there is ample evidence that even short duration auditory deprivation related to OME can have deleterious effects on speech and language development and on academic achievement (Northern & Downs, 1984; Sak & Ruben, 1982). OME is more common in children with other handicaps than in normally developing children. Children with Down syndrome or children with cleft lip and palate, for example, have frequent episodes of recurrent OME and conductive hearing loss. Children at risk for OME should receive frequent otological/audiological monitoring.

Case 2: H-Flu (Bacterial) Meningitis

G.R. is a 15-month-old boy who was hospitalized with H-flu meningitis. He received audiological assessment on the seventh day of hospitalization.

Results of the behavior measure of visual reinforcement audiometry (VRA) are shown in Figure 4.6. G.R. responded to speech and to tonal signals from 500 to 4,000 Hz at intensity levels ranging from 60–70 dB HL. For a child of this age with normal hearing, responses to signals at lower intensities (10–20 dB HL) are expected. The fact that G.R. did not respond to sound until it was moderately intense suggested presence of significant bilateral hearing loss. Individual ear measures could not be obtained as G.R. would not tolerate earphone placement.

The results from the behavior audiometry measure were confirmed by acoustic immittance measures. Acoustic reflexes were absent in both ears, while tympanometry and static compliance measures revealed normal middle ear function bilaterally. In the presence of normal middle ear function, absence of the acoustic reflex is consistent with severe to profound sensorineural hearing loss.

In this case, both behavior audiometry and acoustic immittance measures are consistent with severe sensorineural bilateral hearing loss. In order to obtain a prediction of hearing sensitivity in each ear individually (since such data could not be obtained from the VRA due to G.R.'s resistance to wearing the earphones), auditory brain stem response (ABR) audiometry was performed with G.R. sedated and asleep. The results showed responses to clicks at 80 to 100 dB HL in each ear, but there were no responses to clicks presented at lower intensity levels. These results predict severe (60–79 dB

SOUND FIELD AUDIOMETRY

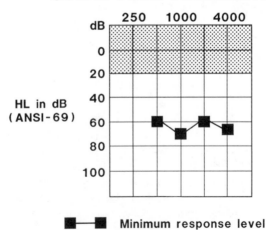

■——■ Minimum response level

Figure 4.6. Sound field audiogram of a 15-month-old boy with H-flu meningitis. This audiogram was obtained using visual reinforcement audiometry. Results are consistent with significant bilateral hearing loss. (Speech awareness = 60 dB HL.) (ANSI-69: American National Standards Institute 1969 standard for audiometric normal hearing.)

SOUND FIELD AUDIOMETRY

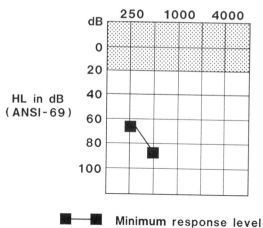

Minimum response level

Figure 4.7.   Sound field audiogram of a 35-month-old girl with congenital cytomegalovirus. Behavioral responses are consistent with profound bilateral hearing loss. (Speech awareness = 65 dB HL) (ANSI-69: American National Standards Institute 1969 standard for audiometric normal hearing.)

HL) hearing loss in the 1,000 to 4,000 Hz region of the pure tone audiogram in each ear.

Based on the overall picture of severe bilateral sensorineural hearing loss, G.R. was fitted with binaural hearing aids and enrolled in speech-language therapy. G.R. will require some level of special education services throughout his school years.

Summary   Meningitis is a major cause of acquired sensorineural hearing impairment in childhood. Depending on the causative organism, approximately 7%–30% of all children with meningitis develop sensorineural hearing loss (Dodge et al., 1984). Hearing impairment can range from mild to profound, but, unfortunately, for most children the expected degree of loss is at least severe in each ear. All children who develop meningitis should receive audiological assessment during treatment for the disease.

Case 3: Cytomegalovirus (CMV)

S.D. is a 35-month-old girl with a congenital viral infection known as cytomegalovirus. Hearing loss was first suspected at age 23 months when she failed a hearing screening at a preschool program, in which she was enrolled because of general developmental delay.

The results of VRA audiometry at age 35 months are shown in Figure 4.7. S.D. responded to noise signals at 250 and 500 Hz, but there were no responses to noise signals centered at higher frequencies. In addition, the responses at 250 and 500 Hz were present only at moderate and high intensities of 65–90 dB HL. Similarly, S.D. responded to speech only at moderate levels of 65 dB HL. These results are consistent with profound bilateral sensorineural hearing loss.

Acoustic immittance measures revealed the presence of a middle ear disorder in each ear. Both tympanograms and static compliance results suggested middle ear dysfunction related to extra mass in the middle ear space. Visual inspection of the ears revealed otitis media with effusion.

ABR audiometry was performed to confirm sensorineural hearing loss. S.D. was sedated for this procedure. There were no responses from either ear. Thus, the overall pattern of results confirms profound bilateral sensorineural hearing loss and middle ear disorder.

S.D. received pressure equalizing (PE) tubes for her OME. She was fitted with binaural hearing aids and enrolled in an individual aural rehabilitation program consisting of auditory training and total communication (sign language). She continued to attend a preschool program for children with developmental disabilities. S.D. will require special education services throughout her school years.

Summary CMV is one of a number of congenital perinatal infections that place a child at risk for hearing impairment. These agents are known as the TORCH complex (T=toxoplasmosis; O=other, usually considered syphilis; R=rubella; C=cytomegalovirus; H=herpes). Each of these infections may result in several handicapping conditions in childhood, including hearing loss, mental retardation, and developmental delay. The TORCH complex is one of the conditions on the *High Risk Register for Deafness* (Gerkin, 1984). Because of the effectiveness of the rubella vaccination program in the United States, CMV is now considered to be a more important cause of childhood handicaps than rubella.

Case 4: Sensorineural Unknown

W.M. is a 5-year-old girl who failed the kindergarten hearing screening. Her prenatal, birth, and early childhood history revealed no serious illness or high-risk condition for hearing impairment. Although speech and language development were described as "slow," W.M. was a sociable, attractive child who got along well with both children and adults.

The results of a conditioned play audiometry measure that was performed immediately after W.M. failed the kindergarten screening are shown in Figure 4.8. W.M. responded to pure tone signals at levels ranging from 25–60 dB HL in both ears. Responses to bone-conducted signals were identical to responses to air-conducted signals. These results indicate mild to moderate bilateral sensorineural hearing loss.

Acoustic immittance measures were consistent with the behavior audiometry measure. Tympanometry and static compliance measures revealed

Right Ear   Left Ear
PURE TONE AUDIOMETRY

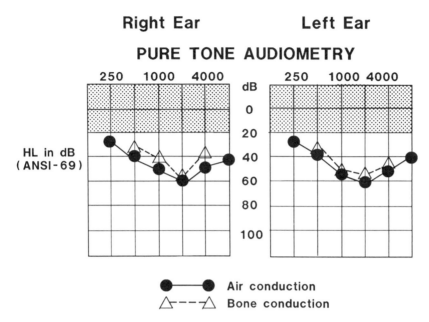

●———● Air conduction
△——△ Bone conduction

Figure 4.8.   Pure tone audiogram of a 5-year-old girl who failed a school hearing screening. Results indicate a mild to moderate bilateral sensorineural hearing loss. (ANSI-69: American National Standards Institute 1969 standard for audiometric normal hearing.)

normal middle ear function in both ears. In addition, the threshold of the acoustic reflex predicted the presence of bilateral sensorineural hearing loss. In view of the reliable behavior measure results and the consistency of acoustic immittance measures with these results, ABR audiometry was not performed.

W.M. was fitted with binaural, mild gain hearing aids and enrolled in speech therapy in the public school. She will require speech therapy throughout her elementary school years to improve her vocabulary development and speech skills. With appropriate support services, W.M. should be successful in a regular classroom.

Summary   Children with no significant medical/developmental history are not easily identified as having a hearing impairment. Depending on the degree of hearing loss, these children often remain undetected until age 2 years and older. In the absence of any medical/developmental risk condition or family history of childhood hearing loss, successful detection of these children often depends on parental observation of and concern about auditory behavioral and speech/language development. Whenever a child is identified as having sensorineural hearing loss of unknown etiology, that child's siblings should also receive audiological assessment. Approximately 50% of all childhood sensorineural hearing loss is related to hereditary factors (Proctor & Proctor, 1967).

Case 5: Cis Platinum Ototoxicity

J.Y. is an 8-year-old boy with a frontal lobe brain tumor. Medical management of his tumor includes radiation therapy and cis platinum (an anti-cancer drug) chemotherapy.

Figure 4.9 shows serial audiograms obtained by conventional behavioral techniques (e.g., the child pushes a button in response to test signals). J.Y. was tested three times during the course of cis platinum treatments. Test 1 shows normal hearing bilaterally. Tests 2 and 3, however, show progressive high-frequency sensorineural hearing loss. At test 2, J.Y.'s hearing remained normal through 4,000 Hz with loss at 6,000 and 8,000 Hz. By test 3, however, J.Y. demonstrated hearing loss for all frequencies above 2,000 Hz. At all three evaluations, acoustic immittance measures revealed normal middle ear function. At evaluations 2 and 3, however, acoustic reflex thresholds indicated the presence of sensorineural hearing loss.

Summary Ototoxicity is common in children receiving cis platinum therapy. In general, the resulting audiogram shows moderate-to-severe high-frequency hearing loss. Sensitivity for frequencies below 2,000 Hz is usually

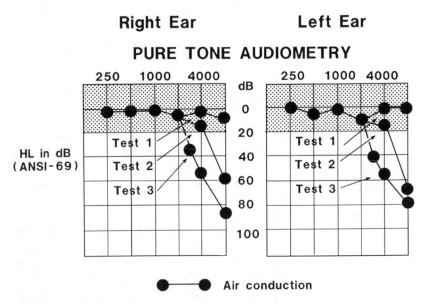

Figure 4.9. Successive pure tone audiograms of an 8-year-old boy receiving cis platinum treatment for a frontal lobe brain tumor. The audiograms show progressive high-frequency sensorineural hearing loss. (ANSI-69: American National Standards Institute 1969 standard for audiometric normal hearing.)

Right Ear   Left Ear
PURE TONE AUDIOMETRY

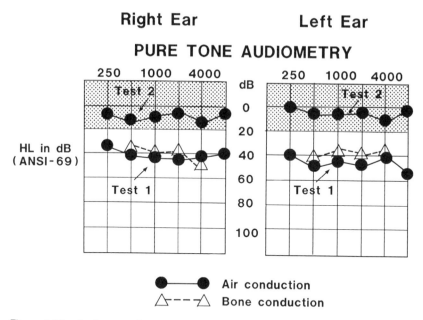

● —— ● Air conduction
△---△ Bone conduction

Figure 4.10. Audiograms from a 12-year-old girl with functional hearing loss. Initial testing showed a relatively flat bilateral sensorineural hearing loss. Thresholds for speech (20 dB HL) were significantly better than thresholds for pure tones. Acoustic reflexes and ABR audiometry predicted normal hearing. Repeat behavioral testing under structured test conditions revealed normal hearing sensitivity. (ANSI-69: American National Standards Institute 1969 standard for audiometric normal hearing.)

normal. For some children, hearing loss is sufficient to warrant the use of hearing aids. Children who are receiving cis platinum chemotherapy should receive regular audiological assessment.

Case 6: Functional Hearing Loss

H.D. is a 12-year-old girl who complains of gradual onset hearing loss. She describes her hearing loss as developing gradually over the past year for no apparent reason. She has greatest difficulty hearing in the classroom.

The results of behavior audiometry are shown in Figure 4.10, Test 1. H.D. responded to pure tone signals at 40–60 dB HL in each ear. Sensitivity was nearly equivalent for both air-conducted and bone-conducted signals. She responded to speech at much lower intensities; with each ear, H.D. was able to identify words at 20 dB HL. This discrepancy in threshold for pure tones and threshold for speech is a common characteristic of functional hearing loss.

Acoustic immittance measures showed normal middle ear function and predicted normal cochlear function in each ear. No evidence of hearing loss was shown by acoustic immittance measures.

H.D. cooperated for ABR audiometry without sedation. Responses were present to air-conducted clicks at 15 dB HL in each ear. This predicts normal bilateral hearing sensitivity in the 1000 to 4000 Hz region of the pure tone audiogram.

Repeated behavior audiometry (Test 2) is also shown in the figure. Under strictly structured test conditions, H.D. responded to pure tones at normal hearing levels.

Summary Functional or nonorganic hearing loss is not uncommon in childhood. Many school-age youngsters demonstrate nonorganic hearing loss at some time during the school years. In contrast to nonorganic hearing loss in adults, the motivation for nonorganic hearing loss in children is almost never monetary. Rather, hearing loss provides a good excuse for poor academic performance or for gaining needed attention. Children are not sophisticated hearing test takers; it is usually not difficult to detect functional hearing loss in children. In these cases, "rehabilitation" consists of management of the underlying emotional/behavior problem.

Conclusion

These cases demonstrate the range of hearing loss observed in children. Hearing is critical for speech and language development, for socialization and emotional maturation, and for academic achievement. Any degree of hearing impairment in childhood can have significant effects on overall growth and development.

Sophisticated techniques are available that permit the identification of hearing impairment in even the most difficult-to-test child. Audiological assessment should not be delayed in any child regardless of his or her age or level of function. If the possibility of hearing impairment is suspected, the child should be referred for immediate audiological assessment.

REFERENCES

Carpenter, M. B. (1972). *Core text of neuroanatomy*. Baltimore: Williams & Wilkins.
Davis, P. (1939). Effects of acoustic stimuli on the waking human brain. *Journal of Neurophysiology, 2*, 494–499.
Dodge, P., Davis, H., Feigin, R., Holmes, S., Kaplan, S., Jubelirer, D., Stechenberg, B., & Hirsh, S. (1984). Prospective evaluation of hearing impairment as a sequela of acute bacterial meningitis. *New England Journal of Medicine, 311*, 869–874.
Gerkin, K. (1984). The High Risk Register for Deafness. *American Speech-Language-Hearing Association, 26*, 17–23.
Green, D. M. (1976). *An introduction to hearing*. Hillsdale, NJ: Lawrence Erlbaum Associates.
Jerger, J., Burney, P., Mauldin, L., & Crump, B. (1974). Predicting hearing loss from the acoustic reflex. *Journal of Speech and Hearing Disorders, 39*, 11–22.

Jerger, J., & Hayes, D. (1976). The cross-check principle in pediatric audiometry. *Archives of Otolaryngology, 102,* 614–620.

Jewett, D., & Williston, J. (1971). Auditory-evoked far fields averaged from the scalp of humans. *Brain, 94,* 681–696.

Liden, G., & Kankkonen, A. (1961). Visual reinforcement audiometry. *Acta Otolaryngolgica, 67,* 281–292.

Lloyd, L., Spradlin, J., & Reid, M. (1968). An operant audiometric procedure for difficult-to-test patients. *Journal of Speech and Hearing Disorders, 33,* 236–245.

Moller, A. (1970). The middle ear. In J. Tobias (Ed.), *Foundations of modern auditory theory: Volume 2* (pp. 133–194). New York: Academic Press.

Northern, J., & Downs, M. (1984). *Hearing in children* (3rd ed.). Baltimore: Williams & Wilkins.

Paparella, M. (1980). Sensorineural hearing loss in children: Nongenetic. In M. Paparella & D. Shumrick (Eds.), *Otolaryngology: Vol. II. The ear* (pp. 1707–1717). Philadelphia: W. B. Saunders.

Proctor, C., & Proctor, B. (1967). Understanding hereditary nerve deafness. *Archives of Otolaryngology, 85,* 23–40.

Sak, R., & Ruben, R. (1981). Effects of recurrent middle ear effusion in pre-school years on language and hearing. *Journal of Behavioral Pediatrics, 3,* 7–11.

United States Department of Labor. (1977). *Dictionary of occupational titles.* Washington, DC: Author.

Chapter 5

Speech-Language Assessment

~~

Trudi Norman-Murch
and Anthony Bashir

Delays or differences in speech and language learning are often the first "red flag" marking the presence of a host of medical and developmental problems in children. While parents may not be sophisticated observers of all aspects of development, they notice if their child starts to talk later or is more difficult to understand than other children in the family or in the neighborhood. Such speech and language problems may be present as specific, primary areas of disability, but more frequently they are related to, and reflective of, problems in other areas of functioning (e.g., hearing, cognition, fine and gross motor skills) as well as emotional and environmental status. A multidisciplinary assessment is often, therefore, critical to understanding the etiology of described speech-language problems and in planning appropriate intervention. Clearly, a child who cannot hear a particular sound pattern should be treated differently from a child who has difficulty with the physical coordination aspects of sound production. In a similar manner, a child who does not say the word "ball" because he or she does not yet know what a ball is and what it is used for, needs a different treatment program than a child who does not say "ball" because he or she is socially withdrawn and has no interest in or need to communicate a desire for that ball. Conversely, the speech-language pathologist can make an important contribution to the multidisciplinary assessment team since communication skills draw on such a broad range of physical, cognitive, and social skills. A precise analysis of speech-language functioning can significantly contribute to a better under-standing of overall status and service needs.

A description of the academic/clinical training and accreditation of speech-language pathologists is provided in this chapter. The conditions treat-ed by the speech-language pathologist are described, as are the assessment procedures appropriate to each disorder. Issues regarding the differential diag-nosis of speech-language problems are discussed, and recommendations as to referral criteria are made.

The importance of early investigation of speech-language problems can-not be stressed enough. First, as noted, they may be an indication of difficul-ties in other areas of functioning and development, such as mental retardation or hearing impairment, which may require prompt recognition and treatment. Second, they may identify the children as being at risk for future learning problems. Follow-up studies clearly indicate that children with early speech-language delays are in a high-risk category for future academic difficulties (Aram & Nation, 1980; Strominger & Bashir, 1977). While the symp-tomatology may change over time, and therefore give the appearance of resolution, the underlying deficits often persist. Finally, a disruption in or failure of the parent-child and child-peer communication system, in and of itself, can have profound emotional and behavioral consequences. Early inter-vention is critical.

PROFESSIONAL TRAINING

The American Speech-Language-Hearing Association (ASHA) is the national organization of speech-language pathologists and audiologists. The Certifi-cate of Clinical Competence in Speech-Language Pathology (C.C.C.-SLP) is offered by ASHA and is the nationally recognized certification of professional expertise. In states where licensure exists for speech-language pathologists, it is, with some exceptions, at least equivalent to the C.C.C.-SLP. In order for a speech-language pathology department to be accredited by the Professional Services Board of ASHA, all its members must have the C.C.C.-SLP or its equivalent, or be supervised by someone who does. The C.C.C.-SLP is recognized by, for example, the Joint Commission on Accreditation of Hospi-tals, the Commission on Accreditation of Rehabilitation Facilities, Medicare, and by various national insurance carriers as a prerequisite for the provision of clinical services in speech-language pathology. ASHA maintains a registry of holders of the C.C.C.-SLP that is published in a directory. Because there are few laws regulating private practice, it is strongly recommended that an individual's professional credentials be reviewed when one is seeking the services of a speech-language pathologist.

The following is a brief summary of the academic and clinical training required for obtaining the C.C.C.-SLP. The candidate must have a master's degree or equivalent with major emphasis in speech-language pathology or speech-language-hearing science. This includes study of general background information (e.g., child development, sociology, physical development), normal communication processes, and communication disorders. Coursework in particular speech-language disorders, assessment procedures, and treatment is specified. At least 6 semester hours of coursework in audiology are required, including assessment of auditory disorders and habilitative or rehabilitative procedures.

In addition to the academic coursework, 300 clock hours of supervised clinical experience in an academic clinical practicum are required. A minimum of 200 of these hours must be in speech-language pathology, and a minimum of 35 hours must be in audiology. Experience with patients of various ages and disorders is also specified, as is practice in both assessment and treatment.

On completion of the academic and clinical practicum requirements for the C.C.C.-SLP, an individual is eligible to sit for the National Examination in Speech-Language Pathology. This examination must be passed within 3 years of initial eligibility.

Finally, the clinician has a Clinical Fellowship Year during which time he or she is closely supervised. The amount and type of clinical supervision required during this year is specified by ASHA. At the completion of the Clinical Fellowship Year, the Certificate of Clinical Competence in Speech-Language Pathology (C.C.C.-SLP) is awarded.

While ASHA does not offer certification in specialty areas (e.g., pediatrics or voice disorders), it is advisable to consider an individual's professional experience when seeking speech-language pathology services. For readers of this volme, the authors suggest that the more pediatric experience a clinician has had, the more he or she may be able to contribute to the multidisciplinary assessment effort.

CONDITIONS TREATED BY SPEECH-LANGUAGE PATHOLOGISTS

Language Learning Disorders

Early Language Learning   Before language learning disorders can be considered, the scope and complexity of normal speech and language development must be appreciated. In the first year of life, the child learns to realize that he or she is separate from the environment and capable of controlling it. The child learns of the independence of objects, the function of objects, and the ways in which objects act upon each other. This early learning forms a basis for language development, a system that the child will acquire for representing what he or she knows of the world.

Learning the language system of his or her community is one of the most complex tasks required of a young child. It is generally expected that by the age of 3–4 years, the child will be an active, competent, verbal participant at home and with peers. He or she knows the names of most of the objects in his or her environment, follows directions, enjoys listening to stories, and understands verbal explanations. He or she can construct simple grammatically correct sentences, tell a story, carry on a conversation, and use his or her language for a wide variety of social functions. Achieving this level of competence involves mastery of discrete though related language skills.

The child learns the meanings of the words that will be used to mark events and the relationships between events (*semantic learning*). He or she also learns to order words into sentences that express relationships (*syntax learning*) and to produce the sounds of the language (*phonological learning*). The child acquires language in a social context and as a result develops an awareness and an ability to alter language styles to meet social situations. For example, the language of politeness is learned along with the appropriate situations in which it is to be used (*pragmatic learning*). Language learning problems may be conceptualized as a breakdown in the development of any of these skills.

Language learning problems may be related to hearing impairment, mental retardation, primary emotional disturbance, or environmental deprivation. They may also be present in isolation and represent a specific form of learning disability. In these cases, unless there is a known traumatic event (e.g., a head injury or a near-drowning episode), the etiology generally remains unknown. A strong familial history of language learning deficits or a positive medical history of seizure disorder or difficult birth are highly suggestive, but causation cannot be determined precisely.

For the sake of discussion, in the next section language learning problems are broken down into a number of discrete disorders. It should be understood that because these areas of functioning are highly interrelated, an individual child might be affected in one or more areas.

Disorders of Comprehension Children may have difficulty understanding the meaning of words (semantic learning); words representing more abstract concepts, such as time and space, may be especially troublesome. If they understand individual words, they may have difficulty understanding more complex word relationships (e.g., opposites and analogies). They may not understand word order rules and therefore not appreciate the difference between "The girl hit the boy" and "The boy hit the girl" (syntax learning). More subtle language comprehension deficits can be present when children fail to understand the implied social content of language (pragmatic learning). For example, a mother may say, "Can you be quiet for a few minutes?" If the child interprets the question literally, he may say "Yes," and continue yelling at his sister.

Some children may be able to understand separate sentences, but when these sentences are joined to form a story, they do not get the meaning or topic. Some children's ability to understand language is especially vulnerable to information "load" factors. That is, they have difficulty following rapid speech, or understanding long or grammatically complex sentences. If they are asked to process auditory information too fast, they experience a breakdown in language comprehension. This may also be reflective of specific auditory processing disorders, which are discussed below.

Disorders of Auditory Processing Some children appear to be especially ineffective in coping with their auditory environment (Stark & Bernstein, 1984). Whether these deficits are perceptually or linguistically based is unclear, but language comprehension is affected (Keith, 1984).

Auditory Attention Problems Problems in this area include distractibility to irrelevant stimuli, difficulty maintaining auditory attention, difficulty shifting from one task to another, and slow adaptation to relevant auditory stimuli. Children with these disorders work best in a quiet, distraction-free environment. They need to be given lead time for change-of-task, and this change-of-task needs to be made explicit for them.

Auditory Discrimination Problems Such problems (i.e., difficulty discriminating one sound pattern from another) have been ascribed to children with language learning disabilities, but recent research has questioned this assumption (Stark & Bernstein, 1984). Further studies are needed before the value of remedial auditory discrimination programs can be substantiated.

Auditory Sequential Memory Deficits Deficits in auditory sequential memory are often present among children with language learning disabilities and are reflected in poor ability to retain auditory verbal information in order on a short-term basis. This kind of problem is a true handicap to children in an academic setting where success depends, to some degree, on the ability to remember ideas and follow directions. When told to "turn to page 23, look at the bottom of the page, and do the third item" these children become confused. If they could find the third item, they might be able to do it successfully—but they never get that far. The behavior of children with such problems may be interpreted as daydreaming or as being lazy, and disciplinary measures may be inappropriately applied. These children benefit from having directions repeated and broken down into short units, from simultaneous demonstration, and from being given extra time for processing what has been said to them. In instances where performance anxiety is a factor, auditory memory is especially vulnerable.

Auditory Figure-Ground Problems Auditory figure-ground problems reflect difficulties in selecting the primary message from a background of noise. Some children's ability to comprehend language deteriorates in situations of increasing or fluctuating background noise. This may go unobserved in a traditional evaluation that is conducted in a quiet, structured, one-to-one exchange, but it can be formally assessed during an audiological evaluation. These children may be at special risk in an open classroom situation where there is more environmental noise than in a traditional structured classroom setting. Consequently, an appropriate educational environment must be selected carefully.

Disorders of Language Expression Comprehension or auditory processing problems are often difficult for the nonspecialist in speech/language to recognize because they cannot be directly observed: one only sees apparent inattention or poor direction-following. Expressive problems may be more obvious. Expressive language disorders represent deficits in one or more aspects of the child's use of spoken verbal symbols. They may occur in isolation or in conjunction with comprehension difficulties. Expressive language skills are described in terms of: 1) primary means of communication (signs, gestures, jargon, words, phrases, and sentences); 2) ability to use words for specification of objects and events, and relations between them (semantics); 3) the child's overall sentence-building skills (syntax); 4) word retrieval skills; 5) narrative appropriateness (pragmatics); and 6) narrative organization as well as elaboration, and sequential development and cohesion. Children with problems in acquisition of these skills are referred to speech-language pathologists.

With preschool children, the difficulty is often identified in terms of primary means of communication (e.g., the child is pointing or gesturing when he or she should be using words). Parents and teachers of the late preschool or early elementary school-age child may also note that the child experiences difficulty in constructing grammatically correct sentences, and they often cite errors of pronoun use, use of telegraphic syntax (e.g., "Me push wagon"), and poor mastery of question formation rules (e.g., "Where my mommy is?"). These deficits in sentence-building skills may, in fact, persist into late childhood and adolescence (Vogel, 1974).

Word retrieval problems constitute a major source of frustration for children with expressive language disorders. They represent a momentary inability to recall the name of an object or event of which the child has previous knowledge (e.g., "It's on the tip of my tongue"; "I know what it is, I just can't say it"). Word retrieval problems are most commonly observed under confrontation situations of naming, answering questions, or in prolonged explanations. Children may compensate by circumlocution. They may use associated labels (e.g., "comb" for "brush") or compound words (e.g., "fish scooper" for "pelican"). They may make sound pattern errors (e.g., "colvano" for "volcano"), or use a word that sounds like the target (e.g., "tornado" for "volcano"). In many cases, they simply abandon the effort to communicate by withdrawing or changing the subject. The emotional consequences of these kinds of problems are often considerable.

More subtle expressive language disorders may be indicated by the inability to organize a coherent narrative or sustain conversational interchange. Parents may report that they cannot follow their child's conversation or understand their communicative intent. Their child's stories are fragmented and disorganized; it is difficult to understand who did what to whom, and why. Again, the frustration for both parent and child represents a significant problem in and of itself (see Figure 5.1).

Articulation Disorders

Many people think of articulation (pronunciation) problems as being the primary focus of speech-language pathologists. Although they diagnose and treat other kinds of communication disorders, as described in this chapter, articulation remains a major concern since it so crucially affects a person's ability to communicate effectively.

Articulation disorders refer to problems with speech-sound production. A child may substitute one sound for another, omit sounds, distort sounds, and occasionally add sounds. Since some sounds are learned at an earlier age than others, clinicians must judge the developmental appropriateness of a child's error pattern. In addition, the speech-language pathologist considers the number of errors made and the overall intelligibility of the child's speech in making a determination as to the presence of an articulation problem. For example, the "r," the "l," the "s," and consonant blend sounds often are not mastered until the child is 6–7 years old (Templin, 1957). A 5-year-old child who persists in making errors in one or two of these sounds may not be a good candidate for speech therapy. However, if he or she makes errors in all of these sounds and if overall intelligibility is affected, therapy may be appropriate.

The child's speech-sound production skills are assessed in a number of different contexts: single word naming, sentence production, and spontaneous conversation. Considerable variability may be present, depending on the complexity of the speaking situation and the degree of communicative pressure present. It is as important to observe the consistency, or lack of consistency, in articulation functioning as it is to describe specific error patterns.

Ultimately, the majority of articulation problems are of unknown origin, but the question of etiology must be considered in order to plan effective treatment. Several causative factors may be considered.

Hearing impairment should be considered. Normal hearing sensitivity must be demonstrated in order to rule out hearing impairment as a possible cause.

Deficits in auditory discrimination have been proposed as primary factors in articulation problems, and may be considered as a possible cause of articulation problems, although recent studies suggest that further research is needed to resolve this issue (Stark & Bernstein, 1984). It is possible that children have difficulty with the auditory discrimination tasks because of problems in understanding the vocabulary, difficulties in following the directions, auditory short-term memory deficits, the presence of competing noise,

A child (C) and an examiner (E) are looking through the child's daily journal, in which he has drawn pictures with themes of his own choice. In this segment, he is talking about a picture he drew after seeing the movie, Bambi.

E: Let's find a picture that has a story with it, okay?

C: I want this, this, this, this [pointing to a picture about Bambi].

E: Oh, Okay.

C: This a squirrel, a squirrel. [Points to another figure in the drawing] I can't, I don't, I don't know he name. Chris [his teacher] don't like him.

E: What kind of thing is it? Is it an animal?

C: [Moving on to another figure], Bambi.

E: That's Bambi.

C: And that Thumper.

E: Yes, that's Thumper.

C: [Pointing to another figure in the drawing] "I want a cracker, I want a cracker."

E: That's what the parrot says, "I want a cracker, I want a cracker."

C: And that one, that one is . . . . [pointing to another figure].

E: Hold it a second, can you remember what happened to Bambi?

C: He can't talk.

E: Bambi can't talk? Why not?

C: I watch a movie.

E: You watched the movie, right—and what happened in *Bambi*? Remember, there was a fire . . . .

C: Uh huh.

E: And then what happened?

C: Bambi did not get dead.

E: Bambi did not get dead—Bambi did not die, but what did he do?

C: He run.

E: Yes, he ran away, and then what happened?

C: All over, all over place.

E: He ran all over the place, yes, and then what happened?

(continued)

Figure 5.1. Conversation between a 6-year-old child (C), with mild to moderate language comprehension deficits and severely disordered expressive language and articulation, and an examiner (E). The child's scores on the Wechsler Intelligence Scale for Children–Revised (WISC-R) were verbal–85 and performance–119, yielding a full scale–101. Note his tendency to label objects rather than construct a narrative, his use of sentence fragments, his incorrect use of pronouns and verb tense, his omission of auxiliary verbs, and his general difficulty in getting his point across. He often starts a sentence over several times, trying to get it right. It is obvious that he actually knows a good deal more about the story than he is able to express on his own.

C: And next day, he house.
E: He went to his house?
C: Uh huh, he safe.
E: That's right, he was safe. But I don't know if he saved himself or if somebody helped him.
C: I don't know.
E: Hmm . . . can't remember that part? . . . Thumper came along, remember?
C: Uh huh . . . helped.
E: Can you remember how Thumper helped him?
C: Uh huh, he help, he can talk [bangs on table to indicate thumping—gets carried away and keeps on banging].
E: That's right, he thumped, he thumped his feet. When he thumped what happened?
C: And the fire "W-W-W-W" [makes a blowing wind noise to indicate a fast moving fire].
E: Yes, the fire moved very fast, didn't it?
C: This, what's this, this? [pointing to mark on the tape recorder].
E: You see that little mark? I think someone put a magic marker on there.
C: How?
E: I'm not sure. Is there anything else you would like to say about this Bambi picture? I think it's a wonderful picture.
C: I don't know, let's go next one.

Figure 5.1. (*continued*)

or hearing impairment. That is, what appears to be an auditory discrimination deficit may actually be reflective of difficulties with the task being used to test those skills.

Dental irregularities (i.e., alignment of upper and lower teeth, spacing between teeth) may be the cause of articulation problems. However, this needs to be examined closely by the speech-language pathologist since dental irregularities do not necessarily cause speech impairment. Normal speech is possible under a wide variety of oral structural conditions.

Lesions in the central and/or peripheral nervous system may result in articulation problems. These lesions are related to weakness, paralysis, or severe incoordination of the oral musculature, and are called "dysarthrias" (Darley, Aronson, & Brown, 1969). During childhood, they are most commonly associated with cerebral palsy. Children with these kinds of problems may not develop intelligible speech and need to be assessed as potential users of augmentative communication systems, such as signs or communication boards. In the case of a more mildly affected child, who may not have received a neurological examination, this possible causative factor could be considered on the basis of the speech symptoms alone.

It has been postulated that *difficulties using sensory information from the mouth* may result in articulation problems (Borden, 1984). Further research into this area is needed.

Developmental dyspraxia of speech refers to difficulties with the voluntary selection, direction, and organization of sequences of movement for speech-sound production. Severity varies from mild (e.g., trouble with multisyllabic words) to incapacitating. Children with developmental dyspraxia often make obvious groping attempts at sound production. A child with this problem may be recognized by the great difficulty he or she has with voluntary imitation of oral movement and sound patterns, such as when asked to move the tongue from side to side, or to move it quickly from the front to middle to back of the mouth (i.e., production of the "p," "t," and "k" sounds in sequence). Communication may be extremely frustrating for these children.

Another group of children has articulation problems related to *underlying language learning deficits.* Although the physical ability to accurately produce sounds in sequence is present, the child makes articulation errors because of an initial failure to process the word correctly, remember it, and retrieve it when needed. These children may, in turn, have language-based reading problems, and require a special reading program adapted to their needs.

Finally, a number of researchers (such as Hodson, 1984) have investigated regularities underlying children's articulation patterns and postulate *faulty learning of sound production rules* as a basis of articulation disorders. These theories are described in the section on articulation assessment, as they relate to evaluation procedures.

Resonance and Voice Disorders While resonance and voice disorders are not directly related to learning disabilities and mental retardation, brief mention should be made of them, as they may occur in conjunction with the developmental disabilities. The speech-language pathologist can identify resonance and voice problems, make recommendations for further medical or psychological assessment, and then help design a treatment program.

Resonance disorders Normal speech production depends on maintenance of the proper relationship between the oral and nasal cavities (Figure 5.2). Production of the "nasal" sounds ("m," "n," and "ng") requires that air be able to pass adequately between the oral and nasal cavities through the velopharyngeal mechanism, giving the characteristic "nasal" resonance. Production of all other English sounds, including vowels, requires some

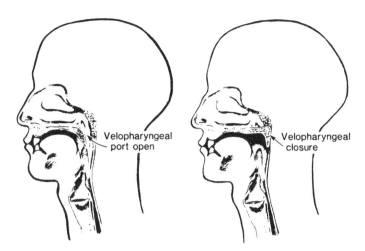

Figure 5.2. Velopharyngeal mechanism. Open for "nasal" sounds, closed for all other English sounds. (From Case, J. L. [1984]. *Clinical management of voice disorders* [p. 288]. Rockville, MD: Aspen Publishers. Copyright © 1984 by Aspen Publishers, Inc. Reproduced by permission.)

degree of separation between the cavities. This is accomplished by a sphincter-like movement in which the soft palate (velum) is elevated against the pharynx at the back of the throat. Failure to achieve adequate closure (velopharyngeal incompetence) results in a leak of air into the nasal cavity, giving an overly nasal ("hypernasal") resonance to sounds that are meant to be non-nasal. Most commonly affected consonants include, for example, "p," "t," "k," and "s" related sounds. Hypernasality is most commonly associated with oral structural problems, such as cleft palate. Conversely, obstruction of the nasal passage (as, for example, by a cold) prevents air from passing adequately through the nasal cavities for production of the nasal sounds ("n," "m," and "ng"), giving a denasal ("hyponasal") resonance.

Voice Disorders Voice disorders include problems with vocal pitch, loudness, and rate.

Vocal Pitch A problem with vocal pitch indicates that it may be too high or too low for a person's age and sex. This can be physically damaging to the vocal cords. Use of an inappropriate pitch or a monotonic pitch can be related to psychosocial problems, and might warrant a psychiatric referral. The speech-language pathologist can provide vocal retraining in use of optimal pitch.

Vocal Quality Disorders in vocal quality refer to hoarseness, breathiness, huskiness, or harshness of the voice due to disruption of normal vocal cord vibration. In children, these conditions are often caused by vocal abuse related to talking too loudly, yelling, or singing, which causes nodules to form on the vocal folds. Allergic conditions and growths (papillomata) on the cords are other possible causes. Disruptions in the motor and sensory tracts of the central and peripheral nervous system can also affect coordination and mobility of the vocal folds (Case, 1984, p. 158). Before the speech-language pathologist can intervene, medical evaluation is critical in order to rule out vocal cord pathology or neurological damage.

Stuttering

Stuttering was defined by the World Health Organization as "disorders in the rhythm of speech in which the individual knows precisely what he wishes to say, but at the same time is unable to say it because of an involuntary repetition, prolongation, or cessation of sound" (W.H.O. 1977, as cited in Andrews et al., 1983). These key behaviors, repetition, prolongation, and cessation of sound, are most likely to occur on initial syllables, words starting with consonants, words in the beginning of a sentence, and long words. The speaker's self-perception as a stutterer is also considered a key element of the disorder.

Stuttering and stutterers have been the object of extensive research. This literature was recently reviewed by Andrews et al. (1983), who looked at replicated studies to establish a set of "facts" about medical history, etiology, and treatment. While some of their conclusions are disputed (Kent, 1983; Perkins, 1983; Wingate, 1983), the following seem to be well accepted.

Most children experience periods of normal nonfluency and these are interpreted simply as a lack of full automoticity in speech production for a still developing language system. Stuttering is different from this normal dysfluency of childhood ("developmental dysfluency"), largely by virtue of the frequency of occurrence of the various dysfluent behaviors. Stuttering problems generally begin with repetitions and prolongations of sound; only later do the other speech behaviors and so-called secondary symptoms (e.g., eye blinking and head turning) develop.

Most stuttering begins between the ages of 2 and 5 years. The prevalence of stuttering in the prepubertal population is estimated to be 1%, and it is estimated that boys are 3 times more likely to be stutterers than are girls. Children generally show a very high rate of recovery (i.e., 78% recover by the age of 16, most of them spontaneously).

Numerous theories have been put forth as to the causes of stuttering. Andrews et al. (1983) have grouped these theories into three categories: 1) those that interpret stuttering as a neurotic response; 2) those that view stuttering as a learned behavior; and 3) those that seek underlying physiological deficits. (The latter, specifically those studies that postulate deficits in the complex coordination of sensory and motor information required for speech, seems especially fruitful for further investigation.)

There appears to be a genetically based predisposition to stutter, which makes a family history of stuttering a risk factor. There is also a higher prevalence of stuttering in persons with various neurological syndromes, including seizure disorders and cerebral palsy. Many studies have examined possible differences between stutterers and nonstutterers. No differences in personality factors have been found, except in regard to difficulties with social adjustment, which may be caused by the stuttering itself. On intelligence tests, stutterers score lower (by one-half standard deviation) than nonstutterers and are more likely than nonstutterers to have additional language and/or articulation problems.

Speech-language pathologists can offer a wide range of therapies to stutterers. With a young child, there is typically an emphasis on parent counseling. It is stressed that parents should not contribute to anxiety surrounding speaking situations with implicit messages concerning the child's inadequacy as a speaker (e.g., by telling a child to slow down or to take a deep breath, or by saying "Don't worry" or "Think before you talk"). Ways of providing successful communicative experiences are stressed. With older children, adolescents, and adults, more direct approaches are recommended. These may include therapies that actually teach the stutterer different ways of talking (initially by gaining more direct, conscious control over speaking), as well as psychotherapeutic and cognitive mediation strategies. It appears that success in therapy is related to length of treatment, specifically with respect to speech retraining programs (Andrews et al., 1983).

SPEECH-LANGUAGE ASSESSMENT

The speech-language pathologist assesses the child's functioning by integrating information obtained from parent and teacher interviews, direct observation, and formal test measures. It should be stressed from the outset that speech-language behaviors are highly inconsistent, readily affected by a host of environmental and task-related factors. For example, children are likely to talk less in unfamiliar settings and may not, therefore, display their full range of capabilities and disabilities during the assessment period. Since these assessments generally take place in a quiet room with a great deal of structure provided by the test format, there may not be the opportunity to observe the child's distractibility or lack of organization, which may critically affect language comprehension and expression. Therefore, in discussing the assessment procedures appropriate to each area of functioning, relevant historical data and behavior observations as well as formal test procedures are stressed. It is not the authors' intent to provide a comprehensive list of speech and language test measures available, but rather to indicate by example the kinds of test materials appropriate to each area of functioning. Of course, test format will vary according to the age and developmental level of the particular child. Also, it must be noted that the tests available to the speech-language pathologist may not possess the degree of reliability and validity needed to make informed decisions regarding a child's impairment (McCauley &

Swisher, 1984). Therefore, test data should be evaluated in conjunction with other observational and historical information before a clinical judgment is made.

Language Assessment

Language Comprehension   The child's ability to understand the names of things (single word vocabulary) is evaluated by means of instruments such as the Peabody Picture Vocabulary Test–Revised (Dunn & Dunn, 1981) in which a child is asked to identify (by pointing) one of four pictures presented. At a simpler level, a child may be asked to select objects that have been named (e.g., "Give me the ball"), as on the Receptive Scale of the Sequenced Inventory of Communication Development (Hedrick, Prather, & Tobin, 1975). Performance is compared to age-level expectations.

The child's understanding of more abstract concepts is measured on most formal test batteries. In addition to mastery of prepositions, color names, and size concepts, a child is asked to classify objects according to category (e.g., "Show me all the animals") and to identify objects by function (e.g., "Show me what you tell time with"). The Auditory Comprehension section of the Preschool Language Scale (Zimmerman, Steiner, & Pond, 1979), the Receptive Scale of the Sequence Inventory of Communication Development (Hedrick et al., 1975), and the Vocabulary Comprehension Scale (Bangs, 1975) are frequently used test measures that include these types of items. The ability to complete simple analogies and opposites is another aspect of language comprehension that goes beyond single word recognition. This is tested, for example, on the Auditory Association subtest of the Illinois Test of Psycholinguistic Abilities (Kirk, McCarthy, & Kirk, 1969), an extensive psycholinguistic battery.

Understanding of word order and word endings is tested by tasks such as asking a child to indicate which of three pictures shows "the children's boots," as opposed to one that shows "one child's boots" (Grammatical Understanding subtest of the Test of Language Development, Newcomer & Hammill, 1977). In like manner, the child may be asked to identify the picture depicting "She shows the girl the boy," with the opposite being a picture of "He shows the boy the girl" (Test of Auditory Comprehension of Language, Carrow, 1973).

It is important to assess comprehension across a range of tasks because a breakdown often occurs as test complexity or degree of abstractness increases. A child who succeeds within the average range on a single word recognition measure (Peabody Picture Vocabulary Test–Revised, Dunn & Dunn, 1981) may have increased difficulty with higher order comprehension tasks.

Parents, particularly parents of preschool children, may not be reliable reporters of language comprehension skills. They often present their concerns by saying that their child "understands everything, he just doesn't talk." This statement must be examined carefully and objectively. With the best of intentions, a parent often supplies a great deal of cueing via gestures to help the child understand. The child's familiarity with household routines and surroundings also supplies a great deal of contextual information that supplements verbal comprehension.

In the clinical setting, it is important to try to assess behaviorally the degree to which the child is relying on gestures and contextual cueing. Overall alertness or responsiveness to language should also be noted.

Auditory Processing Some children have special difficulty interacting with their auditory environment, and may be described as having "auditory processing disorders." These problems may refer both to perceptual and linguistic deficits, that is, deficits in perceiving and interpreting auditory information (Keith, 1984). A hallmark of children with auditory processing disorders is short-term auditory memory deficits. In the extreme, they may have difficulty localizing the source of sound and, for example, may turn to someone other than the person who spoke to them. Their distractibility to auditory stimuli, difficulty maintaining auditory attention, and problems in shifting from one task to another are described earlier in this chapter. Also noted previously are their vulnerability to background noise and their difficulties in distinguishing the main message from other conversations going on around them. All of these problems will, of course, affect language comprehension.

The assessment of auditory processing disorders largely depends on behavioral observations. The characteristics noted above can be observed in the clinical interview, but the quiet, structured, one-to-one interaction may serve to mitigate some of the problems. Clinicians are urged to note their own behavior during testing—if they find themselves slowing down their rate of speech, repeating frequently, breaking directions down into shorter, less complex utterances, and allowing the child extra time for understanding what has been said, they may be intuitively responding to auditory processing deficits.

Some objective measurements of these skills can be made. Most language test batteries include a measure of auditory short-term memory, via sentence or digit repetition (e.g., the Auditory Sequential Memory Subtest of the Illinois Test of Psycholinguistic Abilities, Kirk et al., 1969). A test such as the Assessment of Children's Language Comprehension (Foster, Giddan, & Stark, 1972) systematically tests the child's ability to cope with an increasing number of critical elements (e.g., "Show me the boat," "Show me the big boat," and "Show me the big broken boat under the table"). The Oral Directions subtest of the Clinical Evaluation of Language Functions (Semel & Wiig, 1982), the Oral Directions subtest of the Detroit Tests of Learning Aptitude (Baker & Leland, 1967), and the Token Test for Children (DiSimoni, 1978) are all examples of tests that require increasingly complex direction-following. It should be stressed that factors such as anxiety and distractibility affect a child's ability to perform on these kinds of tasks; therefore, poor achievement does not necessarily reflect specific auditory short-term memory problems.

Reference can also be made to the audiologist's test battery for tasks that measure the child's ability to succeed on auditory figure-ground tasks, the effect of background noise on speech/sound discrimination, and his or her ability to integrate auditory information at higher cortical levels successfully (Katz, 1977; Willeford, 1977).

Language Expression Speech-language pathologists assess the maturity of the child's grammar system, the kinds of meanings the child is able to express, and the social functions for which the child is able to use his or her language. Once again, a combination of formal test measures and behavioral observations is important.

With young children, the mean length of utterance (MLU; mean number of words per utterance) is often calculated, and is a good measure of linguistic maturity (Brown, 1973). The child who is at the 1-word stage is thus distinguished from the child who typically combines words into 3- or 4-word phrases or simple sentences.

The child's knowledge of word order and word ending rules is tested, for example, by the Grammatic Completion subtest of the Test of Language Development (Newcomer & Hammill, 1977) or the Grammatic Closure subtest of the Illinois Test of Psycholinguistic Abilities (Kirk et al., 1969). A spontaneous speech sample may be analyzed and scored according to the presence of various linguistic structures (e.g., use of pronouns, correct use of the auxiliary verb "to be," and use of embedded clauses). A judgment is made of the level of linguistic maturity based on this analysis (cf. Lee's Developmental Sentence Analysis, 1974).

The expressive language of preschool children is also analyzed according to the kinds of meanings expressed. The basic "semantic relations" include: 1) actor-action ("me eat"), 2) action-object ("eat cookie"), 3) attribution ("big cookie"), 4) recurrence ("more cookie"), 5) negation ("no cookie"), 6) location ("here cookie"), and 7) possession ("my cookie") (Bloom & Lahey, 1978). These data are gathered from analysis of a sample of the child's spontaneous language.

In recent years, speech-language pathologists have become aware of the importance of social language usage. Language can be used for a wide range of social functions (e.g., interacting socially, requesting information, making comments, and directing the actions of others) (Bates, 1976). Some children are very restricted in their range of functional usage. Others have special difficulty obeying the subtle social rules of language (e.g., distinguishing between the language of the classroom and the language of the playground). Formal assessment measures for these "pragmatic" language skills are being developed (see the Interpersonal Language Skill Assessment, Blagden & McConnell, 1985), but judgments of adequacy and level of function still depend on informal observation. Children with deficits in these areas are more likely to have behavioral problems, social difficulties with their peers, and poor self-esteem. They may be helped by being taught explicitly to understand and interpret implied social meanings. Role-playing activities that highlight the language appropriate to different settings can also be useful.

Word retrieval problems are often present when other expressive language skills are deficient (Norman, 1982). They can be observed in spontaneous speech when a child gropes for a word, circumlocutes, or says, "I know what I want to say, I just forgot it." Administration of a confrontation naming test (naming pictures on demand) such as the Expressive One-Word Picture Vocabulary Test (Gardner, 1981) or the Boston Naming Test (Goodglass & Kaplan, 1983) often indicates the presence of word retrieval problems. On these tests, the child is required to name the picture presented: if there is a significant discrepancy between his or her ability to perform on this kind of task and a receptive vocabulary measure (where he or she points to a picture named by the examiner, as in the Peabody Picture Vocabulary Test) then word retrieval problems might be suspected. The child understands more than he or she can express on request.

Narrative organization (as in telling a coherent story or giving an explanation) is generally an area of major difficulty for children with expressive language problems. Their stories are confusing, they use gestures and indefinite words ("that thing"; "you know what I mean"), and they are easily sidetracked from the main topic. Formal assessment measures of narrative organization skills are being developed (Snyder, 1984); for now, informal judgments still need to be made.

Articulation Assessment

Sound production skills are assessed in a number of different contexts. The child's ability to produce individual sounds in isolation, single words, sentences, and spontaneous conversation is documented. The effect of the position of the target sound within a word (i.e., if the sound occurs in the initial, medial, or final position) as well as the effect of other neighboring sounds upon the target sound can be evaluated.

A child's articulation error patterns can be described in terms of the processes occurring, such as systematic reduction of consonant clusters ("str" becomes "t") or "fronting" in which sounds that should be produced in the back of the mouth are produced in the front ("g" becomes "d") (Hodson, 1984).

Different test designs reflect different theories about the nature of articulation problems and best approaches to treatment. For example, the Goldman-Fristoe Test of Articulation (Goldman & Fristoe, 1969) tests individual sounds in initial, medial, and final position, but does not give information as to the effect of neighboring sounds on the target. A Deep Test of Articulation (McDonald, 1964) and Coarticulation Assessment in Meaningful Language (Kenney & Prather, 1984) are examples of tests that provide such information. The Assessment of Phonological Processes (Hodson, 1980) describes the underlying sound production processes that result in the child's specific error pattern.

It should be stressed that audiological assessment, examination of the oral mechanism, and language testing, as described elsewhere in this book, are important complements to articulation testing. It is critical to determine the relative importance of hearing status, oral-motor functioning, and language learning skills to the child's articulation.

It is equally important to determine whether there is a great deal of situational variability in a child's overall articulation status. Some children show a deterioration of sound production skills under conditions of communicative pressure. When they have a particularly complex thought to express, are in a confrontation speaking situation, are tired, excited, or in a hurry, their speech may be more difficult to understand.

Articulation skills are always evaluated in terms of developmental expectations. As noted in the description of articulation disorders, late developing sounds such as the "r," "l," or "s" sounds often have not been mastered by the preschool or early elementary school child. Articulation therapy is not recommended on the basis of errors on those sounds alone; the child's overall intelligibility of speech also affects the decision of whether to recommend speech services. If the cumulative effect of the child's articulation errors makes him or her difficult to understand, then some type of speech-language intervention is recommended. By the time a child is age 3–4 years, he or she should be understood by most people, most of the time.

Resonance Assessment

Assessment of vocal resonance depends initially on listener judgment. If no disturbance in resonance can be heard ("hypernasality," as in the speech of a person with a cleft palate, or "hyponasality,"as in the speech of a person with a nasal congestion or a cold) then there need be no further investigation of resonance patterns. However, resonance patterns may be difficult for the lay listener to judge and discriminate.

When hypernasality is heard, further evaluation takes place. The speech-language pathologist does articulation testing in order to observe the patterns and severity of the hypernasality and also assesses the child's ability to modify his or her resonance patterns. Referrals may then be made to an otolaryngologist and a radiologist for medical examination of the velopharyngeal mechanism. An audio-video fluoroscopic study can be done to observe velopharyngeal functioning during speech. Determination can be made as to whether the physical structures are intact and the movement patterns are appropriate. Other instrumentation is available for the measure of air flow between the oral and nasal cavities during speech (Case, 1984, p. 84). If the patient is physically incapable of achieving adequate velopharyngeal closure, medical treatment (surgical correction or prosthetic device) is necessary. This can then be followed by speech therapy.

The speech-language pathologist may note the presence of hyponasality, and make a medical referral. Possible causes of hyponasality include enlarged tonsils and adenoids, deviated nasal septum, rhinitis, nasal polyps, and obstructive foreign bodies.

Voice Assessment

In assessing a child with voice disorders, the speech-language pathologist first obtains a case history that focuses on medical factors (e.g., presence of allergies) as well as behavioral and emotional status. A child who is described by his or her mother as being a "screamer" or as being exceptionally anxious and easily stressed may be a child at special risk for vocal abuse.

A variety of rating scales are available for judging parameters of vocal quality, pitch, resonance, intensity, and range. An example is the Voice Profile (Wilson & Rice, 1977). Training tapes are available so that the speech-language pathologist can learn to calibrate his or her own perceptual judgments.

Finally, instrumentation is used to obtain the most objective measurement of functioning. One such instrument is the VisiPitch 6087, which evaluates pitch and loudness.

Stuttering Assessment

Stuttering is assessed by estimating the frequency and types of dysfluencies, across a variety of speaking situations. A child may be more dysfluent, for example, when carrying on a conversation or telling a story, and more fluent when asked to do automatic speech tasks (e.g., saying the alphabet or echoing the examiner's speech). Frequency of secondary symptoms such as eye blinking or head turning are also noted. These data result in an estimation of severity and, in some cases, an estimation of chronicity. Formal scales such as the Stuttering Severity Instrument for Children and Adults (Riley, 1980) yield a numerical score as an indication of severity.

In addition to measuring the speech behavior itself, evaluation also includes gathering historical information as to age of onset, presence of family history of stuttering, and situational factors that appear to make the child more or less fluent. An attempt is also made to discover how well the family might support change and how committed the child is to work on the problem, and to identify the child's feelings and beliefs about his or her speech. Children often construct complex theories as to why they stutter and the physical disability underlying the stuttering. These need to be addressed in the course of therapy.

Assessment of the Oral Mechanism

Examination of the oral mechanism is an important part of any speech-language evaluation. It includes inspection of the teeth (looking for underbite, overbite, or irregular spacing between the teeth), the hard palate (looking for an unusually high arched palate or submucosal cleft), and the tongue. This is often done informally, although formal test batteries are available (Dworkin & Culatta, 1980). In the past, "tongue-tie" (an unusually foreshortened frenulum) was often held responsible for articulation problems, a position generally rejected today except in cases where the impairment is physically extreme.

Assessment of oral-motor skills is also a part of the oral examination. The child is asked to imitate nonspeech movements (e.g., tongue protrusion and lateralization) as well as sound patterns of increasing complexity. The child with oral-motor planning problems ("developmental dyspraxia") has special difficulty with these voluntary imitations. The child, for example, is asked to repeat "p," "t," and "k" sounds rapidly, as this pattern requires quick movement of the tongue from the front to middle to back of the mouth, an action difficult for the child with deficits in motor planning for sound sequencing.

Observations are also made as to oral-motor tone, strength, and control of saliva (drooling). A feeding history is obtained, including a description of current feeding skills. Persistence of infantile oral reflexes or the presence of abnormal oral reflexes are noted. Children with cerebral palsy are at special risk for having speech problems related to oral-motor dysfunction.

Test Standardization, Validity, and Reliability

Many of the tests used by speech-language pathologists are norm-referenced. Test scores are interpreted to identify performance that is significantly different from that achieved by age-peers in the normative sample. Age-equivalent scores, percentiles, and standard scores are often derived from the raw score. However, when the psychometric properties of speech-language measures are reviewed, certain problems in standardization, validity, and reliability are identified.

In the most extensive review completed to date of speech-language tests used with young children, McCauley and Swisher (1984) cite a number of serious concerns. They evaluated 30 tests, using criteria related to important psychometric properties (e.g., clear identification of standardization sample, adequate sample size for subgroups, information regarding central tendency and variability, evidence of concurrent and predictive validity, estimation of test-retest reliability, and promotion of test reliability and validity via systematic item analysis during test construction). They conclude that "on the whole, the reviewed tests failed to provide compelling empirical evidence that they can reliably and validly be used to provide information concerning the existence of language or articulation impairment'' (McCauley & Swisher, 1984, pp. 40–41).

As the authors note, clinical decisions should not, in any case, be made solely on the basis of test results. Test scores must be considered together with other observational and historical information before any clinical judgment can be made. A study such as this also suggests that speech-language pathologists should exercise a great deal of caution because the standardized instruments available to them may lack the psychometric sophistication necessary for important decisions. Consumers of tests produced by speech-language pathologists must also recognize that a test's title may not reflect its content or what it measures (i.e., the ''jingle,'' ''jangle,'' and ''jungle'' fallacies mentioned in Chapter 2) and that the clinician's interpretation and judgment are the most important factors.

DIFFERENTIAL DIAGNOSIS

Speech and language disorders occur frequently in conjunction with other developmental problems. The speech-language problem may be simply another indication of a pervasive problem such as mental retardation. The multidisciplinary team assessment provides a format for coordinating and integrating diagnostic information. Before speech-language therapy is recommended, the following issues of differential diagnosis must be addressed.

Hearing Status

A child with articulation or language deficits must have an audiological evaluation to rule out hearing impairment as a basis for speech-language delay. Peripheral hearing may be screened by the speech-language pathologist, or a referral may be made to an audiologist.

Cognitive Status

Speech-language delays are typically one of the earliest noted symptoms of mild to moderate retardation (Capute & Accardo, 1978). This is especially true for children who do not have the physical characteristics of a syndrome (such as Down syndrome) or do not show motoric delays. Such children often do not ''look'' retarded. While speech-language therapy services may be of great benefit to children with overall developmental delays, it is important to understand the full range of their needs (i.e., not restrict their services to speech-language therapy). Speech-language needs should be seen in a developmental context so that parents can begin to have a realistic appreciation of their child's status.

For these reasons, normal cognitive functioning in nonverbal areas should be documented before a child is diagnosed as having specific primary language learning disabilities. This is best done with well-standardized comprehensive instruments (e.g., Wechsler Intelligence Scale for Children–Revised; WISC-R) administered by a psychologist.

Emotional Status

Children with a wide variety of emotional problems may be seen first by a speech-language pathologist because of concern about abnormal communicative behaviors. Again, it is important to rule out significant emotional involvement before diagnosing a speech-language problem. The child's overall communicative status should be considered. If he or she is not talking, what is he or she doing to communicate? It is always a concern when, for example, the mother of a 2½-year-old boy says, "He doesn't need to communicate, he really doesn't want anything." These behaviors probably indicate an emotional rather than a language problem because a 2½- to 3-year-old child with specific expressive language problems points, gestures, or pantomines in order to get his or her point across. He or she is expected to enjoy social interaction and to become frustrated if not understood. An atypical or autistic-like child, however, may have very little interest in communication and may not have developed this repertoire of nonverbal behaviors. A depressed child may be noncommunicative, but still have intact knowledge of vocabulary and grammar rules.

The wise speech-language clinician should pay close attention also to the content and social appropriateness of a child's language. Some children's comments are not relevant to the situation at hand, or are bizarre in content. They may make up words ("neulogisms") on their own, and these inventions may not appear to be related to difficulties with word retrieval. In such cases, while grammatical usage or articulation patterns may be mature, the language issues are secondary in importance to emotional issues.

Speech-language pathologists are alert to the possible emotional status of the children they see and recognize that parents and teachers may find it easier to make a referral for speech-language services than for psychiatric or psychological consultation. If the speech-language pathologist suspects an emotional problem, he or she can, of course, make the referral to the appropriate professional. Also, it should be recognized that children with severe speech-language problems are at very high risk for developing psychiatric problems secondary to their speech and language difficulties (Cantwell & Baker, 1980; Gualtieri, Koriath, Van Bourgondien, & Saleeby, 1983).

Environmental Status

Environmental deprivation can result in a depressed acquisition of language skills. This is a differential diagnosis that can be made definitively only in retrospect, when a substantial change in environmental conditions results in a surge in language learning (e.g., starting school). It can be suspected, however, on the basis of social and family history, and in the presence of good functioning in other areas (e.g., motor skills, nonverbal skills, and adaptive behaviors).

Summary

Once hearing impairment, cognitive disorders, emotional disorders, and environmental deprivation are ruled out, then it becomes likely that a specific speech-language disorder is present. The speech-language assessment procedures discussed earlier result in a description of the child's particular speech and language needs. For example, expressive language delays that are basically a reflection of poor comprehension are distinguished from specific expressive language disorders such as word retrieval deficits, or from severe oral-motor planning deficits that may be compromising expressive language capabilities. At that time, planning and implementation of appropriate speech-language therapy can begin.

INDICATIONS FOR REFERRAL TO A SPEECH-LANGUAGE PATHOLOGIST

Rationale for Early Referral

Early speech and language delays place a child at significant risk for later learning problems. This is often not appreciated because the symptomatology changes over time, giving the superficial impression that the child has gotten over or "outgrown" the problem, whereas the problem is simply manifesting itself in another way.

Consider children who have delayed speech-language milestones. At 2 years of age, they may use no words or very few words. One can reassure the parents that the children will talk, and they do. But, at 3–4 years of age, they may have poor articulation and immature grammar. One can assure the parents that the children will develop intelligible speech, and generally they do. However, at 4–5 years of age, the children may be having difficulties with readiness skills such as learning colors, numbers, shapes, and letters. One can then tell the parents that the children will learn these concepts, and they do, but in first grade they often have difficulty learning to read. They may then learn to read, but in third or fourth grade more generalized academic problems become evident. At this point the curriculum requires them to read to learn, rather than learn to read, and their language problems interfere. In late elementary school and on through high school, these children are likely to show written language problems and higher order comprehension difficulties.

Longitudinal studies of children identified in the preschool years as having speech and language delays have demonstrated continuing academic difficulties at highly significant levels (Aram & Nation, 1980; Bashir, Kuban, Kleinman, & Scauuzzo, 1983; Strominger & Bashir, 1977). Silva, McGee, and Williams (1983) looked at early speech-language delays as predictors of subsequent low intelligence and reading difficulties in a group of children seen at ages 3, 5, and 7. They summarized their major findings as follows:

> Every type of language delay identified at each age was associated with a significantly higher prevalence of low IQ and/or reading difficulties than among the sample as a whole. The effects were strongest amongst those with delays at age 3. General language delays at any age were associated with the highest prevalence of later problems: no less than 60% of these children turned out to have a low IQ with reading difficulty at age 7. (Silva et al., 1983, p. 791)

In summary, early speech-language delays require a differential diagnosis of probable etiology so that appropriate intervention can be initiated. Proper assessment is critical not only for the direct intervention services and planning provided to the child, but for the support and education made available to the family. Helping parents and children learn what to expect reasonably from one another, and how to communicate effectively without frustration and anger is as valuable a goal as remediation, as is suggested in Chapter 1.

Minimal Referral Criteria for Young Children

Language acquisition is variable among ''normal''children, and most parents are aware of the differences. The following are some guidelines as to what consititues a problem requiring professional attention. Children meeting these criteria may be evaluated by a speech-language pathologist, or another developmental specialist (e.g., a psychologist, an audiologist, or a multidisciplinary team) depending on the nature of their other needs.

It should be stressed that these are truly minimal criteria. Most children without problems achieve these milestones at substantially earlier ages.

1. An 18-month-old child with poor language comprehension (i.e., does not understand specific words such as his or her name or the name of common objects, or simple commands such as ''Come here,'' ''Where's your bottle?'' or ''Sit down'')
2. An 18-month-old child using no true single word who also:
   a. Shows no understanding of common words and commands such as ''Come here,'' ''Where's your bottle?'' or ''Sit down,'' or
   b. Does not use expressive jargoning (Jargoning refers to use of strings of consonants and vowel sounds that have recognizable intonation patterns and communicative intent. Parents often describe this as ''it sounds like he's talking another language.''), or
   c. Does not specifically indicate what he or she wants by pointing or gesturing
3. A 2-year-old child who uses only a few words (not including ''Mamma'' and ''Pappa'')

4. A 2½-year-old child who shows poor comprehension (i.e., does not understand names of most common objects; does not know simple body parts; does not point to pictures of familiar objects; and does not get something on request that is not directly in his or her field of vision such as in going to another room and getting his or her shoes)

5. A 2½-year-old child who does not use several two-word combinations (i.e., phrases that combine two ideas such as "No cookie" [negation and object] or "More juice" [quantity and substance]; "Bye-bye" or "All gone" are not considered two-word combinations here, as they do not combine two ideas)

6. A 2½-year-old child who is not using recognizable consonant sounds

7. A 2½-year-old child whose articulation is so poor that he or she is often misunderstood or not understood (i.e., children for whom verbal communication is a specific source of frustration)

8. A 3-year-old child who uses no simple sentences (i.e., subject-verb-object or actor-action-object)

9. A 3-year-old child with poor comprehension (i.e., children with whom one cannot negotiate verbally, who do not understand and enjoy simple story sequences, and who cannot understand simple explanations or discussions of past and future events

10. A 3- to 3½-year-old child whose speech and language many people have difficulty understanding, even though family members may generally understand

Additional Referral Criteria

The following criteria, although unrelated to milestones achieved by specific age levels, also concern difficulties in areas related to speech and language development. Any of these criteria is cause for referral to a speech-language pathologist.

1. Children whose results on psychological testing reveal a significant discrepancy between verbal and performance measures (e.g., more than 15 points on the WISC-R; see Figure 5.1)

2. Children who are experiencing special difficulty in learning to read, and who also have a history of delayed language milestones (Current research on dyslexia suggests that many reading problems are based on underlying language processing deficits [Vellutino, 1979]. These children are likely to benefit from an integration of language and reading support services. In addition, their reading program needs to be designed so that the language problems are taken into consideration.)

3. Children who have persistently experienced frustration around communication, even if the stigmata of articulation problems or grammar errors

are not obviously present (e.g., children who have delayed milestones in acquisition of speech, have difficulty getting their point across, follow directions poorly, and have occasional lapses in intelligibility)

4. A child whose parent expresses significant concern regarding his or her dysfluency, since parent counseling may help prevent a stuttering problem from developing, or any child displaying secondary symptoms or avoiding speaking situations

REFERENCES

Andrews, G., Craig, A., Feyer, A. M., Hoddinott, S., Havie, P., & Neilson, M. (1983). Stuttering: A review of research findings and theories circa 1982. *Journal of Speech and Hearing Disorders, 48,* 226–246.

Aram, D. M., & Nation, J. E. (1980). Preschool language disorders and subsequent language and academic difficulties. *Journal of Communicative Disorders, 13,* 159–170.

Baker, H., & Leland, B. (1967). *Detroit Tests of Learning Aptitude.* Indianapolis: Bobbs-Merrill.

Bangs, T. E. (1975). *Vocabulary Comprehension Scale.* Austin, TX: Learning Concepts.

Bashir, A. S., Kuban, K. C., Kleinman, S., & Scauuzzo, A. (1983). Issues in language disorders: Considerations of cause, maintenance, and change. In J. Miller, D. E. Yoder, & R. Schiefelbusch (Eds.), *Contemporary issues in language intervention* (ASHA Reports 12, pp. 92–106). Rockville, MD: The American Speech-Language-Hearing Association.

Bates, E. (1976). *Language and context: The acquisition of pragmatics.* New York: Academic Press.

Blagden, C. M., & McConnell, N. L. (1985). *Interpersonal Language Skills Assessment.* Moline, IL: LinguiSystems.

Bloom, L., & Lahey, M. (1978). *Language development and language disorders.* New York: John Wiley & Sons.

Borden, G, (1984), Cbnsideration of motor-sensory targets and a problem in perception. In H. Winitz (Ed.), *Treating articulation disorders* (pp. 51–65). Baltimore: University Park Press.

Brown, R. (1973). *A first language.* Cambridge, MA: Harvard University Press.

Cantwell, D. P., & Baker, L. (1980). Psychiatric and behavioral characteristics of children with communication disorders. *Journal of Pediatric Psychology, 5,* 161–178.

Capute, A. J., & Accardo, P. J. (1978). Linguistic and auditory milestones during the first two years of life. *Clinical Pediatrics, 17,* 847–853.

Carrow, E. (1973). *Test of Auditory Comprehension of Language.* Austin, TX: Urban Research Group.

Case, J. L. (1984). *Clinical management of voice disorders.* Rockville, MD: Aspen Publishers.

Darley, F. L., Aronson, A. E., & Brown, J. R. (1969). Differential diagnostic patterns of dysarthria. *Journal of Speech and Hearing Research, 12,* 246–269.

DiSimoni, F. (1978). *The Token Test for Children.* Hingham, MA: Teaching Resources.

Dunn, L. M., & Dunn, L. M. (1981). *Peabody Picture Vocabulary Test–Revised.* Circle Pines, MN: American Guidance Service.

Dworkin, J. P., & Culatta, R. A. (1980). *Dworkin-Culatta Oral Mechanism Examination.* Nicholasville, KY: Edgewood Press.

Foster, C. R., Giddan, J. J., & Stark, J. (1972). *ACLC: Assessment of Children's Language Comprehension.* Palo Alto, CA: Consulting Psychologists Press.

Gardner, M. F. (1981). *Expressive One-Word Picture Vocabulary Test.* Novato, CA: Academic Therapy Publications.

Goldman, R., & Fristoe, M. (1969). *Goldman-Fristoe Test of Articulation.* Circle Pines, MN: American Guidance Service.

Goodglass, H., & Kaplan, E. (1983). *Boston Naming Test.* Philadelphia: Lea & Febiger.

Gualtieri, C. T., Koriath, U., Van Bourgondien, M., & Saleeby, N. (1983). Language disorders in children referred for psychiatric services. *Journal of the American Academy of Child Psychiatry, 22,* 165–171.

Hedrick, P. L., Prather, E. M., & Tobin, A. R., (1975). *Sequenced Inventory of Communication Development.* Seattle: University of Washington Press.

Hodson, B. W. (1980). *The Assessment of Phonological Processes.* Danville, IL: Interstate Printers & Publishers.

Hodson, B. W. (1984). Facilitating phonological development in children with severe speech disorders. In H. Winitz (Ed.), *Treating articulation disorders* (pp. 75–89). Baltimore: University Park Press.

Jorgenson, C., Barrett, M., Huisingh, R., & Zachman, L. (1981). *The Word Test.* Moline, IL: LinguiSystems.

Katz, J. (1977). The staggered spondaic word test. In R. W. Keith (Ed.), *Central auditory dysfunction* (pp. 103–127). New York: Grune & Stratton.

Keith, R. (1984). Central auditory dysfunction: A language disorder. *Topics in Language Disorders, 4,* 48–55.

Kenney, K. W., & Prather, E. M. (1984). *Coarticulation Assessment in Meaningful Language.* Tucson, AZ: Communication Skill Builders.

Kent, R. D. (1983). Facts about stuttering: Neuropsychologic perspectives. *Journal of Speech and Hearing Disorders, 48,* 249–254.

Kirk, S. A., McCarthy, J. J., & Kirk, W. D. (1969). *Illinois Test of Psycholinguistic Abilities.* Urbana: University of Illinois Press.

Lee, L. L. (1974). *Developmental sentence analysis.* Evanston, IL: Northwestern University Press.

McCauley, R. J., & Swisher, L. (1984). Psychometric review of language and articulation tests for preschool children. *Journal of Speech and Hearing Disorders, 49,* 34–42.

McDonald, E. T. (1964). *A Deep Test of Articulation.* Pittsburgh: Stanwix House.

Newcomer, P. L., & Hammill, D. D. (1977). *The Test of Language Development.* Austin, TX: Empiric Press.

Norman, T. (1982). *Naming behaviors of language impaired children.* Unpublished doctoral dissertation, University of Pittsburgh.

Perkins, W. H. (1983). The problem of definition: Commentary on "stuttering." *Journal of Speech and Hearing Disorders, 48,* 246–248.

Riley, G. D. (1980). *Stuttering Severity Instrument for Children and Adults.* Tigard, OR: C. C. Publications.

Semel, E. M., & Wiig, E. H. (1982). *Clinical evaluation of language functions.* Columbus, OH: Charles E. Merrill.

Silva, P. A., McGee, R., & Williams, S. M. (1983). Developmental language delay from three to seven years and its significance for low intelligence and reading difficulties at age seven. *Developmental Medicine and Child Neurology, 25,* 783–793.

Snyder, L. S. (1984). Communicative competence in children with delayed language development. In R. L. Schiefelbusch & J. Pickar (Eds.), *The acquisition of communicative competence* (pp. 423–478). Baltimore: University Park Press.

Stark, R. E., & Bernstein, L. E. (1984). Evaluating central auditory processing in children. *Topics in Language Disorders, 4,* 57–70.

Strominger, A. Z., & Bashir, A. S. (1977). A nine year follow-up of language delayed children. Paper presented at the meeting of the American Speech and Hearing Association, Chicago, IL.

Templin, M. (1957). *Certain language skills in children.* Minneapolis: University of Minnesota Press.

Vellutino, F. (1979). *Dyslexia: Theory and research.* Cambridge, MA: MIT Press.

Vogel, S. (1974). Syntactic abilities in normal and dyslexic children. *Journal of Learning Disabilities, 7,* 103–109.

Wiig, E., & Semel, E. (1980). *Language assessment and intervention.* Columbus, OH: Charles E. Merrill.

Willeford, J. A. (1977). Assessing central auditory behavior in children: A test battery approach. In R. W. Keith (Ed.), *Central auditory dysfunction* (pp. 43–72). New York: Grune & Stratton.

Wilson, D. K. (1972). *Voice problems of children.* Baltimore: Williams & Wilkins.

Wilson, F. B., & Rice, M. (1977). *A programmed approach to voice therapy.* Hingham, MA: Teaching Resources.

Wingate, M. E. (1983). Speaking unassisted: Comment on a paper by Andrews et al. *Journal of Speech and Hearing Disorders, 48,* 255–263.

Zimmerman, I. L., Steiner, V. G., & Pond, R. E. (1979). *Preschool Language Scale.* Columbus, OH: Charles E. Merrill.

Chapter 6

Occupational Therapy Assessment

~~~

Margaret A. Short-DeGraff

Occupational therapy is an area of study and clinical practice focusing on the abilities of human beings at all ages to function as independently and efficiently as possible in the physical, psychological, and social realms of everyday living. Any field as broad in scope and dealing with such a wide age range of clients must, by definition, be eclectic and flexible. This flexibility and wide scope of occupational therapy means that therapists perform an array of services for many diverse types and ages of client populations.

A problematic aspect is that it is not easy to define occupational therapy, and many people are confused by the term "occupation" in the title (e.g., parents may ask why an occupational therapist is on a pediatric team because, "Children don't need job training.") The term "occupation"in occupational therapy refers not to a specific job or vocation but to productivity—personal, physical, social, and emotional productivity. Occupation has to do with constructive or purposeful activity; it is "goal-directed use of time, energy, interest and attention" ("Occupational therapy," 1972). Purposeful activity motivates and directs human energies: 1) in accomplishing what is necessary for vocations as well as successfully performing daily living skills; 2) in

The author gratefully acknowledges the editorial feedback provided by Kenneth Otten-bacher, University of Wisconsin, and the reference materials provided by Stephanie Presseller, Director, Educational Division of the American Occupational Therapy Association.

participating in meaningful hobbies as well as complex social interactions; and 3) in feeling fulfilled by contributing to personal growth, as well as to a family and to society at large. Purposefulness involves learning, skill, growth, and change.

Definitions of occupational therapy must reflect the varying nature of therapists' roles. Occupational therapists work in a wide range of facilities such as acute care hospitals, sheltered workshops, neonatal intensive care units, hospices, school systems, and hand rehabilitation clinics. The roles that occupational therapists play in these diverse settings may vary, but there is a common element across all of these services: the need of all humans to feel and be productive by engaging in meaningful activity. Occupational therapists help people to define and to perform those activities that are important to productive and meaningful lives. "Occupational therapy was founded on the concept that it is natural for humans to be engaged in activity, and the process of being occupied contributes . . . to health and well being" (Pedretti, 1981, p. 93).

While the variability and name of occupational therapy are a source of confusion to some laypeople, that variability can be an enormous asset. The scope of the field often enables therapists to play versatile roles within diagnostic and treatment settings. More professions are beginning to recognize the significance of treating "the whole child," but this is already the focus of pediatric occupational therapy. At a time when many professions are becoming increasingly specialized, it is important for the evaluation and treatment team to perceive the child from an integrated point of view. Occupational therapists are particularly comfortable with such a perspective, as their training comprises a diverse background in art, science, theory, and clinical practice. They focus on all aspects of development—physical, psychological, and sociocultural—which often enables them to work effectively with medical, behavioral science, and educational team members.

In pediatric occupational therapy assessment, the focus is on the child's abilities to function independently. One of the greatest demands of infancy and early childhood is the coordination of sensory and motor abilities for performance of skills necessary for becoming independent. Occupational therapists can make unique and valuable contributions to the assessment effort by focusing on one or all of the following areas of development: gross motor, fine motor, neuromotor, reflex, oral-motor, perceptual-motor, sensory, and adaptive. Assessment of these areas of function are highlighted in this chapter.

TRAINING

The American Occupational Therapy Association, which was formed early in the 20th century, defines occupational therapy as an art and a science, the goal of which is to direct a person's participation in selected tasks to restore, reinforce and enhance performance, facilitate learning of those skills and functions essential for adaptation and productivity, diminish or correct pathology, and to promote and maintain health. Reference to occupation in the title is in the context of man's goal-directed use of time, energy, interest, and attention. Its fundamental concern is the development and maintenance of the capacity throughout the life span to perform with satisfaction to self and others those tasks and roles essential to productive living and to the mastery of self and the environment. (American Occupational Therapy Association, 1983a, p. 1)

An analysis of this definition reveals that the course of study for occupational therapy must include principles of human growth and development; basic and applied sciences dealing with anatomy, physiology, and movement of the human body; physical and psychological pathologies; the meaning of and means for promoting health and normal functions during daily living; the rationale for the selection and use of various tasks or activities designed to reduce or correct specific physical or psychological dysfunctions; and clinical training for application of this knowledge.

Entry-Level Training

Certified Occupational Therapy Assistant (COTA) training is given at approximately 40 vocational technical schools, and in colleges or universities that offer the associate's degree or its equivalent (Gray, 1978).

There are approximately 50 programs in the United States for Registered Occupational Therapist (OTR) training, most of which are baccalaureate degree programs. There are, however, other modes of training for the professional level. Some colleges and universities offer a certificate or a master's degree in occupational therapy for students who have undergraduate degrees in other fields. Other programs offer master's or doctoral degrees for persons who already are registered occupational therapists.

Currently, a study is underway that is examining the feasibility of establishing the master's, in lieu of the bachelor's, degree as the entry-level for OTR status (American Occupational Therapy Association, 1984). Henderson (1983) points out that a master's degree is often required for clinical practice in pediatrics and that a large proportion of such advanced training programs in occupational therapy offer specializations related to the treatment of children with handicaps (p. 1124).

Standards, Certification, and Licensure

Standards for the education of the COTA and the OTR are established by the American Occupational Therapy Association. Every educational program must be accredited and is periodically evaluated for compliance with the Association's standards for academic as well as clinical field experience. The programs that prepare students at the professional (OTR) level are also accredited by the American Medical Association in collaboration with the

American Occupational Therapy Association (American Occupational Therapy Association, 1983a, 1983b; Gray, 1978).

After satisfactory completion of academic and field work, one is eligible to sit for a national certification examination conducted by the American Occupational Therapy Association. Upon successful completion of the national examination, the assistant or registered therapist is qualified to perform functions commensurate with his or her level of training (i.e., the COTA provides direct services and evaluates client performance in collaboration with or under the supervision of an OTR [Gray, 1978]).

In addition to national certification, many states have adopted occupational therapy licensure programs which, often in conjunction with other allied health and related fields, include licensing boards responsible for setting and monitoring therapists' qualifications and standards. The letter "L," as in OTR/L, signifies that a therapist has been licensed by the appropriate licensing board in his or her state.

Occupational Therapy Specializations

For ease of communication, it is often convenient to refer to occupational therapy training and treatment specializations in pediatrics, physical dysfunction, and mental health. However, the growing emphasis on multidisciplinary and family-oriented approaches as well as home health care often makes such specializations functionally obsolete. Since this book deals with the assessment of children, this chapter focuses on the pediatric aspects of occupational therapy training and assessment; but it is important to note that there is too much cross-over of clinical training and client pathologies for easy compartmentalization of training or services. For example, children who have multiple handicaps may be referred to occupational therapists in physical rehabilitation clinics, hand clinics, or in mental health settings that may not be specifically pediatric in emphasis. Thus, it is important to recognize that while specializations are convenient for reference, they are often used for ease of communication rather than for implying discrete, compartmentalized services.

Running counter to the generalist tendencies just mentioned are therapists who are trained in specific diagnostic and treatment techniques. For instance, occupational therapists who work with at-risk neonates may seek specific training in the administration of standardized evaluations such as the Neonatal Behavioral Assessment Scale (Brazelton, 1973), or participate in infant development projects, perhaps using the Bayley Scales of Infant Development (Bayley, 1969). Neurodevelopmental therapy (NDT; Bobath, 1972) and sensory integration (Ayres, 1972a) are two examples of specific treatment and evaluation approaches. Training in both areas is offered periodically, and graduates of such workshops receive certification. Such specialists also develop their skills and keep up-to-date by reading current literature and by maintaining communication networks with other specialists in similar areas. Traditionally, NDT has been used with children or adults who display central nervous system damage resulting in abnormal movement patterns (Trombly, 1983a), whereas sensory integration treatment was originally employed in intervention with children with learning disabilities.

OCCUPATIONAL THERAPY ASSESSMENT

Characteristics and Functions

The types of assessments used by occupational therapists vary depending on the nature and extent of the child's disability, the type of facility, the types and the extent of the communication among team members evaluating the child, the age of the child, and the reason for referral. Assessment may include a review of reports and medical records, screening, observation, interview, formal evaluation, and follow-up.

In general, an occupational therapist is called upon to assess all or some of the following: motor abilities, including gross and fine motor, perceptual-motor, oral-motor, and neuromotor skills; how motor skills are carried out functionally in activities of daily living (ADL) and play; and clinical measures of sensation, balance, muscle tone, coordination, joint range of motion, postures, and reflexes. Additional assessments may also include parent-child feeding, handling, and other social interactions; home or classroom observation; and evaluation of the needs for architectural modifications or adaptive equipment to enhance specific functional abilities, such as toileting, dressing, writing, and/or mobility.

The evaluation process serves many functions, including: determining the child's baseline performance; identifying the deficits that can and cannot be addressed by occupational therapy; indicating the child's potential for change; establishing a foundation for treatment; when possible, providing the child and/or the child's family with a therapy set, that is, the rationale, procedures, and goals of treatment (Peloquin, 1983); when possible, involving the child and the family in the self-assessment of deficits as well as abilities and potential; and giving the child and family assistance with planning and implementing a course of action addressed toward taking advantage of existing abilities and toward eliminating deficits (Gilette, 1971).

The occupational therapist, more than any other diagnostician, with the possible exception of the special educator, is likely to have recurring treatment contact with the child, making evaluation an ongoing process. This allows the original treatment goals to be constantly re-assessed along with the child's progress in therapy. Banus reports that, for the occupational therapist, "every treatment session is an evaluation" (1979, p. 191); and as Nelson (1984) states, "The evaluation process and treatment process reinforce each other. . . . The informal evaluation is a vigorous, ongoing process beginning with the evaluator's first contact with the client and continuing throughout therapy. So long as the therapist is able to discover new patterns of client activity and gain new insights into the causes and meaning of the client's activity, the evaluation continues'' (p. 116). Such serial assessment is necessary because children are rapidly changing (Coley, 1978).

Like many other pediatric diagnosticians, occupational therapists believe in the notion that the early diagnosis of handicapping conditions is essential. A portion of this belief rests on the supposition of neural plasticity in infancy and childhood, a discussion of which is beyond the scope of this chapter (see Ottenbacher & Short, 1985).

An additional rationale for early occupational therapy assessment is that many children with mental retardation and learning disabilities also exhibit physical handicaps. It is an accepted principle that muscular weakness and paralysis must receive immediate intervention to prevent permanent contractures or deformities. Range of motion (ROM) therapy, adaptive devices, and assistive equipment need to be prescribed as early as possible. ROM therapy prevents contractures and deformities, and the early use of adaptive equipment enables the child to develop movement strategies while incorporating the use of such devices. For example, prosthetic equipment needs to be reevaluated constantly because of changes in the child's physical growth. "Flexibility of the child, with his greater reserve of all tissues, permits him to adapt quickly to prostheses. The young amputee grows up with his appliance and accepts it as a necessary item for his daily life" (Stoner, 1971, p. 140).

The child who initially acquires motor skills with the use of adaptive equipment only has to learn once, whereas the adult or child who develops first without the equipment often has to re-learn movement strategies and skills when prosthetic appliances or adaptive equipment are eventually prescribed and fitted. Assessment and intervention begun in infancy is often best. As Palisano (1984) reports, "Therapy is considered to produce optimal results if begun prior to an infant's abnormal movement patterns becoming habitual or delays becoming too pronounced" (p. 12).

Types of Assessments

Occupational therapists use a wide range of assessment tools. Some of these tools have been designed by and used almost exclusively by occupational therapists, but it is also not uncommon for therapists to adopt evaluation instruments or to combine parts of instruments widely used by other professionals. Examples of this include the Denver Developmental Screening Test (Frankenburg, Dodds, Fandal, Kazuk, & Cohrs, 1975) and the Motor Scale section of the Bayley Scales of Infant Development (Bayley, 1969). Many assessments that are familiar to, and widely used by, a variety of professionals are not examined in detail in this chapter. However, details are given regarding specific motor skill assessments as well as a variety of recently developed instruments constructed by or widely used by occupational therapists.

Observation   Occupational therapists, like other trained professionals, can make apt clinical judgments based on observations of a child's behavior either during testing or in a natural setting such as the home, nursery, school, or playground. An experienced therapist can obtain important information by observing the child during interactions with people or with objects such as toys, furniture, play equipment, eating implements, clothing, or crayons and paper. Observation often occurs prior to more formal assessment. This pre-liminary means of assessment can be unstructured or may involve a checklist of specific behaviors that will be examined more thoroughly during formal testing (see Figure 6.1). Initial observations can provide a general index of the child's motor and social abilities, a preliminary gauge of age-appropriateness, and immediate information required for subsequent evaluations. (For exam-ple, does the child use a wheelchair, crutches, wear leg braces, use other adaptive equipment, or require assistive devices? Does the child show evi-dence of paralysis, weakness, or visual or hearing impairment? Is the child extremely fearful of strangers, labile, or restless? Each of these factors con-tributes to decisions regarding the nature, location, duration, type, and format of administration for subsequent testing.)

Additionally, observation is an important, ongoing process during which the clinician continually receives feedback regarding the child's re-sponses and progress in therapy and, if possible, the child's behavior outside the context of therapy. As Smith and Tiffany (1978) point out, "If it is possible for the therapist to interact informally and spontaneously with pa-tients in situations where role differentiation may be less clear, information may be available which otherwise might be difficult to obtain. Different perspectives on values, interests, and functional levels, for example, may be gained by . . ." (p. 153) observing the youngster in settings other than in therapy.

Multidomain Screening Tools   Screenings are preliminary means for determining if additional formal evaluation is required. Screening tools vary widely, as many institutions and treatment teams adapt instruments for their own specific needs. For example, Short and Fincher (1983) report an example of a clinical team who compiled their own Head Start screening tool by using items from many different assessments. The team included psychologists, speech and language pathologists, and occupational therapists. The screening was designed to be administered by classroom teachers and aides, and it tested the following areas of development: gross and fine motor, speech and lan-guage, cognitive, and social-emotional. Children who did not perform age-appropriately in any particular area were referred by the teacher to the profes-sional service team, who, when warranted, scheduled the children for more comprehensive examinations. While such instruments fit the specific needs of

Key   *   Activities for lower-functioning children   0   Cannot perform
      2   Performs independently   ?   Does not cooperate
      1   Performs with assistance

NAME											
OBSERVATION Homologous: is symmetrical tonic neck utilized?											
Homolateral: is asymmetrical tonic neck utilized?											
Reciprocal											
No pattern											
REFLEX INHIBITION Moves head side to side in isolation											
*Moves head up and down in isolation											
Creeps: washcloth between chin and shoulder											
*Creeps: head straight											
GROSS MOTOR ACTIVITIES *Forward/backward											
*Sideways											
*Clockwise/counterclockwise											
Creeps: follows hand signals											
Camel-walks											
Crab-walks: follows hand signals											
Trail											
Obstacle course											
*Rocks all directions											

Figure 6.1. Observation checklist of creeping behavior. (From Montgomery, P., & Richter, E. [1977]. *Sensorimotor integration for developmentally disabled children: A handbook* [p. 27]. Los Angeles: Western Psychological Services. Reproduced by permission of the publisher, Western Psychological Services, 12031 Wilshire Blvd., Los Angeles, CA 90025.)

evaluation teams, there are numerous problems with such informally developed assessments that do not meet rigorous test construction criteria.

Miller Assessment for Preschoolers   An example of a standardized preschool screening instrument is the Miller Assessment for Preschoolers (MAP; Miller, 1982). Developed by L. J. Miller, an occupational therapist, the MAP is designed to address the clinical need and legislative requirement for the early identification and assessment of children with potentially handicapping conditions (Miller, 1982). The objectively scored instrument can be reliably administered by education and health professionals and support personnel, without specialized training. Banus (1983), however, reports that inter-administrator reliability for the test was obtained with trained personnel, and it is unclear at this point if the test achieves the same reliability levels when administered by nonprofessional personnel, especially those inexperienced in pediatrics. Both Banus (1983) and DeGangi (1983) report that a weakness of the MAP instruction manual is the lack of clarification of the minimum pediatric and testing experience requirements necessary to insure reliable test administration.

The MAP assesses moderate to severe problems among preschoolers (i.e., children ranging in age from 2 years, 9 months to 5 years, 8 months) in five areas: basic motor and sensory abilities, complex fine motor and oral-motor abilities, speech and language abilities, verbal and nonverbal cognitive skills, and visual-motor integration. An occupational therapist may administer and make decisions about referral for in-depth evaluation independently or in collaboration with diagnosticians from other professions.

One positive feature of the MAP is that it has been standardized on a large number of subjects, with fairly equal distributions for sex, age, region of the nation, and socioeconomic status. Test items are reported, ''to discriminate among the lowest 20 percent of the normal sample'' as well as to ''clearly differentiate across age levels within the normal sample'' (DeGangi, 1983, pp. 410). Banus (1983) reports that the MAP's ''Behavior During Testing'' section, which examines attention, interaction, and sensory reactivity during testing, is ''the best mechanism I have encountered for defining a child's general behavior in a test situation. Most screening tests for this age group look at social interaction, some expect the examiner to comment on the children's attentional abilities, but none to my knowledge assesses a child's reaction to movement and touch'' (p. 334). Such sensory data are thought to provide possible preliminary indications of learning disabilities (Ayres, 1972a), thus the MAP may help to identify preschoolers who may be at risk for later academic problems. Banus, however, (1983) suggests that the predictive validity of the MAP will not be clear until predictive validity studies are completed, some of which are being conducted (in 1985) by author Miller.

A weakness of the test is the need for more explicit cutoff points for determining the need for more in-depth assessment. DeGangi (1983) reports that the MAP's ''at-risk'' and ''suspect'' categories are arbitrary, and that a large number of children may be falsely classified as "normal." "Since the false normal rate is estimated to be quite high, the usefulness of the MAP as a screening tool for delayed children is highly questionable" (DeGangi, 1983, p. 408). Thus, DeGangi suggests that although the MAP is a comprehensive and effective tool for screening "normal" children who score below the 20th percentile, it should be used with caution when screening children who are already exhibiting delays. The MAP is a new instrument, and it is expected that future reliability and validity studies will improve what is already considered to be a well-developed, comprehensive preschool screening instrument.

Denver Developmental Screening Test   Many similarities exist between the MAP and the Denver Developmental Screening Test (DDST; Frankenburg et al., 1975), a widely used, standardized screening instrument of four major areas: personal-social, fine motor-adaptive, language, and gross motor. The DDST was designed to be used with children from birth to age 6 years, and it is administered by asking children to perform tasks of increasing difficulty. Parents may also be queried regarding the child's skill level. Testers are cautioned that the test is for screening, not to generate diagnostic labels (Frankenburg et al., 1975, p. 1).

The DDST and the MAP have been compared in a small study of 30 subjects, and DeGangi (1983) reports that the "MAP was found to identify 24 percent more children as high risk or delayed . . . . This may be an indication that the MAP either misclassified normal children as delayed, or it may reflect the sensitivity of the test in detecting children with delays" (p. 409). There are several differences between the two screenings: the MAP does not accept parental report, but it is flexibly administered, enabling optimal performance of each child. The DDST lacks neurodevelopmental items, as well as items for 5- to 5½-year-olds, and the DDST uses standardization data from only one city, compared to the MAP's data that was obtained from subjects representing nine Census Bureau regions of the United States (Banus, 1983). The DDST is more commonly used; it is widely familiar to most professionals and can easily be demonstrated to students. The MAP is a new instrument that is unfamiliar to many practicing clinicians; however, there is a move by the test publishers and some occupational therapy advocates to educate students and clinicians about the new instrument and to offer training workshops on the administration and uses of the MAP. It is expected that in the future the MAP will be increasingly adopted by practicing occupational therapists and will possibly replace the use of the DDST in many clinics.

Motor or Neurological Screening Tools   While the MAP and DDST are general screening instruments, other instruments assess specific motor abilities of interest to occupational and physical therapists. Such instruments are used for screening when occupational therapists participate in teams and evaluate motor skills, or as part of a battery when a child is referred for an in-depth evaluation.

Milani-Comparetti Motor Development Screening Test The Milani-Comparetti Motor Development Screening Test (Trembath, 1978) is designed for the early identification of motor delays and abnormal movement patterns in children from birth to age two years. According to Price (1980), the designers of the instrument recognized the need for a motor development test that did not require a specific setting, extensive training preparation, or administration time. The Milani-Comparetti Motor Development Screening Test is easily scored and, depending upon the user's skill, can be administered in 4–8 minutes. It can be used to differentiate ''normal'' children from those exhibiting motor delays, as well as differentiating children with simple developmental delay from those with possible central nervous system dysfunction. According to Price (1980), the test is safe, easily repeated, and easily included in a routine physical examination, but it lacks standardization, reliability, validity data, and adequate criteria for determining when a referral for in-depth evaluation is required.

Quick Neurological Screening Test The Quick Neurological Screening Test (QNST; Mutti, Sterling, & Spalding, 1978) was developed for identifying academic difficulties in children ranging in age from 5 to 17 years. It consists of items adapted from other pediatric neurological exams and measures soft neurological signs, often discerned in children exhibiting learning problems. Ingolia, Cermak, and Nelson (1982) report that the QNST may be more useful to occupational therapists than some other screening tools because it covers such a large age range and because it assesses nonacademic, clinical signs often discerned in some children with learning disabilities.

In-Depth Motor Measures: Movement Assessment of Infants and the Peabody Developmental Motor Scales In the past several years, there has been an increase in the number of assessments designed to provide specific measures of motor development. Two of these assessments are the Movement Assessment of Infants (MAI; Chandler, Andrews, & Swanson, 1980) and the Peabody Developmental Motor Scales (PDMS; Folio & Fewell, 1983).

The MAI was developed by physical and occupational therapists and designed to be administered by health and medical personnel trained in infant development. The purposes of the test are: to identify motor problems in children up to age 1 year, to determine the need for early intervention, to monitor the effects of therapy, to enhance research by use of a systematic assessment, and to ''teach skillful observation of movement and motor development through evaluation of normal and handicapped children'' (Campbell, 1981, p. 54). Muscle tone, reflexes, automatic reactions, and voluntary movements are assessed, yielding a wide-ranging profile of a child's overall motor and reflex status that may be predictive of later developmental disabilities.

The PDMS was designed to assess a wider range of behaviors as well as a wider age-range of children than the MAI. The two sections of the PDMS examine the following skill categories in children from birth to age 6 years, 11 months: reflexes, balance, grasp, hand use, eye-hand coordination, manual dexterity, locomotion and nonlocomotion, and receipt and propulsion of objects. The test was designed by educators, including physical education personnel, and requires for administration no specific qualifications except familiarity with developmental test administration and preliminary practice using the PDMS with at least 3 children (Palisano & Lydic, 1984).

Like the MAI, the PDMS has a number of purposes: to identify children with abnormal or delayed gross and fine motor skills, to compare gross and fine motor abilities, to measure changes in motor abilities over time, and to bring together motor programming and assessment. There is an older version of the test (Folio & DuBose, 1974), and a recent revision (Folio & Fewell, 1983) that is normed on a representative sample stratified according to geographical region, race, and sex in the United States. Ottenbacher, Short, and Watson (1981) describe several of the older version's clinical and research advantages that are still applicable to the revision. One such advantage is "the assessment of a fine gradation of performance, ranging from total dependence to complete independence. These gradations enable the quantification of progress within each developmental age and facilitate the assessment of neuromotor performance in children whose severe motor impairments prevent them from making large gains in terms of moving from one developmental level or age to the next" (p. 3).

In contrast to many motor evaluations, the PDMS is divided into separate Gross Motor and Fine Motor Scales. Palisano (1984) points out that some children may perform differently on these two scales because of the different competencies required for each. The Gross Motor Scale assesses motor abilities that are not often included in other evaluations, whereas the Fine Motor Scale includes items that are similar to those on the Mental Scale of the Bayley Scales of Infant Development. High correlations have been reported between scores on the Fine Motor Scale and the Bayley Mental Scale (Folio & Fewell, 1983).

The PDMS has been more fully developed and more widely used than the MAI, which is still under development and should be cautiously interpreted because of the lack of reliability and validity studies (Campbell, 1981). The MAI has been most highly developed for the assessment of 4-month-old infants, although recent research indicates that both the MAI and PDMS may be useful in following the motor progress of infants with mental retardation (Lydic, Short, & Nelson, 1983; Lydic, Windsor, Short, & Ellis, 1985).

Both the MAI and the PDMS appear to be useful gauges of motor development, and may be more useful than "older, more commonly used tools such as the Bayley and the Gesell . . . when one is especially interested in measuring specific motor abilities" (Lydic, 1984, p. 86). Campbell

(1981), however, points out that the selection of specific motor assessments over more general developmental evaluations depends on many factors such as: the stage of the youngster in the evaluation process, the nature of the child's referral, the extent of evaluation by other team members, the choice of specific instruments by evaluation teams, and the extent of intercommunication among team members.

Long, comprehensive motor assessments such as the MAI or PDMS may not be used in settings where diagnostic services are limited and a screening instrument such as the DDST can be used. For children past infancy, assessment of fine and gross motor abilities may be accomplished through examination of functional performance during activities of daily living (ADL). These assessments are covered in the next section.

General ADL Assessments   The area of assessment that is most closely identified with occupational therapy and in which the occupational therapists' unique contributions are most obvious is ADL assessment (Coley, 1978). ADL assessments, which Henderson (1983) terms "the core of the developmental assessment in occupational therapy" (p. 998), are a traditional means of determining performance of motor or daily living skills. However, Henderson cautions, ADL assessments typically take the form of performance checklists, which differ markedly in purpose and procedure from standardized developmental tests. The checklist, she reports, provides a detailed description of a child's performance in a circumscribed area, rather than an overall measure of developmental level. Performance checklists include a survey of chronologically arranged developmental sequences for specific behaviors. The "approximate chronological ages at which individual items are accomplished are taken from research literature or standardized scales and are included on test forms to serve as guides to normative levels of behavior" (Henderson, 1983, p. 998).

ADL assessments have a long history. First developed by Sheldon in 1935, they were commonly used during the Second World War in rehabilitation clinics. Such assessments enable both the therapist and the patient to examine the amount of skill and effort required to perform independently at home and in the community (Coley, 1978). In the *Pediatric Assessment of Self-Care Activities*, Coley (1978) adapts an ADL measuring device for children. Her text includes a 76-item assessment divided into sections evaluating bed, feeding, toileting, hygiene, undressing, dressing, and fastening activities (see Figure 6.2). Additionally, for older children and adolescents, as well as children with special needs, she includes comprehensive supplemental evaluations of communication; adolescent self-care; household activities, including food preparation, shopping, cleaning, laundry, and sewing; and transfer and wheelchair activities.

Coley (1978) uses widely accepted maturational principles as rationales underlying her childhood ADL assessment. These principles state that gross

CHILDREN'S HOSPITAL AT STANFORD
OCCUPATIONAL THERAPY

TIME-ORIENTED RECORD

ACTIVITIES OF DAILY LIVING ASSESSMENT

Key to scoring:
4 .... Independent
3 .... Independent with equipment and/or adaptive technique
2 .... Completes but cannot accomplish in practical time
1 .... Attempts but requires assistance or supervison to complete
0 .... Dependent—cannot attempt activity
— .... Nonapplicable

The Year-Month vertical column represents the [Order of developmental sequence] or approximate age when the child accomplishes the activity; the horizontal column represents the chronological age of the child being assessed.

Visit number			1		2		3		4		5		6		7		8	
FEEDING—cont'd	Yr. Mo.		R.	L.	R.	L.	R.	L.	R.	L.	R.	L.	R.	L.	R.	L.	R.	L.
	Order of dev. seq.																	
Utensils																		
Bottle	0.10																	

ACTIVITIES OF DAILY LIVING

22	Spoon	3.0
23	Cup	1.6
24	Glass	2.0
25	Fork	3.0
26	Knife	6.0–7.0
	TOILETING	
27	Bowel control	1.6
28	Bladder control	2.0
29	Sit on toilet	2.9
30	Arrange clothing	4.0

Figure 6.2.   Partial checklist for activities of daily living assessment. (R. = right hand. L. = left hand.) (From Coley, I. [1978]. *Pediatric assessment of self-care activities* [p. 12]. St. Louis: C. V. Mosby. Reproduced by permission.)

motor precedes fine motor development and that development proceeds in cephalocaudal and proximodistal directions. Thus, control of the head is established before control of lower portions of the body, and trunk control is established prior to precise manipulation of the extremities, as in finger dexterity. These principles are also applied to therapeutic principles, as it makes little sense to focus only on enhancing manual dexterity and grip strength for precise ADL skills if the arm and shoulder cannot provide an adequately strong and stable support for their performance. Similarly, it is widely accepted that therapy needs to focus first on head, neck, and trunk control before precise, complex, distal manipulations can be initiated effectively. Coley (1978) claims that the arrangement of data in her handbook "allows the assessment to flow in concert with the appearance and integration of primitive reflexes and the evolution of more advanced patterns of movement" (p. 5). She reports that each ADL task is examined as a neuromotor developmental process and that "the results of this approach yield unexpected clarity as the developmental relationships between function, reflexes and reactions unfold" (p. 5). Several chapters of her book detail neuromotor development as well as perceptual and cognitive development underlying the evolution of self-care tasks.

Regarding the assessment itself, Coley states that it meets Banus's criteria for a formal evaluation that usually examines a limited area of behavior, is often adapted for the use of a specific institution and patient population, is often developed by combining observations and subtests from standardized tests, and is developed to permit repetition (Banus, 1971). ADL assessments are commonly adapted by different facilities as their caseloads and treatment needs vary. Coley's is no different; it was adapted from an occupational therapy ADL evaluation used at Children's Hospital at Stanford (see Bleck, 1975) and is based on commonly accepted neuromotor principles of development. The test itself is not standardized; it comprises items that are selected from different standardized tests as well as observations. Coley (1978) reports that an advantage of this over a standardized test is that it is much more flexible, enabling the tester the freedom "to explore what factors enhance performance and exercise more latitude in drawing out potential" (p. 2). In addition, Coley points out that maturation is affected by environmental (sociocultural) forces and that users of this ADL assessment "should always remain open to adjusting established schedules and avoid the fallacy of a timetable approach to developmental tasks" (p. 7).

Many other ADL assessments have been published. In general, they are similar to Coley's in that they also examine self-care, home-care, and communication-related behaviors, and they provide sufficient space and means for recording graded levels of independence as well as use of adaptive equipment in performing these skills. ADL assessments can be used to assess function in clinic as well as home environments. Henderson (1983) reports that once the baseline measure has been obtained, the item is often readministered in a variety of ways to determine whether factors such as altered position, adaptive equipment, extra demonstration, nonverbal presentation, or time of day will enhance the child's performance . . . . In addition . . . the therapist observes the quality of performance to determine to what degree perceptual or motor disabilities interfere with performance. Physical factors such as poor coordination and timing of movement, joint limitation, maladapative postures, evidence of weakness, and undue stress or fatigue are indications of the need for treatment or for further evaluation. Failure in fine motor tasks despite apparently adequate intellectual and motor abilities suggests a need to explore sensory and perceptual functions. (p. 999)

Specific ADL Assessments   Performance on general ADL assessments may indicate the need for additional, more comprehensive evaluation of specific functions such as oral-motor abilities, range of motion, specific hand functions, endurance, and reflexes. The assessment of some of these specific abilities is discussed in more detail in the following sections.

Occupational therapists use a variety of procedures for assessing specific functions that are necessary for performing daily living tasks. Some procedures are more objective than others. Some assessments may be easily administered by inexperienced therapists or aides, while other techniques require sophisticated instrumentation for administration and/or apt clinical judgments for interpretation.

Oral-Motor Functions   Feeding is an activity of daily living in which occupational therapy can often provide unique assessment and treatment expertise. In their review of the development and treatment of oral-motor dysfunction, Ottenbacher, Bundy, and Short (1983) point out that abnormal oral patterns and reflexes occur in conjunction with many handicapping conditions such as mental retardation and cerebral palsy, that disorganized sucking has been associated with high-risk status in infants, and that many children with severe to profound mental retardation exhibit multiple handicaps that prevent them from feeding themselves. Feeding is an important physiological and social event. Unfortunately, the feeding of children with oral-motor problems can be dangerous and very time-consuming, can cause social stigmas, and can initiate such issues as rejection and conflict in parent/caregiver interactions.

Feeding is treated by many clinical theories as an element of general development, tied in with head and trunk control, articulation, and breathing. The treatment procedures used by many occupational and physical therapists and speech pathologists tend to emphasize sensory input that enables the child to perform appropriate motor acts. This, in turn, allows the child to benefit from the sensory and motor feedback associated with the appropriate responses (Ottenbacher et al., 1983). Specific treatment and assessment techniques vary across programs. Many assessments of feeding are performance checklists, such as the comprehensive Check List for Oral-Motor Involvement and Communication (see Figure 6.3; Howison, Perella, & Gordon, 1978, pp.

	Date:	Date:	Comments

2. Oral movements for facilitation
(1) Normal (2) Moderate (3) Poor
  a. Lip closure
    1. While sucking			

2. While chewing			
3. While swallowing			
4. Bilabials in individual words			
5. Bilabials during spontaneous speech			
6. Lips at rest			

b. Sucking
    Infant feeding—age when solid food
    was introduced			

1. Grooving of tongue while sucking			
2. Straw placement—on sides			
3. Straw placement—in middle			
3. Chewing (1) Dev. to side (2) Rotary (3) Up and down			

Figure 6.3. Part of the Check List for Oral-Motor Involvement and Communication. (From Howison, M. V., Perella, J. A., & Gordon, D. [1978]. Cerebral palsy. In H. L. Hopkins & H. D. Smith (Eds.), *Willard and Spackman's occupational therapy* [5th ed., p. 514]. Philadelphia: J. B. Lippincott. Reproduced by permission.)

513–515). Some feeding assessments are included as parts of other ADL measures. Often, informal means of examining oral-motor abilities are included within texts for therapeutic techniques, and they take the form of descriptive, illustrative guides rather than sophisticated testing instruments (e.g., Farber, 1974; Finnie, 1975). It is very difficult to quantify tongue movements, strength of jaw stability, suck-and-swallow responses, and their interactions; thus the assessment of oral-motor behaviors requires astute clinical observation more than testing expertise.

Range of Motion, Muscle Strength, and Grasp and Pinch Strength Joint range of motion (ROM) is quantitatively assessed with a goniometer, a flexible instrument, similar to a protractor, that measures the degrees through which the moving joint passes (see Figure 6.4). Study by the occupational therapist of comprehensive photographs and measurement forms, such as those provided by Scott and Trombly (1983, pp. 128–225), can enhance measurement knowledge and abilities.

Although the goniometer provides a quantitative index, the accuracy and reliability of its use are affected by the clinician's accuracy in placing the axis of the goniometer over the axis of joint motion, the means of support for body parts without interference with joint movement, clothing that obstructs movement, and numerous environmental and patient-related factors (Trombly, 1983b). In addition, clinical goniometery can only provide a gross index of ROM. Small increments of change cannot be obtained unless more sophisticated technologies are adopted (Zemke & Zemke, 1982).

Measurement of joint range also includes qualitative factors, as many children, because of structural limitations or muscular weakness, are able to

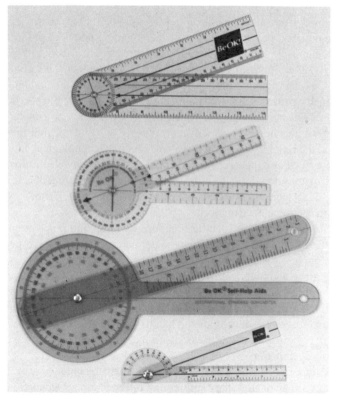

Figure 6.4. Goniometers used to measure joint range of motion. (Photograph compliments of Fred Sammons, Inc./Professional Self-Help Aids, 145 Tower Drive, Burr Ridge, IL 60521.)

complete only partial movements, especially with antigravity motions. Recognition of and judgments regarding qualities of movement require additional clinical expertise. Drews, Vraciu, and Pellino (1984) suggest that more ROM norms be made available for newborns and children; such norms may be useful diagnostically in discriminating "normal" infants from those displaying congenital problems that result in abnormalities of muscle tone.

Muscle strength is often evaluated in conjunction with assessing ROM. Comprehensive, well-illustrated handbooks note the locations of muscles and discuss methods for testing and grading strength of muscles throughout the neck, trunk, and extremities (e.g., Daniels & Worthingham, 1972). Interpretation of that data, however, requires such clinical expertise as the ability to judge grades of strength and to provide consistent resistance to client movements, as well as clinical knowledge of neurological, orthopedic, and muscular conditions.

As Drews et al. (1984) report, "Descriptions of joint motion have reflected the increased sophistication in research methodologies and instrumentation gained from allied medical fields" (p. 49). Electromyography and electrogoniometry provide an index of the electrical potential produced by a contracting muscle and an electronic measure of joint angle, respectively (Trombly, 1983c, p. 258). The use of such technology enables clinicians to increase the quantification of muscle and ROM measures. For example, electrogoniometry provides an accurate method for judging small, specific movements, thus quantifying specific reflex behaviors (Zemke & Zemke, 1982). Such technology, however, is still more widely used in research than in the clinic; and the reliable use of such systems requires technological and clinical expertise as well as expensive instrumentation. Day-to-day electromyography measures of muscle contraction, used, for example, in biofeedback, require accurate, exact placement of clean electrodes. Even then, Trombly (1983b) reports, measurement error occurs.

The measure of such specific functions as grasp and pinch strength can be quantified in pounds with a dynamometer and a pinch gauge, respectively. There are numerous studies providing systematic methods of testing as well as providing grasp and pinch norms for adults and children of various ages (e.g., see Ager, Olivett, & Johnson, 1984; Bowman & Katz, 1984; Scott & Trombly, 1983). Bowman and Katz (1984) report that, in addition to height, weight, and cognitive development, hand strength also increases with age. Thus, it may be useful as an index of normal development and a gauge for identifying dysfunction.

It is important to note that while assessment techniques may become increasingly sophisticated, they still require interpretation. Occupational therapists must apply their clinical expertise in compiling and interpreting data so that assessment results are understood within a context of functional abilities. The functional significance of measures such as ROM, muscle strength, and grasp and pinch strength often must be understood in terms of their effects on

ADL skills as well as on the child's progress in enhancing strength, ROM, or preventing weakness or contractures. Grasp and pinch strength are also examined within the context of functional hand skills, or prehension.

Prehension   Understanding the development of prehension is important for individuals treating children exhibiting developmental delays as well as learning disorders. As Dunn (1983) reports:

> The development of accurate and efficient prehension patterns is important because so much of independent living requires smooth hand use. Furthermore, perceptual and cognitive development relies upon exploration of the environment; these areas might also be affected adversely when prehension is inadequate. (p. 59)

The Erhardt Developmental Prehension Assessment (EDPA; Erhardt, 1982) attempts to provide an objective prehension assessment for children of any age who are developing abnormally. As Dunn (1983) reports, the EDPA has been under development for at least 10 years. It is based on compiled data from many theorists, but it is not standardized. The most recent form of the test is published in Erhardt (1982).

The test consists of three sections, which examine reflexive arm and hand positions, voluntary arm and hand positions, and prewriting skills. There are over 100 items for each arm/hand. Administration, which may take from 30 to 60 minutes, is conducted by an experienced therapist who observes hand positions while the child is in different supported and antigravity positions. Similar to ADL assessments, the EDPA is based on a developmental, maturational perspective. Test administrators, especially those testing children with abnormal development, must be familiar with postural development in order to observe the influence of abnormal movement patterns adequately. Both occupational and physical therapists are appropriate administrators of the EDPA; however, other professionals familiar with developmental principles can also administer the test to children with immature motor patterns (Dunn, 1983).

While the test does not meet the rigid psychometric criteria necessary to qualify it as a valid and reliable assessment, it is still clinically important. As Dunn (1983) reports:

> The present version of the EDPA contains a variety of observations of prehensile patterns from the fetal and natal stages through the fifteenth month; additionally pencil grasp and drawing is rated from one year to six years . . . . It provides an excellent framework from which to accurately describe a difficult series of behaviors. Additionally, it provides a very organized plan from which a treatment approach can evolve. The format of the test forms allows for easy sharing of test findings with other professionals and especially with parents. The clinical nature of the presentation of the items allows the parent or teacher to observe, which would provide an opportunity for teaching and learning. (pp. 66–67)

Summary   The evaluation of specific abilities such as prehension, range of motion, or oral-motor function is often indicated following the observation of deficits during a child's performance on gross or fine motor or ADL assessments. A child's actual ability to perform age-appropriate daily living skills successfully is dependent not only on the specific muscular development required for manual dexterity and good range of motion, but also on the interaction and coordination of perceptual and motor capacities. Although prehension may be normally developed, the child may still be unable to perform some ADL and other fine motor skills because of inadequate coordination between perceptual and manual abilities. Many ADL and school-related abilities are dependent on the interaction of the eyes and hands as well as on the feedback from other senses such as touch, pressure, movement in space, joint position, visual guidance, and coordinated use of the hands. Such abilities are assessed by sensorimotor or perceptual-motor instruments.

Evaluation of Perceptual-Motor and Sensorimotor Development
Most professionals working with children with learning disabilities acknowledge that "learning disabilities" represents a heterogeneous mix of deficits. Many assessments designed to identify some of the more obvious problems associated with learning disabilities are pencil-and-paper types of tests that examine visual perceptual-motor abilities. The Developmental Test of Visual-Motor Integration (Beery & Buktenica, 1967) or the Frostig Developmental Test of Visual Perception (Frostig & Horne, 1964) are examples of such tests that are likely to be used by a variety of professionals, including occupational therapists.

Clinical Measures of Sensorimotor Abilities   Another approach to the identification of learning disabilities is the examination of clinical measures of sensorimotor abilities. A considerable number of studies suggest the existence of a subgroup of learning disabilities, characterized by deficits in balance and coordination which are regulated by muscle proprioceptors and the vestibular apparatus. As Ottenbacher and Short (1985) point out:

> A developing body of literature supports the independent research of Ayres (1974) and de Quiros (1976) concerning the presence of vestibular-proprioceptive processing disorders in some learning disabled children. Investigators have provided tentative confirmation of a relationship between vestibular proprioceptive dysfunction and certain "soft" neurological signs including decreased muscle tone, and poor righting and equilibrium reactions in some learning disabled children (Clyse & Short, 1983; Fisher & Bundy, 1982; Ottenbacher, 1978; Steinberg & Rendle-Short, 1977). Evidence is also accumulating that suggests a disorder of the vestibular-oculomotor system may be partially responsible for visual motor deficits and ocular scanning dysfunction contributing to certain reading disorders (Levinson, 1980; Ottenbacher, Watson, Short, & Biderman, 1979; Petri & Anderson, 1980). (p. 315)

Theories regarding the impact of these clinical signs and their relationship to learning disabilities vary. One assumption is that the predominance of abnormal reflexes and vestibular-proprioceptive deficits is characteristic of an immature or injured nervous system, one that is ill-prepared for the concentration and refined perceptual-motor, oculomotor skills necessary for successful academic performance. Hierarchical maturational theories assume that gross motor and reflex abilities must be stable before more specific, coordinated, and fine motor skills can develop (Ayres, 1972a). De Quiros (1976) poses the theory that the concentration on interoceptive cues, which is required for a child with balance and sensory problems, interferes with the necessary concentration required for academic tasks.

Clinical assessment includes sensory discrimination, sensorimotor development, oculomotor functions, various "soft" neurological signs, and reflex integration. The last term denotes a complex concept referring to the age-appropriate emergence and withdrawal of reflexes. While some reflexes are evident and useful throughout life, others are normally evident only during a brief time in early development. These may be apparent at birth or gradually emerge; they temporarily affect motor functions, and then become less predominant with age. Studies of infant and child motor development have yielded norms both for the emergence and withdrawal of these reflexes, and these norms are consulted for indications of a child's level of reflex integration (e.g., see Fiorentino, 1973; Morrison, Pothier, & Horr, 1978).

Some reflexes are very specific and commonly recognized, such as the sucking and rooting reflexes that affect the oral-motor behaviors essential for eating. Other less widely known reflexes are more global in nature. These reflexes exert effects on the entire body, such as on posture and on interactions between the eyes and head in relation to the position of the body and limbs. Some of these global reflexes are protective, and many are preliminary to the coordinated, bilateral movements underlying quadrapedal and bipedal locomotion or coordinated body, eye, and hand movements. When some of these reflexes predominate, motor behavior may become less controlled; with reflex integration, performance becomes more fluid, and is characterized by the smooth performance of age-appropriate motor skills.

While reflex integration is a part of normal development, it may be delayed or may not occur at all in children with sensory or motor deficits. Delayed reflex integration is often an indicator of delays in other general motor or perceptual-motor skills. For example, some children with learning disabilities or developmental delays display reflexes at ages when the reflexes should no longer be evident (Ayres, 1972a; Montgomery & Richter, 1977). These residual reflexes exert pronounced effects on motor performance, because such nonintegrated reflexes may result in residual motor behaviors that interfere with subsequent coordinated skill development. These reflexes are found in conjunction with other "soft" clinical or neurobehavioral signs such as motor incoordination, abnormal muscle tone, balance difficulties, and other measures of vestibular-proprioceptive abilities that are manifested through postural reactions, body movements in space, and sensory discrimination (see Ayres, 1972a).

Postural, reflex, and other clinical measures are receiving considerable attention in occupational and physical therapy research. Norms, standardization data, and reliability tests have been published for many clinical measures (e.g., Deitz, Siegner, & Crowe, 1981; Gregory-Flock & Yerxa, 1984; Harris, 1981; Kimball, 1981; Morrison & Sublett, 1983; Punwar, 1982; Short, Watson, Ottenbacher, & Rogers, 1983); and relationships have been found between a standardized, vestibular-related measure, the Southern California Postrotary Nystagmus Test (Ayres, 1975), and specific measures such as some antigravity postures, balance, and muscle tone (Clyse & Short, 1983; Ottenbacher, 1978).

Many assessments of sensorimotor function look at reflex abilities in conjunction with other developmental motor assessments. Fiorentino (1973) and Morrison et al. (1978) provide widely used illustrative checklists and guides for assessing reflex abilities in children. Montgomery and Richter (1977) provide a manual useful for educators and therapists developing motor-oriented programs for infants and children with developmental delays. This book, *Sensorimotor Integration for Developmentally Disabled Children: A Handbook,* also includes very general checklists of gross and fine motor abilities (see Figure 6.1) and reflex behaviors, and a useful checklist for obtaining a child's sensorimotor history. Larson (1982) reports that ''the use of a sensory history questionnaire appears to be an appropriate and useful tool to assist in the differential diagnosis of tactile defensiveness.'' Tactile defensiveness is a heightened response to touch stimulation, and it, as well as hypersensitivity in other sensory modalities, is purported to be exhibited by some children with learning disabilities, mental retardation, and developmental delays (Larson, 1982).

Assessment of Sensory Integration Since the early 1960s, A. Jean Ayres has examined characteristics of sensory and motor deficits found in children with learning disabilities. Ayres has identified certain syndromes commonly associated with learning disabilities. These syndromes include disorders in: form and space perception; motor planning; postural and bilateral abilities; and sensory, specifically tactile, responsiveness (Ayres, 1980). Deficits in these areas are labeled sensory integration problems. While the term ''integration'' is often used to refer to a neural liaison between multisensory/ sensory input and motor output, Ayres's use of the term is much more general and less defined. In fact, one of the criticisms of Ayres's work is the lack of adequate operational definitions for her theoretical constructs. For example, Ayres (1979) defines sensory integration as ''the organization of sensation for use'' (p. 5).

Ayres developed an entire battery of tests, called the Southern California Sensory Integration Tests (SCSIT; Ayres, 1972b), to measure sensory integrative abilities; she designed sensory integrative therapy to remedy the syndromes of deficits identified through clusters of scores on the various subtests of the SCSIT. According to Ayres (1979), sensory integrative therapy is designed "to provide and control sensory input, especially the input from the vestibular system, muscles and joints, and skin in such a way that the child spontaneously forms the adaptive responses that integrate those sensations" (p. 140). It is beyond the scope of this chapter to assess the theoretical foundations underlying Ayres's treatment principles and the psychometric properties of each of the subtests included in the SCSIT (Ayres, 1972b); however, the following section reports on the orientation of the tests and some general conclusions. (For a detailed analysis of the SCSIT and sensory integration theory, consult Ottenbacher and Short, 1985.)

The tests constituting the SCSIT were originally combined in 1972 and were partially revised in 1980 (Ayres, 1980). The battery of tests explores a variety of abilities, including the fine motor and visual perceptual abilities examined by other standardized assessments; however, "the battery also provides evaluative information for basic areas of sensory-perceptual function rarely included on other standardized assessments" (Ottenbacher & Short, in press). Those items assessed by the SCSIT but not usually included in other developmental evaluations generally examine posture, joint position, sensory discrimination, and movement in space.

The SCSIT are reported to have a high degree of face validity. A majority of the tests were standardized on children from 4 to 8 years of age, but some normative data are included for children up to age 10 years. In general, the tests have been criticized for various psychometric weaknesses, including: the use of small norm groups, drawing conclusions about syndromes from factor analytic studies that involved administration of multiple tests to small samples of children, some unacceptable ranges of test-retest reliabilities, and inadequate validity data provided in the test manual (Ottenbacher & Short, 1985).

Considerable training is recommended in order to be qualified to administer and interpret the SCSIT, including clinical expertise with children, at least 20 supervised administrations, and graduate training in the neurosciences and in statistics. Members of Sensory Integration International (formerly called the Center for the Study of Sensory Integrative Dysfunction) recommend that testers be certified in SCSIT test administration and interpretation (Ayres, 1980; Ottenbacher & Short, 1985). Such certification is offered through various workshops sponsored by Sensory Integration International or by completing coursework offered by certified instructors in various occupational therapy academic programs.

Extensive work to provide better standardization data and to revise the SCSIT is underway, and these efforts are expected to eliminate many existing criticisms. Some unreliable tests from the SCSIT are eliminated, and other tests of apraxia are included in the new tests, called the Sensory Integration and Praxis Tests, to be published in 1986 (Koomar, 1984).

Greater understanding of the relationship between learning disabilities and sensorimotor development is expected to be forthcoming with the extensive amount of research investigating these areas. Already, data indicate that some clinical measures may be useful for delineating specific forms of learning disability or developmental delay as well as evaluating the response of children with learning disabilities to specific kinds of therapy (Ottenbacher & Short, 1985; Ottenbacher, Short & Watson, 1979; Ottenbacher, Short & Watson, 1980).

Many clinical measures have been incorporated into two sensory integration assessments directed at young children (DeGangi & Berk, 1983; Dunn, 1981). With the development of tests for younger age groups, it is hoped that the assessment of deficits associated with learning disabilities (and other problems) can occur as early as possible. This focus on early assessment is particularly evident in neonatology, discussed in the following section.

Neonatal Assessments An area of increasingly significant focus is the assessment of premature infants and neonates. Due to advancements in medical technology, more infants who are premature and smaller than average are surviving; but there are concerns about the developmental prognosis of some of these infants, especially those with birth weights under 1,500 grams or those considered at high risk for developmental disorders because of neonatal medical complications. As Palisano and Short (1984) point out, these infants may be at higher risk for subsequent developmental problems related to motor, learning, language, perceptual-motor functions, or neuromotor functions. Thus, the emphasis of professionals treating these infants is on greater understanding of premature infant development, creation of assessment tools that accurately predict at-risk status, and continued follow-up evaluation and treatment of children diagnosed as being at risk.

Occupational and physical therapists are often members of neonatal treatment and follow-up teams. Tyler and Chandler (1978) point out that the roles of physical and occupational therapists, while separate in many environments, "in pediatrics in some areas have merged until it is frequently difficult to distinguish one from the other. A specialist called the developmental therapist or the pediatric therapist (Banus, 1971) has emerged. The coming together of the two professions has been encouraged by a growing understanding of the interdependence of the sensory and motor systems and the view that the head, trunk, and extremities function as a unit" (p. 170). The focus of these therapists is on the evaluation of motor and sensory (sensorimotor) development, which is assessed by examination of gross and fine motor development plus clinical assessment of: muscle tone; motor functions, including bilateral symmetrical movement; oral-motor functions; developmental reflexes; and automatic reactions. "While opinion varies as to the use of neonatal assessments for predicting long-term neurological and intellectual outcomes, indices such as muscle tone and motor function have been reported to differentiate among neonates with similar medical complications, those which are more likely to have developmental disabilities'' (Palisano & Short, 1984, pp. 43–44).

Unfortunately, standardized neonatal sensorimotor assessments are scarce, and pediatric therapists often resort to developing their own tools or to using standardized scales developed by members of other disciplines. The standardized neonatal assessments that include aspects of muscle tone and motor functions are classified by Palisano and Short (1984) into three types: neurological, gestational age, and behavioral. Neurological assessments (Amiel-Tison, 1976; Parmelee & Michaelis, 1971; Prechtl & Beintema, 1964) are designed to evaluate the functional status of the peripheral and central nervous system, with a focus on reflexes, postures, and movements that are thought to reflect the status of brain stem and spinal cord mechanisms. Gestational age assessments (Amiel-Tison, 1968; Dubowitz, Dubowitz, & Goldberg, 1970) have been used for estimating the age of premature infants and differentiating small-for-dates full-term neonates from premature infants. Behavioral assessments (Brazelton, 1973; Graham, 1956; Rosenblith, 1961) are based on interactive and organizational capacities of neonates and are designed to elicit the infants' best psychological and motor performances.

None of these assessments, however, is ideally suited to the needs of the occupational therapist assessing neonatal motor behaviors. Premature infant development has not been fully studied, and it is only in the 1980s that such large numbers of young and small infants are surviving. Some therapists have found success using developmental assessments that are designed for infants rather than specifically oriented to neonates or premature infants; but it is important to recognize that many premature infant behaviors are not fully understood and may be qualitatively different from those of the full-term infant. Thus, before detailed assessments can be created, comprehensive normative studies must be conducted regarding normal premature infant and neonatal motor development. Some understanding of premature infant development and assessment should be provided by the Assessment of Premature Infants' Behavior (Als, Lester, & Tronick, 1982). However, occupational and physical therapists need to develop specific assessments that focus on the quality, variety, and adaptability of movement patterns and postures (Palisano & Short, 1984). In addition, all members of the diagnostic and treatment team must increase their focus on the multiple variables, such as family and social factors, that affect premature infant growth and development.

INDICATIONS FOR REFERRAL TO AN OCCUPATIONAL THERAPIST

Diagnostic team members should refer to occupational therapists children who are exhibiting motor-related or performance-related problems. Examples include problems with: adaptive or daily living skills such as dressing, hygiene, and other self-care skills requiring prehension and fine motor abilities; feeding and oral-motor actions; sensory or perceptual-motor abilities; or movement (i.e., tremors, rigidity, incoordination, weakness, restricted movement, or limb deformities that compromise the ability to perform age-appropriate tasks). Such problems may affect daily functional skills, social-emotional interactions, play, and school activities. Many such deficits may be obvious, manifested through physical abnormalities or motor delays that accompany delays in other domains such as cognitive or speech and language.

For children exhibiting sensory or motor delays or abnormalities, occupational therapists can be consulted for prescribing adaptive equipment or assistive devices to meet specific home, school, or daily living needs. Suggestions may be made with regard to improving architectural access, facilitating feeding, enhancing posture during classroom activities, enhancing independence in toileting or dressing, or integrating children with special needs into the classroom and community.

It has been the author's experience that, with their unique approach to sensory and motor deficits, occupational therapists are often called on to examine children who remain "unclassified" after other team members have completed their assessments. Such children may exhibit subtle sensory and motor problems that are sometimes associated with learning disorders or developmental delays. Some combinations of the following problems may be seen: incoordination, clumsiness, lack of balance, acting out, poor self-image, abnormal reflexes or awkward movements, withdrawal or abnormal reactions to touch or other sensory stimuli, avoidance of motor activities and games, oculomotor deficits, or abnormal muscle tone such as rigidity or floppiness. Combinations of these problems are often seen in children who exhibit deficits in sensory integration, sensorimotor integration, or reflex integration, which are often assessed and treated by occupational therapists.

REFERENCES

Ager, D. L., Olivett, B. L., & Johnson, C. L. (1984). Grasp and pinch strength in children 5 to 12 years old. *American Journal of Occupational Therapy, 38,* 107–113.

Als, H., Lester, B. M., & Tronick, E. C. (1982). Toward a research instrument for the assessment of preterm infants' behavior (APIB). In H. E. Fitzgerald, F. M. Lester, & M. W. Yogman (Eds.), *Theory and research in behavioral pediatrics: Vol. 1.* New York: Plenum.

American Occupational Therapy Association. (1983a). *Essentials and guidelines of an accredited educational program for the occupational therapist.* Rockville, MD: Author.

American Occupational Therapy Association. (1983b). *Essentials and guidelines of an approved educational program for the occupational therapy assistant.* Rockville, MD: Author.

American Occupational Therapy Association. (1984). *Studying entry level education for occupational therapists* (Resolution #604-84). Rockville, MD: Author

Amiel-Tison, C. (1968). Neurological evaluation of the maturity of newborn infants. *Archives of Diseases of Children, 43,* 89–93.

Amiel-Tison, C. (1976). A method of neurologic evaluation within the first year of life. *Current Problems in Pediatrics, 7,* 1–50.

Ayres, A. J. (1972a). *Sensory integration and learning disorders.* Los Angeles: Western Psychological Services.

Ayres, A. J. (1972b). *Southern California Sensory Integration Tests, manual.* Los Angeles: Western Psychological Services.

Ayres, A. J. (1974). *The development of sensory integrative theory and practice.* Dubuque, IA: Kendall/Hunt.

Ayres, A. J. (1975). *Southern California Postrotary Nystagmus Test.* Los Angeles: Western Psychological Services.

Ayres, A. J. (1979). *Sensory integration and the child.* Los Angeles: Western Psychological Services.

Ayres, A. J. (1980). *Southern California Sensory Integration Tests, manual revised.* Los Angeles: Western Psychological Services.

Banus, B. S. (1971). *The developmental therapist.* Thorofare, NJ: Charles B. Slack.

Banus, B. S. (1979). Evaluation. In B. S. Banus, C. A. Kent, Y. S. Norton, D. R. Sukiennicki, & M. L. Becker (Eds.), *The developmental therapist* (pp. 165–199). Thorofare, NJ: Charles B. Slack.

Banus, B. S. (1983). The Miller Assessment for Preschoolers (MAP): An introduction and review. *American Journal of Occupational Therapy, 37,* 333–340.

Bayley, N. (1969). *Bayley Scales of Infant Development.* New York: Psychological Corporation.

Beckwith, L. (1976). Caregiver-infant interaction as a focus for therapeutic intervention with human infants. In R. N. Walsh & W. T. Greenough (Eds.), *Environments as therapy for brain dysfunction.* New York: Plenum.

Beery, K. E., & Buktenica, N. A. (1967). *Developmental Test of Visual-Motor Integration.* Chicago: Follett.

Bleck, E. E. (1975). Cerebral palsy. In E. E. Bleck & D. A. Nagel (Eds.), *Physically handicapped children—A medical atlas for teachers.* New York: Grune & Stratton.

Bobath, B. (1972). The neurodevelopmental approach to treatment. In P. Pearson & C. Williams (Eds.), *Physical therapy services in developmental disabilities.* Springfield, IL: Charles C. Thomas.

Bowman, O. J., & Katz, B. (1984). Hand strength and prone extension in right-dominant, 6 to 9 year olds. *American Journal of Occupational Therapy, 38,* 367–376.

Brazelton, T. B. (1973). *Neonatal Behavioral Assessment Scale.* Philadelphia: J. B. Lippincott.

Campbell, S. (1981). Movement assessment of infants. An evaluation. *Physical and Occupational Therapy in Pediatrics, 1* (4), 53–58.

Chandler, L., Andrews, M., & Swanson, M. (1980). *Movement Assessment of Infants.* Rolling Bay, WA: A. H. Larson.

Clyse, S. J., & Short, M. A. (1983). The relationship between dynamic balance and postrotary nystagmus in learning disabled children. *Physical and Occupational Therapy in Pediatrics, 3* (3), 25–32.

Coley, I. L. (1978). *Pediatric assessment of self-care activities.* St. Louis: C. V. Mosby.

Daniels, L., & Worthingham, C. (1972). *Muscle testing. Techniques of manual examination* (3rd ed.). Philadelphia: W. B. Saunders.

DeGangi, G. A. (1983). A critique of the standardization of the Miller Assessment for Preschoolers. *American Journal of Occupational Therapy, 37*, 407–411.

DeGangi, G. A., & Berk, R. A. (1983). Psychometric analysis of the Test of Sensory Integration. *Physical and Occupational Therapy in Pediatrics, 3* (2), 43–60.

Deitz, J. C., Siegner, C. G., & Crowe, T. (1981). The Southern California Postrotary Nystagmus Test: Test-retest reliability for preschool children. *The Occupational Therapy Journal of Research, 1*, 165–178.

Drews, J. E., Vraciu, J. K., & Pellino, G. (1984). Range of motion of the joints of the lower extremities of newborns. *Physical and Occupational Therapy in Pediatrics, 4* (2), 49–62.

Dubowitz, L. M. S., Dubowitz, V., & Goldberg, C. (1970). Clinical assessment of gestational age in the newborn infant. *Journal of Pediatrics, 77* (1), 1–10.

Dunn, W. (1981). *A guide to testing clinical observations in kindergartners.* Rockville, MD: American Occupational Therapy Association.

Dunn, W. (1983). Critique of the Erhardt Developmental Prehension Assessment (EDPA). *Physical and Occupational Therapy in Pediatrics, 3* (4), 59–68.

Erhardt, R. P. (1982). *Developmental hand dysfunction: Theory-assessment-treatment.* Laurel, MD: Ramsco.

Farber, S. D. (1974). *Sensori-motor evaluation and treatment procedures for allied health personnel* (2nd ed.). Indianapolis: Indiana University Foundation.

Finnie, N. R. (1975). *Handling the young cerebral palsied child at home* (2nd ed.). New York: E. P. Dutton.

Fiorentino, M. R. (1973). *Reflex testing methods for evaluating C.N.S. development* (2nd ed.). Springfield, IL: Charles C. Thomas.

Fisher, A. G., & Bundy, A. C. (1982). Equilibrium reactions in normal children and in boys with sensory integrative dysfunction. *The Occupational Therapy Journal of Research, 2*, 171–183.

Folio, M., & DuBose, R. F. (1974). *Peabody Developmental Motor Scales.* Nashville, TN: George Peabody College for Teachers.

Folio, M., & Fewell, R. (1983). *Peabody Developmental Motor Scales.* Hingham, MA: Teaching Resources.

Frankenburg, W. K., Dodds, J. B., Fandal, A. W., Kazuk, E., & Cohrs, M. (1975). *Denver Developmental Screening Test manual. Revised edition.* Denver: University of Colorado Medical Center.

Frostig, M., & Horne, D. (1964). *The Frostig Program for the Development of Visual Perception. Teacher's guide.* Chicago: Follett.

Gilette, N. (1971). Occupational therapy and mental health. In H. S. Willard & C. S. Spackman (Eds.), *Occupational therapy.* Philadelphia: J. B. Lippincott.

Graham, F. K. (1956). Behavioral differences between normal and traumatized newborns: The test procedures. *Psychological Monographs, 70* (21, No. 427), 1–16.

Gray, M. (1978). Occupational therapist. In R. M. Goldenson (Ed.), *Disability and rehabilitation handbook* (pp. 739–741). New York: McGraw-Hill.

Gregory-Flock, J. L., & Yerxa, E. J. (1984). Standardization of the prone extension test on children ages 4 through 8. *American Journal of Occupational Therapy, 38*, 187–194.

Harris, N. P. (1981). Duration and quality of the prone extension position in four-, six-, and eight-year-old normal children. *American Journal of Occupational Therapy, 35*, 26–30.

Henderson, A. (1983). Occupational Therapy. In M. D. Levine, W. B. Carey, A. C. Crocker, & R. T. Gross (Eds.), *Developmental-behavioral pediatrics* (pp. 998–1000; 1123–1126). Philadelphia: W. B. Saunders.

Howison, M. V., Perella, J. A., & Gordon, D. (1978). Cerebral palsy. In H. L. Hopkins & H. D. Smith (Eds.), *Willard and Spackman's occupational therapy* (5th ed.; pp. 501–546). Philadelphia: J. B. Lippincott.

Ingolia, P., Cermak, S. A., & Nelson, D. (1982). The effect of choreoathetoid movements on the Quick Neurological Screening Test. *American Journal of Occupational Therapy, 36,* 801–807.

Kimball, J. G. (1981). Normative comparison of the Southern California Postrotary Nystagmus Test: Los Angeles vs. Syracuse data. *American Journal of Occupational Therapy, 35,* 21–25.

Koomar, J. A. (1984). Development of praxis tests for children. *Sensory integration special interest section newsletter 7*(3), 1–4. (Available from American Occupational Therapy Association, 1383 Piccard Drive, Rockville, MD).

Larson, K. A. (1982). The sensory history of developmentally delayed children with and without tactile defensiveness. *American Journal of Occupational Therapy, 36,* 590–596.

Levinson, H. N. (1980). *A solution to the riddle dyslexia.* New York: Springer-Verlag.

Lydic, J. S. (1984). *Effects of controlled rotary vestibular stimulation on the motor performance of infants with Down syndrome.* Unpublished doctoral dissertation, Boston University, Boston.

Lydic, J. S., Short, M. A., & Nelson, D. L. (1983). Comparison of two scales for assessing motor development in infants with Down's syndrome. *The Occupational Therapy Journal of Research, 3* (4), 213–221.

Lydic, J. S., Windsor, M. M., Short, M. A., & Ellis, T. A. (1985). Effects of controlled rotary vestibular stimulation on the motor performance of infants with Down Syndrome. *Physical and Occupational Therapy in Pediatrics, 5,* 93–118.

Miller, L. J. (1982). *Miller Assessment for Preschoolers (manual).* Littleton, CO: Foundation for Knowledge in Development.

Montgomery, P., & Richter, E. (1977). *Sensorimotor integration for developmentally disabled children: A handbook.* Los Angeles: Western Psychological Services.

Morrison, D., Pothier, P., & Horr, K. (1978). *Sensory-motor dysfunction and therapy in infancy and early childhood.* Springfield, IL: Charles C Thomas.

Morrison, D., & Sublett, J. (1983). Reliability of the Southern California Postrotary Nystagmus Test with learning disabled children. *American Journal of Occupational Therapy, 37,* 694–698.

Mutti, M., Sterling, H. M., & Spalding, N. V. (1978). *QNST: Quick Neurological Screening Test Manual* (rev. ed.). Novato, CA: Academic Therapy Publications.

Nelson, D. L. (1984). *Children with autism and other pervasive disorders of development and behavior: Therapy through activities.* Thorofare, NJ: Charles B. Slack.

Occupational therapy: its definition and functions. (1972). *American Journal of Occupational Therapy, 26,* 204–205.

Ottenbacher, K. (1978). Identifying vestibular processing dysfunction in learning disabled children. *American Journal of Occupational Therapy, 32,* 217–222.

Ottenbacher, K., Bundy, A., & Short, M. A. (1983). The development and treatment of oral-motor dysfunction: A review of clinical research. *Physical and Occupational Therapy in Pediatrics, 3* (2), 1–21.

Ottenbacher, K., & Short, M. A. (1985). Sensory integrative dysfunction in children:

A review of theory and treatment. In M. L. Wolraich (Ed.), *Advances in developmental and behavioral pediatrics* (Vol. 6., pp. 287–329). Greenwich, CT: JAI Press.

Ottenbacher, K., Short, M. A., & Watson, P. J. (1979). Nystagmus duration changes of learning disabled children during sensory integrative therapy. *Perceptual and Motor Skills, 48,* 1159–1164.

Ottenbacher, K., Short, M. A., & Watson, P. J. (1980). The use of selected clinical observations to predict postrotary nystagmus change in learning disabled children. *Physical and Occupational Therapy in Pediatrics, 1* (1), 31–38.

Ottenbacher, K., Short, M. A., & Watson, P. J. (1981). The effects of a clinically applied program of vestibular stimulation on the neuromotor performance of children with severe developmental disability. *Physical and Occupational Therapy in Pediatrics, 1* (3), 1–11.

Ottenbacher, K., Watson, P. J., Short, M. A., & Biderman, M. (1979). Nystagmus and ocular fixation difficulties in learning disabled children. *American Journal of Occupational Therapy, 33,* 717–721.

Palisano, R. J. (1984). *Chronological versus adjusted age in evaluating motor development of healthy premature infants.* Unpublished doctoral dissertation, Boston University, Boston.

Palisano, R. J., & Lydic, J. S. (1984). The Peabody Developmental Motor Scales: An analysis. *Physical and Occupational Therapy in Pediatrics, 4* (1), 69–75.

Palisano, R. J., & Short, M. A. (1984). Methods for assessing muscle tone and motor function in the neonate: A review. *Physical and Occupational Therapy in Pediatrics. 4* (4), 43–54.

Parmelee, A., & Michaelis, R. (1971). Neurological examination of the newborn. In J. Hellmuth (Ed.), *Exceptional Infant* (Vol. 2). New York: Brunner/Mazel.

Pedretti, L. W. (1981). *Occupational therapy. Practice skills for physical dysfunction.* St. Louis: C. V. Mosby.

Peloquin, S. M. (1983). The development of an occupational therapy interview/therapy set procedure. *American Journal of Occupational Therapy, 37,* 457–461.

Petri, J. L., & Anderson, M. E. (1980). Eye and head movements in reading-disabled and normal children. *American Journal of Occupational Therapy, 34,* 801–808.

Prechtl, H. F. R., & Beintema, D. (1964). *The neurological evaluation of the fullterm newborn infant* (Little Club Clinics in Developmental Medicine, No. 12). London: National Spastics Society.

Price, M. M. (1980). Critique of the Milani-Comparetti Motor Development Screening Test. *Physical and Occupational Therapy in Pediatrics, 1* (1), 59–68.

Punwar, A. (1982). Expanded normative data: Southern California Postrotary Nystagmus Test. *American Journal of Occupational Therapy, 36,* 183–187.

de Quiros, J. B. (1976). Diagnosis of vestibular disorders in the learning disabled. *Journal of Learning Disabilities, 9,* 50–58.

Rosenblith, J. F. (1961). The modified Graham behavior test for neonates. *Biology of the Neonate, 3,* 174–293.

Scott, A. D., & Trombly, C. A. (1983). Evaluation. In C. A. Trombly (Ed.), *Occupational therapy for physical dysfunction* (2nd ed.; pp. 126–229). Baltimore: Williams & Wilkins.

Short, M. A., & Fincher, G. (1983). Intercorrelations among three preschool screening instruments. *Occupational Therapy Journal of Research 3,* 180–182.

Short, M. A., Watson, P. J., Ottenbacher, K., & Rogers, C. (1983). Vestibular-proprioceptive functions in 4-year-olds: Normative and regression analyses. *American Journal of Occupational Therapy, 37,* 102–109.

Smith, H. D., & Tiffany, E. G. (1978). Evaluation overview. In H. L. Hopkins & H. D. Smith (Eds.), *Willard and Spackman's occupational therapy* (pp. 151–157). Philadelphia: J. B. Lippincott.

Steinberg, M., & Rendle-Short, J. (1977). Vestibular dysfunction in young children with minor neurological impairment. *Developmental Medicine and Child Neurology, 19,* 639–651.

Stoner, E. K. (1971). Care of the amputee. In F. H. Krusen (Ed.), *Handbook of physical medicine and rehabilitation* (2nd ed.; pp. 97–144). Philadelphia: W. B. Saunders.

Trembath, J. (1978). *The Milani-Comparetti Motor Development Screening Test.* Omaha: University of Nebraska Medical Center, Meyer's Children's Rehabilitation Institute.

Trombly, C. A. (1983a). The Bobath neurodevelopmental approach. In C. A. Trombly (Ed.), *Occupational therapy for physical dysfunction* (2nd ed.; pp. 83–96). Baltimore: Williams & Wilkins.

Trombly, C. A. (1983b). Treatment. In C. A. Trombly (Ed.), *Occupational therapy for physical dysfunction* (2nd ed.; pp. 230–241). Baltimore: Williams & Wilkins.

Trombly, C. A. (1983c). Biofeedback. In C. A. Trombly (Ed.), *Occupational therapy for physical dysfunction* (2nd ed.; pp. 254–263). Baltimore: Williams & Wilkins.

Tyler, N. B., & Chandler, L. S. (1978). The developmental therapists: The occupational therapist and physical therapist. In K. E. Allen, V. A. Holm, & R. L. Schiefelbusch (Eds.), *Early intervention—A team approach* (ch. 7; pp. 169–197). Balitmore: University Park Press.

Zemke, R., & Zemke, W. P. (1982). Electrogoniometry: A proposed research tool for the measurement of the asymmetrical tonic neck reflex. *Physical and Occupational Therapy in Pediatrics, 2* (1), 51–62.

Chapter 7

Developmental Pediatric Assessment

~~~

Michael E. Msall
and Rebecca Ichord

The developmental pediatrician is first and foremost a pediatrician and, ideally, he or she serves in many roles: as the provider of services to individual patients and their families, as an educator to pediatricians in training, as a consultant to pediatricians and family practitioners in primary care, and as a consultant to the community on public policy for persons with disabilities. His or her training, therefore, must provide the scope and depth of knowledge and experience necessary to meet these responsibilities.

TRAINING

As the developmental pediatrician is called upon to assess the developmental integrity of children, he or she must have a thorough knowledge of the range of normal growth and development. An understanding of the common diseases of childhood, their diagnosis, their impact on growth and development, and their impact on the family, is also needed. These form the heart of pediatric residency training for general pediatricians and pediatric subspecialists alike. Currently, pediatric residencies consist of three years of intense training involving inpatient, outpatient-ambulatory, and pediatric subspecialty experiences, which include biopsychosocial aspects of child development (American Academy of Pediatrics, 1978). Extensive experience with adverse biological events and their impact on the developing child and his or her family occurs throughout training. Perhaps no other pediatric subspecialty (including neurology, genetics, and psychiatry) provides the depth and scope of hands-on experience with respect to newborn medicine, meningitis, trauma, abuse and neglect, coma, seizures, cyanotic heart disease, abnormalities of growth and development, and adolescent medicine as does developmental pediatrics.

After the pediatric residency, the developmental pediatrician must complete 2 years of subspecialty training in a fellowship program. Although training programs vary in detail, all include a core of direct experience with children who have developmental disabilities and a variety of related subspecialty experiences (Capute & Accardo, 1980). The fellowship experience should not be limited to any one developmental period but should include problems of the adolescent and young adult who have developmental disabilities. This provides a longitudinal perspective that is crucial in order to appreciate the impact of developmental disabilities on the individual, on the family, and on society at large.

Training in the care of children with developmental disabilities is the most important component of the developmental pediatrician's fellowship. This training includes specific instruction and practice with assessment tools for the whole spectrum of developmental disabilities, experience with the multidisciplinary process, and experience with parent counseling. The value of this training cannot be overemphasized. It is not sufficient for a practitioner who sees children with multiple handicaps in a seizure clinic one afternoon per week to claim competence in counseling parents on developmental levels without meeting first with psychologists or educators. In addition, the developmental pediatrician may be called upon frequently, both in individual cases and in the public arena, to make judgments with regard to medical-legal issues affecting handicapped persons. As a consequence of PL 94-142, the pediatrician often acts as a co-advocate with parents in making appropriate use of educational services (Wright, 1982).

The fellowship training for developmental pediatricians also provides direct experience with diagnosis and management of the whole spectrum of disabling conditions, including cerebral palsy, mental retardation, sensory deficits, behavior disorders, language and communication disorders, and learning disabilities. This is important because an individual child with a developmental disability often has associated deficits. Accardo and Capute (1978), summarizing Conley's national survey, point out that among persons with mental retardation, 40% have behavior-psychiatric disorders, 10% have cerebral palsy, 4% have epilepsy, 3% have hearing loss, and 1% have visual impairment. Scheiner and Moomaw (1982) note a similar spectrum of associated handicaps in an early intervention network for children with severe visual impairments. In a sample group of 48 children living in Massachusetts, ranging in age from birth to 4 years, the following conditions were found: mental retardation, 42%; seizures, 33%; cerebral palsy, 23%; learning-behavior-emotional problems, 19%; and hearing impairments, 2%. Similarly, children with learning disabilities often have associated problems such as hyperactivity, adjustment disorders, and social learning deficits. In order to comprehensively coordinate a habilitation plan, the developmental pediatrician must be competent in diagnosing and managing the associated deficits. Again, the multidisciplinary approach is of great value in that liaison with mental health practitioners and knowledge of family counseling and therapy are essential to attaining such competence.

Finally, since among biomedical factors the growth and development of the nervous system has the greatest impact on behavioral development, the subspecialty fellowship should give the developmental pediatrician a thorough grounding in the neurological substrate of child development. Thus, pediatric neurology is a critical component of the subspecialty experiences, which also include genetics, rehabilitation medicine, and psychiatry. These subspecialty experiences, coupled with ongoing pediatric developmental consultation services to other pediatric subspecialists such as cardiologists and endocrinologists, provide training in the conditions that carry a high risk of disabilities. These conditions include low birth weight, traumatic coma, and genetic metabolic disease, as well as those medical disorders known to cause disabilities (e.g., Down syndrome, spina bifida, and craniofacial malformations). As Rapin (1982) states, in comparing the pediatric neurologist with the developmental pediatrician:

> The competencies of the child neurologist and the pediatrician with special training in child development and in the care of the handicapped child [developmental pediatrician] have large areas of overlap. . . . In truth, when it comes to the care of the statically handicapped child the choice of consultation with a child neurologist or a developmental pediatrician is largely one of availability. (p. 187)

(Authors' note: The choice should also be one of interest. That is, the appropriate specialist is one who devotes a significant portion of his or her practice and efforts to persons with developmental disabilities.)

The emphasis is biological in the subspecialty fellowship training in order to insure that families receive appropriate medical diagnoses and accurate prognoses. For example, to label a child with Sanfilippo's syndrome simply "delayed" without specific medical diagnosis not only compounds the tragedy in terms of genetic counseling but also in terms of providing family supports. Subsequent sections of this chapter highlight the importance of establishing both developmental diagnoses and their biomedical determinants in children with mental retardation and learning disabilities.

ROLE OF THE DEVELOPMENTAL PEDIATRICIAN

The role of a developmental pediatrician may assume a wide variety of forms, as determined by the needs of the community, the availability of other developmental and medical services, and the specific individual's interests and training. The most important responsibility is to insure that medical diagnoses are made of the treatable and preventable disorders that cause or accompany developmental disabilities. This responsibility may be fulfilled through a variety of services: 1) as an integral part of a primary care pediatric practice; 2) as a medical consultant to community agencies providing services to handicapped persons, such as Association for Retarded Citizens, United Cerebral Palsy, and Association for Children and Adults with Learning Disabilities; 3) as the pediatrician on a multidisciplinary team providing comprehensive assessment and treatment for individuals with disabilities; and 4) as a teacher and researcher in an academic center where service and training are combined, such as neonatal intensive care follow-ups, comprehensive epilepsy centers, and genetic birth defects evaluation centers.

Developmental pediatrics has evolved in response to powerful and rapidly changing social and medical forces. The care of children with developmental disabilities has moved steadily toward early identification and intervention. More children now survive life-threatening medical conditions through more complex therapeutic technologies than ever was imagined in the 1960s. The developmental pediatrician is in a unique position to provide answers to the questions about developmental outcome for these children posed by their parents and by the physicians involved in their acute care. On the opposite end of the spectrum, primary care pediatricians face an increasing demand for developmental services among the healthy children who dominate their practices. They turn to developmental pediatricians for training in developmental screening and for consultation in more complicated cases.

In a multidisciplinary assessment of a child with mental retardation or learning disabilities, the developmental pediatrician contributes by providing medical and neurodevelopmental diagnoses that influence the team process at every important stage: 1) initial assessment, 2) planning habilitation, 3) parent education, and 4) monitoring outcome. The developmental pediatrician's primary responsibility is to identify the biomedical conditions that may be contributing to or simply accompanying the developmental problem. At best, such information may lead to medical therapy that ameliorates or prevents recurrence of the developmental disorder. At the least, medical and neurodevelopmental diagnostic information can provide a more rational basis for parent counseling as to prognosis and habilitation needs. In either case, the developmental pediatrician helps to accomplish the principal purposes of assessment outlined in Chapter 1.

The developmental pediatrician's approach to medical diagnosis is shaped by several key questions. First, is there an identifiable biomedical cause for the child's developmental problem? If so, is it an active or progressive process in which further diagnosis may lead to definitive therapy or a radical revision of the prognosis? Because of the breadth of training, the developmental pediatrician is able to determine which disease processes may be present and whether they affect the child's development, and, subsequently, to obtain appropriate medical subspecialty services. For example, an infant may be referred for developmental evaluation because of gross motor delays and failure to thrive. Upon systematic medical evaluation, a diagnosis of heart failure due to obstructive sleep apnea (breathing irregularities) leads to definitive and immediate medical intervention, with subsequent normalization of his or her development.

Second, is the child's developmental problem due to a disorder that may recur but can be prevented? For example, is mental retardation due to fetal alcohol syndrome, lead poisoning, or a chromosomal disorder?

Third, are there medical problems caused by or associated with the developmental disorder, in which medical diagnosis and treatment may have an impact on developmental function? For example, feeding and growth disorders are common in persons with severe disabilities.

Finally, what do the parents perceive as the cause for their child's problem? Even if no definitive treatment or prevention exists, a proper medical diagnosis can provide a measure of reassurance to parents who previously bore the burden of misdirected blame.

An Illustrative Case

Mr. and Mrs. Smith were first concerned about their son Joe when he was a toddler. He learned to sit and crawl at the appropriate times during his 1st year, but always seemed a little unsteady. He walked at age 14 months but was slow and unstable. He could not run without falling even at age 24 months. A neurological evaluation at that time led to a diagnosis of congenital ataxia and was said to be of no great significance. There was no identifiable cause, as he had been a healthy newborn following an uncomplicated pregnancy and delivery. Joe was a slow feeder and grew poorly at first, but he seemed to lose this problem by 12 months of age.

His parents were reassured by his progress over the next 6 years. He was a happy, manageable child who received satisfactory marks in kindergarten and 1st grade. By the end of 2nd grade, Joe's teacher noticed a decrease in attention span and an inability to complete assignments. Instructions had to be repeated and made simpler for him. Educational and psychological testing at age 8 years showed variable intelligence in the normal range and academic underachievement, leading to a diagnosis of learning disability. Despite receiving professional educational assistance and constant support from a very concerned and stable family, his academic performance deteriorated. Joe was highly distractible, emotionally labile, impulsive, and seemingly unable to carry on a conversation with family or friends. (In retrospect, his parents admit that other subtle changes occurred between ages 10 and 12 years, including slurred speech, a slow shuffling gait, worsened fine motor coordination and less legible writing.)

Joe's parents sought professional help and were advised that the behavior changes and school problems were due to a combination of poor motivation, a primary emotional disorder, and his learning disability. They spent many years searching their consciences for the cause, and dutifully took him to a counselor.

By age 16, Joe's motor impairment had worsened, an eye movement disorder had become apparent, his thinking and memory had worsened, and his emotional characteristics became dull and restricted. Repeat IQ testing resulted in scores scattered over the borderline range. Joe was placed in an adult vocational rehabilitation center. Meanwhile, his parents despaired as they watched one of his two older brothers begin to show the same problems. The teachers and psychologists were equally baffled. Finally, the parents sought expert neurological and multidisciplinary developmental evaluation, which led to the diagnosis of a neurodegenerative lipid storage disease.

Their response to this diagnosis was a mixture of dismay and relief. They knew that the degenerative process would continue slowly over many years, ending in death. However, knowledge of its cause allowed them to marshall their resources and support each other through the difficult times. They were greatly relieved by the genetic counseling that reassured them that their oldest son was unlikely to develop the disease or to pass it on to his children.

This case demonstrates the importance of continual neurodevelopmental monitoring of children with minor developmental dysfunction. Because neurodegenerative disease is very uncommon, it frequently is dismissed in its early stages. Appropriate parent counseling must be able to encompass questions of medical etiology. A more timely medical evaluation in this case might have saved this family years of guilt and self-blame.

Summary

The developmental pediatrician is an integrator of genetics, medicine, and neurology, all of which contibutes to major etiologies of developmental disabilities. He or she recognizes: 1) the strengths of the medical model in establishing priorities for the known and treatable causes of developmental disabilities, and in devising strategies for prevention; 2) the limitations of the medical model, especially in areas of incomplete and unknown information; 3) the value of rehabilitation and habilitation strategies in the management of chronic handicaps; 4) the untapped power of parents in promoting self-esteem and coping behaviors; and 5) the strengths of multidisciplinary teams, consisting of medical, rehabilitation, behavior and psychological and educational specialists.

The role of the developmental pediatrician is to assist the multidisciplinary team in unifying both medical and educational strategies so that a picture of the whole child is maintained. With this perspective, long-term advocacy for the child and support to the parents is possible.

CONDITIONS FREQUENTLY ASSESSED
BY THE DEVELOPMENTAL PEDIATRICIAN

Children come to the attention of a developmental pediatrician by a variety of routes, which may be divided into three major groups (see Table 7.1). First are those children with medical diagnoses known to have a high incidence of handicaps, such as Down syndrome. Second are children with medical disorders that carry a high risk of handicap, such as birth asphyxia, but whose development to date may or may not be abnormal. Third are children with no previous medical diagnosis but whose parents suspect a primary problem with development. The pediatrician in each case links his or her knowledge of the medical disorder with his or her knowledge of the developmental disorder. A systematic review of these medical-developmental correlations can be accomplished through the use of an etiological classification system.

A variety of such classification systems have been developed for both diagnostic and research purposes. The first approach is to classify by severity of mental retardation. For example, Penrose (1963) demonstrates that in children with IQs below 55, biological insults operating on the central nervous system are much more likely to occur than in children with IQs above 55. Several authors have stressed a second approach of determining the most likely timing of insult to the developing nervous system, that is by classifying the dysfunction as prenatal or congenital, perinatal, postnatal, mixed, and unknown (Crocker, 1983; Gustavson, 1977; Opitz, 1980). Smith (1975) offers a third approach. He emphasizes the importance of determining the age of onset of the developmental dysfunction in concert with identifying major organ malformations, such as congenital cyanotic heart disease and patterns of clustered minor malformations, such as an unusual facial appearance or abnormal palmar creases. (For an in-depth review of much of the research, see Freeman [1985]) For purposes of further discussion, the following classi-

Table 7.1. Referral patterns for developmental pediatricians

Reason for referral	Example
1. Medical diagnosis with known handicapping effects	Down syndrome; hereditary deafness
2. Medical diagnosis with increased risk for handicap	Prematurity; birth asphyxia; traumatic coma
3. Healthy child with a primary developmental complaint	Child who is slow to walk, slow to talk, or not learning in school

fication is considered: 1) congenital genetic and nongenetic disorders, 2) perinatal and postnatal disorders, and 3) at-risk conditions (see Table 7.2 and Table 7.3). The assessment techniques needed to use this classification are discussed at length in subsequent sections of this chapter.

Congenital Disorders

In a congenital disorder there has been some biological disturbance present at birth that in some way reflects alteration of the developmental potential *in utero*. The disturbance may be genetic or nongenetic. Genetic disorders are caused by a defect in the arrangement or translation of genetic information. This may result in a chromosomal disorder, a single biochemical defect (inborn error of metabolism) or errors in major organ system development (errors in morphogenesis, such as DiGeorge syndrome). The chromosomal disorder is a variation from the normal number (46) of chromosomes present in each cell. Multiple internal systems as well as appearance are affected, as in Down syndrome (trisomy 21). An inborn error of metabolism is a specific aberration in a single metabolic pathway that produces toxic products or deficiencies in necessary products. Often a specific enzyme is missing due to improper genetic coding, but chromosomes look normal.

Congenital syndromes are also caused by nongenetic biological disturbances. These include: gestational disorders such as maternal hemorrhage,

Table 7.2. Classification of causes of mental retardation

Cause	Classic example or result
A. Congenital syndromes, genetic	
1. Chromosomal	Down syndrome
2. Single gene defect	Phenylketonuria (PKU)
3. Major malformations	Spina bifida
4. Presumed genetic	Isolated familial mental retardation
B. Congentital syndromes, nongenetic	
1. Intrauterine infection	Congenital rubella
2. Maternal systemic disease	Maternal diabetes
3. Maternal drug ingestions	Fetal alcohol syndrome
4. Maternal gestational disorders	Low birth weight infant because of preeclampsia
C. Perinatal and postnatal disorders	
1. Prematurity and its complications	<1,000 grams birth weight
2. Birth asphyxia	Apgar less than 3 at 10 minutes
3. Head trauma	8-year-old hit by car
4. Central nervous system infection	Herpes encephalitis
5. Toxins	Acute lead poisoning
6. Hypoxic events	Near drowning
7. Chronic severe systemic disease	Chronic lung disease
D. Unknown	50% of children with mental retardation

Table 7.3. Conditions related to increased risk for mental retardation or learning disabilities

A. Neonatal problems
   1. Birth weight below 1,500 grams
   2. Premature infants with severe medical complications
   3. Severe birth asphyxia
   4. Small-for-gestational-age infants
   5. Neonatal meningitis

B. Severe chronic medical diseases
   1. Failure to thrive in infancy
   2. Congenital cyanotic heart disease
   3. Chronic renal failure in infancy
   4. Childhood leukemia
   5. Chronic lung disease

C. Severe episodic diseases affecting the central nervous system
   1. Traumatic coma
   2. Coma of non-traumatic origin, (e.g., Reye's syndrome)
   3. Bacterial meningitis
   4. Lead poisoning

D. Developmental disorders
   1. Minor or transient motor disorders in infancy
   2. Cerebral palsy
   3. Preschool language disorder

E. Severe environmental and social disturbances
   1. Child abuse and neglect
   2. Major psychiatric disorder or substance abuse in parents

F. Genetic
   1. Mental retardation in parents
   2. Familial reading disability
   3. Sex chromosome disorders: Turner's syndrome (monosomy X); Klinefelter's syndrome
   4. Malformation syndromes: cerebral gigantism; Prader-Willi syndrome; spina bifida; congenital heart disease
   5. Single gene disorders: Duchenne muscular dystrophy; Marfan syndrome; homocystinuria; neurofibromatosis

which compromises fetal development; intrauterine infections such as rubella; maternal drug or alcohol ingestion, the latter of which may result in fetal alcohol syndrome; and maternal diseases that have a direct impact on the developing fetus, such as maternal diabetes. Often, the only sign of a maternal or fetal disorder at birth is an infant who is small for gestational age.

Fetal Alcohol Syndrome: An Illustrative Case A two-year-old white male was referred for growth failure and developmental delay. He weighed 2,300 grams at birth, small for a full-term gestation. His mother's pregnancy was complicated by significant ethanol exposure during the first trimester. Additional maternal stresses included depression, primarily caused by the death of her father, for which an unknown tranquilizer was prescribed, as well as numerous psychosocial stresses due to the infant's father's exposure to heroin addiction. The woman did not know she was pregnant until the third month and denied any alcohol, drugs, or radiation after that.

At birth the infant had microcephaly (small head), decreased weight and decreased linear growth, eye movement problems, and congenital dislocation of the hip. Appropriate medical and surgical care was obtained. During the first 3 months of life, difficult feeding and poor growth continued. Laboratory assessment included a skull X ray and blood and urine tests, which revealed no signs of congenital viral infection.

The gross motor skill of walking developed near normally (at age 14 months). Receptive language was significantly delayed. At the age of 2 years he was not speaking in phrases or sentences. His mother was concerned about frequent episodes of otitis media (inflammation of the middle ear), which seemed to occur monthly.

Family history revealed alcohol abuse and learning disabilities on both the maternal and paternal sides of the family. The maternal and paternal grandparents were alcoholics. The boy's mother exhibited learning difficulties and poor attention during her elementary school years and never finished high school. Her 9-year-old daughter was considered to have a learning disability.

A physical examination of the child showed facial and extremity dysmorphic (atypical-appearing) features. These minor malformations included small eye openings, increased distance from nose to lips, and small hands and feet. In addition, abnormal patterns of hand and finger crease were noted. Other findings included microcephaly, crossed eyes, and low eyelids. The developmental exam revealed clumsiness, language delays, and fine motor delays. Observation of the child's behavior revealed marked hyperactivity and distractibility.

This pattern of abnormalities was found to be most consistent with fetal alcohol syndrome (cf. Claren & Smith, 1978). Classic chromosome deletions were ruled out by appropriate genetic studies. Subsequent developmental diagnoses included mild to moderate mental retardation, attention deficit disorder with hyperactivity, and minor motor dysfunction, characterized as clumsiness.

Additional Congenital Disorders   Other infants whose malformations are obvious in the newborn period include those with spina bifida (incompletely enclosed spinal cord), congenital heart disease, and head and facial malformations. Children with spina bifida require comprehensive medical teams that include neurosurgeons, orthopedic surgeons, urologists, and physical therapists. Children with congenital heart disease need cardiac surgeons, cardiologists, skilled laboratory personnel, and nutritionists. Children with craniofacial abnormalities, including cleft lip and palate, need teams of otolaryngologists, plastic surgeons, audiologists, and dentists.

In addition to facilitating the coordination of medical services for these children, the developmental pediatrician monitors the developmental progress of both the child and the family. Initially, this may involve clarifying the genetic implications of a specific malformation. Other issues include helping a family cope with the myriad of specialists or providing a forum so that the stresses of prolonged hospitalization on the child and the family can be addressed.

Over time, the developmental pediatrician monitors the developmental impact of these conditions and coordinates appropriate habilitative services. Frequently, these may be underemphasized as attention focuses on the obvious handicap. For example, it is not unusual for parents to focus on motor deficits in a child with cerebral palsy and ignore the less obvious handicap of learning disability. Children with spina bifida often have significant difficulties caused by either learning disabilities or cognitive impairment. Children with congenital heart disease may have hemiparetic cerebral palsy, attention deficit disorder, or learning disabilities. Children with cleft lip and palate may have communication disorders or conductive hearing impairments. It is the responsibility of the developmental pediatrician to understand the complexities of such conditions and, by doing so, facilitate their management.

DiGeorge Syndrome: An Illustrative Case A 4-month-old white male was referred for poor feeding and developmental delay. He was carried full-term and weighed 3,500 grams at birth. His mother's pregnancy, labor, and delivery were uncomplicated. In the delivery room, dysmorphic features involving the face, neck, and fingers were noted. A heart murmur was accompanied by signs of congestive heart failure. Referral to a specialty care center established the diagnosis of significant congenital heart disease, and open heart surgery was performed. The combination of facial and neck dysmorphic features and heart defect alerted the pediatrician to the diagnosis of DiGeorge syndrome (Kelly et al., 1982). Medical problems associated with this disorder include endocrine deficiencies with seizures, irregular heartbeat, and muscular problems. Some individuals may also have a chromosomal disorder.

Postoperatively this child had several complications including prolonged cardiopulmonary arrest, persistent seizures, and systemic infection, which required a 3-month stay in an intensive care unit. At age 4 months, head circumference was at a 1-month level, weight at a 2-week level, and length at a 2-month level. A neurological exam revealed a facial diplegia (bilateral weakness) and motor delays with left-right asymmetry. Visual abilities were at a 3- to 4-month level and auditory abilities were at a 1-month level. An oral-motor evaluation revealed a difficulty with sustained sucking. Tube feedings were required to maintain nutritional status. In addition, motor delays compromised ease of handling by the parents and nursing staff. Poor positioning resulted in further difficulties with feeding.

The child was seen by a multidisciplinary team that included a physical therapist, an occupational therapist, an audiologist, a psychologist, and a developmental pediatrician. They collaborated to devise a feeding and positioning protocol. Over the next month, head circumference began to approach that of a normal 2-month-old child. Weight and length significantly improved and the infant was able to take 2–3 ounces of formula by nipple. A follow-up evaluation at age 9 months revealed continued growth and developmental progress. Testing of brain stem evoked responses revealed no significant auditory abnormalities.

The approach by a multidisciplinary developmental team with specialty experience in children with motor and physical handicaps resulted in easier feeding, handling, and parental management.

Perinatal and Postnatal Disorders

Perinatal and postnatal disorders constitute a very heterogeneous group. Perinatal disturbances refer to problems occurring between birth and 7 days of age, and usually relate to the birth process itself. They include prematurity and all its complications, birth asphyxia, birth injury, and neonatal meningitis. A variety of disorders acquired postnatally (i.e., after 7 days of age) also adversely affect development and may directly involve the child's brain function and behavior. The more common postnatal disorders include head injury, brain infections, hydrocephalus (often acquired from meningitis or bleeding into the brain), hypoxic events (reduction of oxygen), or exposure to toxins. They can be genetically caused, such as phenylketonuria (PKU), or caused environmentally, as in lead poisoning. In addition, there may be postnatal systemic diseases such as malnutrition and failure to thrive, chronic lung disease, or chronic renal disease that indirectly affect the central nervous system.

Genetic Toxin: An Illustrative Case   A 3-year-old girl was referred for consultation because of recurrent vomiting, poor growth, and behavior problems. She weighed 2,900 grams at birth, after a full-term pregnancy. During her first year of life, she was a poor feeder and required three hospitalizations for vomiting, somnolence, and dehydration. Her symptoms always improved with intravenous fluids. The girl's mother noted that the child seemed to prefer low-protein foods, such as fruits and potatoes. At age 16 months, she had an episode of vomiting and lethargy preceded by unsteadiness, shakiness, slurred speech and behavior changes, which included biting, pulling her hair, banging her head, and screaming. Excessive sleep alternated with nocturnal restlessness. A diagnosis of complex partial seizures was entertained and appropriate anticonvulsants were initiated but the symptoms remained. She was hospitalized and again improved with intravenous fluids.

Beginning at 3 years of age, vomiting occurred after meals. At the age of 3½ years, she was readmitted to the hospital for severe lethargy, hyperactivity, and bizarre behavior. The full family history was obtained, which revealed that the mother had 3 maternal half-siblings who died of encephalopathy during childhood. A maternal great-aunt also died at 12 years of age of encephalopathy.

A physical exam revealed progressive growth failure with even head growth less than the fifth-percentile level. A neurological exam revealed clumsiness. Developmental assessments revealed receptive and expressive language delays, and a Stanford-Binet IQ score of 65. Because of recurrent symptoms, failure to thrive, and neurological signs in conjunction with the family history of several deaths due to neurological disease in childhood, metabolic investigations were performed. Additional consultation with the National Institute of Health Genetics Center resulted in genetic studies of family members. The mother was found to be a carrier of a rare enzyme deficiency disorder, while her sister was normal. Following diagnosis, the child was placed on a special diet, and over the next 6 months no further episodes of bizarre behavior or somnolence occurred. Her Stanford-Binet IQ score increased from 65 to 85.

This case highlights several problems a developmental pediatrician encounters, his or her tools of analysis and his or her use of the laboratory and subspecialty consultation. A pattern of cyclical feeding problems, progressive growth problems, and episodic central nervous system irritability were inconsistent with the more common diagnoses of colic, rumination, and impaired maternal-child interaction. Because high suspicion of organic etiology was maintained, there was selective appropriate use of the laboratory and genetic consultation. Growth, behavior, and developmental improvements followed institution of specific medical therapy.

Conditions Related to Increased Risk for Learning Disabilities or Mental Retardation

Children at risk for developmental disabilities may be defined as those who have experienced the occurrence of any biomedical disturbance or serious environmental deficit that has been shown to be associated with an increased incidence of handicap. The list of risk factors has grown exponentially as medical knowledge and treatment techniques have advanced. For example, survivors of childhood leukemia whose therapy included irradiation of the brain plus a high dose of chemotherapy were found to have cognitive deficits when compared to population norms (Whitt, 1984). In a parallel trend, a growing awareness of child abuse and neglect has been accompanied by an increased concern for the developmental impact of these "social diseases" (Oates, 1984). Perhaps, however, the most telling and reliable risk factors are themselves developmental in nature. Prospective studies of developmental abnormalities in preschoolers, such as mild gross motor abnormalities or language disorders, have defined clearly increased risks for cognitive and learning impairments (Rubin, 1980; Stark, 1984).

An exhaustive listing of the conditions associated with increased risk for developmental disabilities is beyond the scope of this chapter. However, a general list is given in Table 7.3.

Although biomedical diagnosis is a critical element of developmental assessment, its limitations need to be kept in mind by the developmental pediatrician. First, identification of a specific etiology is not sufficient to predict the child's developmental status. For example, infants with a certain congenital virus infection eventually may have multiple and severe handicaps, or may have normal intelligence with a learning disability (Hanshaw & Dudgeon, 1978). Second, an adverse perinatal factor, such as birth weight under 1,000 grams or severely depressed Apgar (newborn rating scale) scores, does not predict with great accuracy the future occurrence of any specific handicap (Freeman, 1985). They define risk categories that help guide monitoring efforts and maximize early identification and intervention. For example, the premature population has a high incidence of nearsightedness, and survivors of bacterial meningitis have an increased incidence of acquired hearing loss and learning disabilities. Systematic screening and early treatment for sensory impairments in these populations can minimize their effects on development. Finally, there are many children in whom a specific biomedical factor cannot be identified as either a definite or a suspected cause of problems. Even in these cases, parents derive reassurance from the knowledge that treatable and preventable causes have been examined and ruled out.

Neonatal Factors Advances in neonatal care have rapidly improved the survival of critically ill infants (Hack, 1979). In 1960, the lower limit of viability for premature infants was a birth weight of 1,000 grams. In 1985, this figure is 500 grams. Severe asphyxia carried a mortality rate of 40% in the early 1970s, and in 1985 it is below 5%. Similar trends in survival may be seen in infants with life-threatening birth defects or major malformations, such as congenital heart disease. Improved survival has been the result of more aggressive and intensive therapeutic technology, such as mechanical ventilation, meticulous biochemical monitoring, and prolonged intravenous nutrition.

Often these infants are hospitalized in intensive care settings for many weeks. They are susceptible to life-threatening biological disturbances that may directly affect the developing nervous system. These disturbances occur at a time when the brain's built-in protective mechanisms are immature or are rendered dysfunctional by a disease process. The sick neonate by necessity must experience procedures and an environment that differ radically from a normal home in terms of sensory input (such as light and sound), feeding routines, sleep-wake cycles, and mother-infant relationships. Although these issues are of secondary importance in the intensive care unit as compared to life-and-death problems, their influence on developmental outcome deserves further exploration.

What then are the trends in the developmental outcomes for high-risk neonates? Table 7.4 gives ranges for major disabilities (mental retardation and cerebral palsy) and for minor disabilities (language disorders, learning dis-

Table 7.4. Developmental outcomes for survivors of neonatal intensive care

Classification	Percentage of incidence of disability	
	Major[a]	Minor[b]
Premature births		
birth weight <1,500 grams	4% (2%–15%)	10%–30%
birth weight <1,000 grams	10% (2%–15%)	?
birth weight < 750 grams	18% (6%–26%)	?
Asphyxial brain damage		
mild	0%–5%	20%–25%
severe	60%–85%	10%–35%
Small for gestational age[c]	2%–100%	30%–40%
(Reference population: Individuals in the community with developmental disabilities	0.5%–2%	5%–15%)

Data derived from a variety of studies (Allen, 1984; Drillien, 1980; Finer, 1981; Fitzhardinge, 1981; Stewart, 1981) and given here as an average and range.
[a]Mental retardation with IQ <70 and/or cerebral palsy.
[b]Learning disabilities, language disorders, behavior problems, and clumsiness.
[c]Incidence of handicap for these infants depends on cause of growth failure (see Table 7.5).

abilities, behavior problems and clumsiness) in neonates according to their predominant neonatal classification. Several points deserve emphasis. The vast majority of premature survivors of neonatal intensive care have no disability (Fitzhardinge, 1981). Furthermore, the premature infants who have disability account for probably no more than 10% or 20% of all persons with major handicaps. Also, the incidence of mild disabilities among premature infants, particularly learning disabilities, has not been well defined (Drillien, 1980; Stewart, 1981). As illustrated in the table, the incidence of mental retardation and cerebral palsy in premature infants increases as birth weight decreases, particularly below 750 grams. However, in over 80% of these infants, no major handicap is present.

In infants who are small-for-gestational-age (SGA), the outcome is highly dependent on the cause for their growth retardation (see Table 7.5; for additional information, see Allen, 1984). The outcome for full-term asphyxiated neonates covers a wide spectrum that correlates roughly with the severity of disturbed brain function (asphyxial brain damage) apparent in the postnatal period (Finer, 1981). The incidence of mental retardation and cerebral palsy ranges from a low of 0%–5% in mild neonatal asphyxial brain damage to 60%–85% in the most severe cases.

Monitoring the developmental outcome for high-risk neonates begins in the nursery, and requires selective use of multidisciplinary assessment and treatment services. First, the neonatal staff members identify high-risk infants

Table 7.5. Some causes of intrauterine growth retardation associated with very high risk for disability

Cause	Example
Chromosomal disorder	Trisomy 18
Maternal disease	Phenylketonuria (PKU)
Intrauterine infection	Rubella
Maternal ingestion	Alcohol

in terms of their neonatal disorders. Second, a neonatal neurodevelopmental examination leads to a classification of each infant as part of a normal, suspect, or definitely abnormal group at the time of discharge. Subsequent monitoring should be individually tailored to take into account the severity of the risk factors, the neonatal neurodevelopmental exam, whether an active chronic disease exists, and the family's need for support and information (see Table 7.6).

The infant with less severe risk factors and a normal discharge exam may be monitored by the primary care pediatrician at each well baby checkup. This should include a careful record of developmental milestone attainment and a neurodevelopmental screening examination. When these screenings show abnormalities, referral for definitive developmental assessment is made. A hearing and vision check at 1 year of age should always be included, as these infants have an increased incidence of nearsightedness, strabismus (eye malalignment), and hearing loss, all of which are treatable conditions.

Table 7.6. Monitoring strategies for high-risk neonates

Discharge status	Monitoring strategy
1. High-risk history, normal exam	Hearing and vision tests at age 1 year. Developmental screening with well baby care. Refer for definitive evaluation only as needed.
2. High-risk history, suspect exam	Hearing and vision tests at age 1 year. Developmental screening with well baby care. Definitive evaluation and school programming at age 2 or 3 years if abnormalities persist.
3. High-risk history, definitely abnormal exam	Hearing and vision tests at age 1 year. Specialized developmental monitoring every 3 months, including therapists for ongoing treatment. Ongoing support and information for family.
4. High-risk history, abnormal exam, active chronic disease	Same as #3, plus close linkage with medical care.

In contrast, the infant with multiple high-risk factors and an abnormal discharge exam requires a higher level of monitoring. If the abnormalities have immediate functional implications, therapy may be needed, as in occupational therapy services for an infant with severe oromotor feeding dysfunction. Frequent (every 2–3 months) assessment by a developmental pediatrician and by the most relevant therapists is needed to identify and manage major disabilities at the earliest possible time during the first 2 years of life.

The infant at high risk for disabilities based on history and exam who also has a serious ongoing disease such as chronic lung disease or hydrocephalus should receive intensive developmental monitoring that is closely linked to his or her medical care. Another group needing a more intensive level of monitoring comprises high-risk infants in families with limited coping resources.

An Illustrative Case   A male infant was born 10 weeks premature, weighing 900 grams, to a 17-year-old girl. Because of severe lung disease, he required mechanical ventilation for 6 weeks. At age 3 days, he had a seizure and a sudden drop in blood pressure; he was found to have a brain hemorrhage of moderate severity. He gradually recovered and gained weight slowly, at first with intravenous feedings, then with gastric (stomach) tube feedings. Finally, he was breathing on his own and took all feedings by mouth from a bottle.

At age 3 months, he was big enough and well enough to go home. At that age, his examination showed excessive muscle tone abnormalities in his legs. During frequent developmental follow-ups, he was very slow in learning to sit and never learned to crawl. At age 2 years, he took his first steps, although he was clumsy, stiff, and up on his toes. Finally, at age 3 years, he could walk and run, though he was still clumsy and slow.

Of greater concern to his mother was the fact that he only knew about 50 words, which he only occasionally combined into 2-word sentences. In addition, he was constantly and randomly on the move, highly distractible, and impulsive, and he frequently threw temper tantrums. He entered a preschool language program and subsequently improved in communication functions. Of equal importance was the fact that his mother, who had not completed high school, received frequent guidance about his level of function and also received behavior management suggestions.

At age 6½ years, repeat testing indicated the presence of a learning disability, and led to his placement in an appropriate special education classroom. In the smaller classroom setting with more individualized attention, his learning rate and behavioral adjustment improved. With timely supportive counseling, the boy's young mother, a high school drop-out who came from a chaotic home, was able to cope with her son's behavior, act as his advocate in the educational system, and work toward her own high school equivalency certification.

This case illustrates a common sequence of developmental problems. The initial concerns in the nursery relating to the boy's low birth weight, serious lung disease, and abnormal discharge exam were compounded by his mother's young age, low level of education, and poor family background. However, fears about severely handicapping cerebral palsy could be dismissed by age 2 years. The mild diplegia and language delays present at that time were markers of a mild central nervous system dysfunction, which later declared itself in the form of a learning disability. His mother's coping strategies were continually reinforced with his frequent developmental monitoring visits. She was able to hope for a better future for her son because she knew he received intervention for his disabilities at an early age. This reassurance allowed her the time and energy to invest in her own future.

THE PROCESS OF DEVELOPMENTAL PEDIATRIC ASSESSMENT

The goals of developmental pediatric assessment are to assess the whole child in terms of general health, specific medical conditions, and developmental levels and deficits. This initial assessment allows the developmental pediatrician to act as a coordinator, advocate and principal resource for the family when serving as a case manager, or to answer specific questions for other professionals when serving as an outside consultant. This section describes the developmental pediatrician's general approach, specific developmental assessment techniques, and guidelines for the rational use of laboratory and radiological (X ray) studies.

General Medical Assessment

The developmental pediatrician approaches assessment of the general health and well-being of a child with handicaps in a systematic way, by integrating data from the child's history, the physical exam, and laboratory studies. This process begins with active listening to parental concerns, and involves discriminating colic from organic irritability from infantile spasms. The developmental pediatrician collects information on general health maintenance common to all children; a task often neglected in children with developmental disabilities. These issues include physical growth, diet and nutrition, immunizations, recurrent illnesses, major organ system diseases, and environmental hazards. Particular attention is given to those problems that have a direct impact on behavior and on central nervous system function. In the process of obtaining historical information, it is important to assess continually the parents' knowledge and coping resources, their myths about developmental dysfunction, and their access to health care services.

A physical examination serves to identify specific medical problems, such as hydrocephalus or congenital heart disease. Such a disorder may have an immediate impact on the child's performance in a testing situation, or it may be a treatable cause of the developmental deficits. The physical examination focuses particularly on identifying patterns of major deformations and clusters of minor physical anomalies or dysmorphic features. The analysis of dysmorphic features is in itself a systematic task. It consists of a specific focus on and frequent measurements of the physical appearance of the skull, facial features, external ears, scalp and body hair patterns, hand and foot features, skeletal deformities, and genital anomalies. (Smith [1982] describes this analysis in greater detail and provides age-specific norms.) In the newborn period, the presence of 3 or more minor malformations is accompanied by a 90% chance of major malformation. Major malformations include spinal cord defects, head and facial syndromes, cardiovascular malformations, and major organ lesions requiring surgery. Minor malformations include abnormalities of the hair, eyes, ear, palate, tongue, and extremities.

Accardo (1980) reviews studies in the preschool and older population comparing minor malformation rating scales (stigmata ratings) and the presence of attention deficit disorder, hyperactivity, clumsiness, irritable temperament, and learning disabilities. Accardo (1980) finds a statistically significant correlation between these developmental disorders and stigmata scores in several prospective surveys. Accardo (1980) states, ''These minor malformations thus reflect a specific organic component in disorders of behavior and learning in children, and they can serve as clinical markers for minor deviations in the embryogenesis of the central nervous system.'' Using the data from Waldrop, Bell, McLaughlin, and Halverston (1978), however, he cautions that ''if one uses stigmata scores to screen for behavior and learning problems, there will be few false positives but many false negatives'' (Accardo, 1980).

The general medical assessment also serves to identify medical complications of developmental disorders, whose treatment may lessen the impact of the underlying handicap. (This was illustrated earlier in the case of the child with DiGeorge syndrome.) Since seizures, malnutrition, and recurrent respiratory infections are common in children with multiple handicaps, optimizing their management may have a significant effect on the day-to-day experiences of the child and his or her care-givers. Although the impact of optimal nutrition on long-term brain growth and function remains speculative, there is ample experimental and pathological evidence to indicate a significant effect (Wachtel, 1982).

The Developmental History

As with general medical diagnosis, the developmental pediatric approach to developmental diagnosis involves an understanding of the whole child along a time continuum. This tradition originated with Arnold Gesell, was expanded with Amatruda (Knoblock, 1974), and was elaborated by Ronald Illingworth (1983). Within this approach, the child's development is viewed as a continuous acquisition of progressively more complex behaviors, determined by genetic and biological maturational potential and shaped by the effects of learning and interaction with the environment.

The developmental history forms the basis for developmental diagnosis. It consists of a systematic and meticulous record of the age of attainment of standard developmental milestones in each stream of development. These recorded milestones are compared with the norms for average children and can be converted to a developmental screening instrument and scored (Accardo & Capute, 1978). Particular attention is given to a clear description of the child's current level of functioning, and on areas the parents perceive to be abnormal.

In the average child with average biological potential and an average environment, the acquisition of behaviors follows a predictable sequence at a predictable rate. The behaviors logically cluster into several functional subgroups, or streams of development. Gesell and Amatruda's original subdivision (Knoblock, 1974) includes adaptive (problem solving), gross motor, fine motor, language, and personal-social skills. These developmental "fields" comprise predictable sequences of observable behavior occurring at specific chronological ages in average "normal" children. Over a period of 40 years and more than 10,000 exams, Gesell and his colleagues standardized the sequence and timing of these fields of development. These schedules provide the framework for many neurodevelopmental scales, which emphasize a more systematic standardization.

Gesell's second major contribution was the use of the developmental quotient (DQ) in developmental pediatrics (Knoblock, 1974). A child can be examined and found to possess skills within each field of development that in average children cluster at certain developmental age levels. The ratio of the child's developmental age to his or her chronological age multiplied by 100 is the developmental quotient or DQ; it compares the rate of his or her development in a particular field to that of the average child. For example, suppose a 24-month-old girl has normal gross motor milestones but has only acquired the language skills equivalent to those of an average 12-month-old. Her motor DQ is 100 ($24/24 \times 100 = 100$), while her language DQ is 50 ($12/24 \times 100 = 50$).

The analysis and interpretation of the developmental history has several purposes, all of which relate back to the parents' original questions about their child's developmental diagnosis and prognosis. First, it should accurately describe the specific deficits within each field of development. Second, the pattern of deficits and their severity must be viewed as a whole in order to diagnose the underlying disabling condition, to identify all associated deficits, and to make prognostic statements. The spectrum of neurodevelopmental disabilities includes mental retardation, cerebral palsy, communication disorders, autism, and learning disabilities (Capute & Palmer, 1980). Each dis-

Table 7.7. Dissociation in developmental disabilities: Pattern of DQs[a] in each developmental field

Disability	Gross motor	Fine motor	Language	Problem solving	Personal-social
Mental retardation	nl[b] to del[c]	nl to del	del	del	del
Cerebral palsy	del	del	var[d]	var	var
Communication disorder	nl	nl	del	nl	var
Autism	nl	nl	del	del	del
Learning disabilities	var	var	var	var	var

Source: Expanded from Accardo and Cabute (1978).
[a]Developmental Quotient.
[b]normal.
[c]delay.
[d]variable.

ability has a typical pattern of developmental delays, deviancies, and dissociations in infancy or childhood (Accardo & Caute, 1978). Table 7.7 illustrates the use of dissociation as a key to developmental diagnosis. In learning disabilities, for example, there may be mild delays or deviancies in any developmental field. It is also important to note that behavior problems can occur in concert with any type of developmental disability.

Developmental assessment only begins with establishing the initial diagnosis, as suggested by the information obtained at one point in time from the developmental history. Each developmental diagnosis is a statement of current function and a prediction of future function. It involves assumptions about the stability of both the underlying biological capacities and the environment, which may be more or less substantiated by objective measures. One of the developmental pediatrician's central responsibilities is to monitor the course of the child's development in order to confirm his or her assumptions about the child's biological stability, and to support, where possible, an optimal adjustment between the child's changing needs and his or her environment. If the developmental pediatrician finds an unexpected deterioration in developmental progress, it is his or her unique responsibility to look for biomedical causes such as exposure to toxins, genetically determined metabolic disorders, neurodegenerative conditions, or sensory deficits, any of which may have specific implications for treatment, prognosis, or genetic counseling.

The Neurodevelopmental Examination

The purpose of the neurodevelopmental examination is to provide a comprehensive and objective measure of the integrity of the child's developing brain and his or her behavior. Specifically, it describes each field of development in terms of developmental age level and the deviant patterns present. This information provides a precise and objective basis for the diagnosis first suggested by the developmental history. The process of formulating a diagnosis thus occurs in several stages and requires a synthesis of medical, historical, and neurobehavioral information.

The components of a complete neurodevelopmental examination are best understood in the framework of the major fields of development:

1. Neuromotor status (gross motor and fine motor), including the special senses of vision and hearing
2. Cognitive status, including language and visually based intelligence
3. Social and behavioral status
4. Adaptive function or problem solving (i.e., how all other functions work together to allow the individual to meet basic survival needs and adjust to novel social and environmental circumstances)

Tools of Assessment The specific examination tools used by a developmental pediatrician may vary from one setting to another, and with the age of the particular child. For purposes of definitive assessment, once again, the examination developed by Gesell and Amatruda (Knoblock, 1974) provides the framework for most other comprehensive assessment tools as well as for many screening tools, such as the Denver Developmental Screening Test (Frankenburg, Fondal, & Sciarillo, 1981). Depending on the developmental pediatrician's training and interest and the age of the child to be tested, the developmental pediatrician may combine several tools to assess each field, which he or she synthesizes into an understanding of the whole child. For example, a comprehensive yet practical tool for neonates may be found in the Dubowitz Neonatal Assessment (Dubowitz, 1981). A more focused evaluation of neonatal behavior is available with the Brazelton neonatal exam (Brazelton, 1984). The Reynell language scales (Reynell, 1969) or the Peabody Picture Vocabulary Test–Revised (Dunn & Dunn, 1981) are useful for looking more selectively at language development in preschoolers.

The value of these tools in the hands of a developmental pediatrician is greatly enhanced by his or her participation in a multidisciplinary team, which serves as a source of standardization and precision for more specialized testing. As other chapters in this book deal extensively with cognitive, language, and behavioral assessment, the remainder of this section is devoted to one part of the neurodevelopmental assessment—the neuromotor exam.

The Neuromotor Examination This type of assessment can best be appreciated if the developmental nature of neuromotor function is reviewed. In the normal child, neuromotor maturation follows a predictable sequence that is characterized by several stages. The newborn is dominated by primitive reflexes, flexor tone, and autonomic demands. As he or she approaches 6 months of age, the primitive reflexes are inhibited and replaced by postural control of the neck and trunk, providing a more stable base for voluntary movement. This voluntary movement matures in a head-to-foot direction. Control of the head in relation to visual and auditory sensory inputs paves the way for more complex social interactions and visually directed upper extremity activities between 6 and 12 months. At the same time, mobility evolves from a prone, on all four extremities position to a biped, upright position. This is dependent on mature postural equilibrium responses, efficient weight shifting from one posture to another, and precisely orchestrated movement of individual limbs in coordination with each other. The precise neural mechanisms of this behavioral maturation are not well delineated, but connections are known to occur during the first year of life (Prechtl, 1981).

Components of the Exam   Table 7.8 gives a summary of the components of an expanded neurodevelopmental exam. Included are behavioral state and social awareness, cranial nerve function, special senses, muscle tone and strength, posture and mobility, upper extremity function, balance and coordination (cerebellar function), peripheral sensation, deep tendon reflexes, primitive reflexes, pathological reflexes, and pathological movement patterns.

The classic neurologic exam differs from the neurodevelopmental exam in that it was developed in the setting of acute or discretely localized disorders of the mature brain, such as strokes or tumors. Therefore, when applied to children, it has limited usefulness for understanding the developing brain, particularly in the areas of cognition, behavior, and motor maturation. Chronic disabling conditions of childhood such as mental retardation rarely arise

Table 7.8.   An expanded neurodevelopmental examination

Exam item	Developmental focus
Behavior	Assess level of arousal, activity, and social competence.
Cranial nerves, general	Observe specific localizing signs and oromotor dysfunction.
Cranial nerves, special nerves	Assess vision and hearing, with attention to perceptual maturation.
Gross motor function	Define developmental level and deviancies in posture, mobility, and tone.
Fine motor function	Define developmental levels and deviancies in reach, grasp, and eye-hand movements.
Cerebellar function	Describe abnormalities in balance and coordination.
Peripheral senses	Describe deficits in touch, position sense, and pain (to assist in localizing dysfunction).
Deep tendon reflexes	Describe abnormalities, including pathological reflexes (to assist with localization).
Primitive reflexes	Describe abnormal persistence and localization.
Abnormal movements	Identify presence of chorea, athetosis, and ballismus.

from discrete anatomically localizable lesions such as brain tumors or strokes, but rather from global processes affecting brain growth and function in a diffuse way. In addition, for many neurobehavioral characteristics, abnormality represents a spectrum determined by age-specific norms. For example, a Moro (startle) reflex is perfectly normal in a newborn, but decidedly abnormal if elicited in an 8-month-old. Thus, the developmental pediatrician must have an understanding of the developmental norms for each component of the neurodevelopmental exam.

Formulation of a Diagnosis   Formulation of a neurodevelopmental diagnosis requires interpretation of the exam findings with several key neurological and developmental questions in mind. First, are acute or progressive neurological disorders present that may be subject to specific medical diagnosis or intervention? For example, an expanding intracranial mass, brain infection, hydrocephalus, or seizures requires prompt assessment and treatment by a neurologist.

Second, is there evidence of chronic neuromotor dysfunction? This is shown by delayed motor developmental age, deviant movement patterns, dissociation of gross motor and fine motor developmental levels, or specific pathological signs such as athetosis (repeated, involuntary motions) or abnormal lower extremity posturing.

Third, what is the degree of abnormality? While no single "score" completely describes the motor abnormality, a good estimate can be given in the form of a motor developmental quotient (Capute & Shapiro, 1985). This is calculated from the ratio of motor developmental age to chronological age. The exam then points to specific abnormalities of tone, posture, and reflexes that may be inferred to be predominant factors interfering with motor skill attainment.

Finally, is there a characteristic topography and physiology of motor abnormalities that conforms to a known type of cerebral palsy? While a full discussion of cerebral palsy is beyond the scope of this chapter, it is important to appreciate the high frequency of coexistence between motor and cognitive handicaps. Diagnosis of a specific motor handicap should alert the multidisciplinary team to associated deficits of brain function, such as attention deficit disorder and learning disability, present in certain kinds of cerebral palsy. Children with mild degrees of neuromotor dysfunction as infants and toddlers frequently outgrow their motor disorder, but they do not always outgrow their brain dysfunction (Nelson & Ellenberg, 1982). Many go on to have learning and behavior disorders, the impact of which may be ameliorated by prompt identification and management (Drillien, 1979).

Predictive Value of Developmental Assessment

Illingworth (1961) challenges the commonly stated view, proposed by Bayley (1933), that developmental tests in infancy have no predictive value. He points out that a predictive value appears to be absent because psychologists study a select population (i.e., they exclude children with mental retardation). In an initial study of all infants seen in a child health department, 122 infants without obvious cause of mental retardation such as Down syndrome, hydrocephalus, or congenital hypothyroidism were diagnosed in their 1st year as having mental retardation. Of the 122 infants, 58 were diagnosed prior to 6 months of age; 64 were diagnosed between the ages of 7 and 12 months. Overall, 75% of the children identified as having mental handicaps and 80% of those identified as not having mental handicaps remained so, respectively. In a subsequent study of 230 children who were assessed at 6 months (if the results were doubtful, they were reassessed at 10 months), 30% were considered to have mental retardation. Overall sensitivity and specificity for predicting mental retardation at 7–8 years was 76%, with the predictive value of a positive test being 27.5% (Illingworth, 1971).

Early Detection of Visual Impairment

A key area of concern for all children, especially those with handicaps, is early detection of visual impairment. (See Lobovits [1982] for a review of the principles of visual screening in general pediatric practice and Scheiner and Moomaw [1982] for a discussion of aspects of severe visual impairment and other handicaps.) The role of the developmental pediatrician in vision assessment is to detect amblyopia (failure to develop depth perception), strabismus (deviation of the eye inward or outward), and refractive errors (lack of sharpness of vision) so that early referral to a pediatric opthalmologist can be made. Tests to detect these conditions can be subdivided into examinations for visual acuity, ocular alignment, and stereopsis (3-dimensional vision).

Available instruments for use with children under age 6 years include the Stycar screening test (Sheridan, 1973), Allen Picture Cards (Allen, 1957), and the Illiterate Single E. All three tests have excellent consistency of response and can be administered by the developmental pediatrician in an office setting (Scheiner & Moomaw, 1982). The major advantage of the Stycar over the Illiterate E is that the Stycar has an untestable rate of less than 8% compared to 13% for the Illiterate E when administered at a distance of 10 feet (Lobovits, 1982). The other advantage of the Stycar is that different tests are available for different ages, including children under the age of 2 years.

Methods for detecting strabismus include the cover and cover/uncover test, and the Hirschberg method, also known as the corneal light reflex tests. In the cover and cover/uncover test, the child fixes his or her eyes on an object, and while one eye is covered, the uncovered eye is observed for movement. Observation is made to determine if there is lateral or medial deviation of the eyes. The Hirschberg method involves shining a pen flashlight on each eye and examining the symmetry of light reflected on each cornea. Although all tests for strabismus have not been tested for sensitivity and specificity (Lobovits, 1982), that is not of major importance to the developmental pediatrician. As previously stated, his or her goal is only to detect visual deprivation so that proper opthalmological consultation and monitoring may be undertaken.

Use of the Laboratory in the
Developmental Pediatric Assessment Process

Analysis of the Family History Mental retardation is a developmental diagnosis and often a symptom of developmental dysfunction of the developing nervous system (see Chapter 1). Perhaps in no other instance in clinical medicine is the importance of systematically pursuing a diagnostic work-up more essential. A three-generation family history concentrating on similar developmental problems in other family members, and on instances of miscarriages, stillbirths, and unexplained infant death is extremely valuable. Prior to the initiation of laboratory studies, analysis of the family history gives supportive evidence for genetic etiologies and reveals specific patterns of inheritance that may imply a specific diagnosis. Also, since certain disorders follow a specific pattern (e.g., in some disorders, males are significantly symptomatic and females are carriers but can also be symptomatic), by use of family history analysis, recurrent unexplained family tragedies can be distinguished. Other information of importance in a family history is parental age, ethnicity, and consanguinity. The greatest value of analyzing a family history lies in helping determine etiology, but another is establishing recurrence risks.

Selection of Laboratory Procedures Opitz (1980) and colleagues attempt to develop a rational protocol for selecting laboratory procedures for children with mental retardation by stressing the importance of age of onset of the condition. Smith (1975) emphasizes the importance of the presence of major malformations or clusters of minor malformations as adding additional power to the factor of age of onset. By combining these approaches, significant mental retardation can be categorized as occurring in six ways: 1) prenatal with major malformations; 2) prenatal with central nervous system malformations or central nervous system dysfunctions such as seizures; 3) perinatal; 4) postnatal; 5) mixed; and 6) unknown.

An example of "mixed" is provided by the following case description. An infant with microcephaly and an abnormal fundoscopic (internal eye) exam who was small for gestational age had seizures and apnea during an episode of severe hypoglycemia. The child's mother was single, 14-years-old, and had dropped out of school. A laboratory evaluation of the child revealed evidence of CNS (central nervous system) viral illness. In this case, the cause of developmental disability was mixed, in that prenatal, perinatal, and postnatal environmental factors were operative.

Numerous studies have documented that routine, nonselective tests, such as multichannel chemistries, skull X rays, EEGs, and CT scans are often unnecessary (Lewis & Freeman, 1977; Ling, Sundara, Read, & Holland, 1982; Opitz, 1980; Smith, 1975). The authors recommend a systematic approach that combines age of onset, tempo (acute or chronic), organ systems involved, neurological systems involved, and family history analysis. There is no one type of lab test that is routine in any developmental disorder; all tests must be individualized to the specific child and situation. Therefore, the developmental pediatrician serves as a crucial link between patient, subspecialist, and a rational, individualized use of the laboratory.

Chromosomal Studies The link between family history analysis, physical examination, and use of the laboratory is well exemplified in the area of chromosomal studies. Overall abnormalities of chromosome number have a significant medical impact. Fifteen percent of persons with mental retardation who have IQ scores of less than 55 and 33% of institutionalized individuals with mental retardation have chromosomal abnormalities (Laxova, Ridler, & Bowen-Bravery, 1977). Maternal age, history of previous fetal wastage, intrauterine growth retardation, decreased fetal activity, and breech presentation are family history factors that are frequently associated with chromosomal anomalies. Important physical findings associated with chromosomal abnormalities include clustering of dysmorphic features, cardiac malformations, microcephaly, and continued growth deficiency.

For the developmental pediatrician, the fragile-X syndrome (a type of X-linked mental retardation) exemplifies the relationship between family history, physical examination, and advances in the cytogenetics laboratory (Hagerman, McBogg, & Hagerman, 1983). The developmental consequences of this disorder include mental retardation, attention deficit disorder, self-injurious behavior, seizures, and autism.

Screening Efforts Some of the major advances in laboratory evaluation have been in the development of strategies to prevent mental retardation by detecting conditons prior to the onset of symptoms and in the devising of treatment strategies to prevent or modify the adverse effect on the nervous system. The outstanding example of this effort is phenylketonuria (PKU) screening. Prior to discharge from the hospital, newborns are given a blood test that detects the presence of excessive phenylalanine, an amino acid. An excessive amount of phenylalanine is an indication of PKU. Prompt definitive testing and initiation of a special diet following such testing can reduce the incidence of retardation.

Health professionals must be aware of current screening efforts in their states and the support program necessary to implement them and to maintain a high degree of quality control. It cannot be overemphasized that abnormalities detected by screening need prompt evaluation and confirmation. In addition, the absence of a positive indicator from a screening should not preclude the possiblity of missed cases, variants, or other metabolic conditons that can cause mental retardation.

The Role of the Developmental Pediatrician in the Assessment of Learning Disabilities

So far, this chapter has concentrated on the developmental pediatrician's role in caring for children with mental retardation or for at risk children, who typically come to his or her attention before age 5 years. There is also a great demand for pediatric involvement in children with a lesser degree of neurodevelopmental dysfunction. Typically, these children come to the attention of the developmental pediatrician because of behavior problems or school failure between ages 5 and 10 years.

The disorders within this group are varied; they are sometimes referred to as the "high prevalence–low severity" handicapping conditions of childhood (Levine, 1982). In planning assessment of and intervention for this group of conditions, several points must be kept in mind. First, it is the most common type of childhood disability, with an estimated prevalence of 10%–15% in school-age children. Second, it is very heterogeneous in how it is shown clinically and in its etiologies. Third, although customarily considered a mild handicap, it can nonetheless be a lifelong burden for the individual and the family. Its cumulative impact, in many cases, may take on major proportions.

Perhaps the best early identification strategy for those with low severity handicaps combines historical factors, parent concerns, and screening instruments. Thus, early detection consists of identifying children with etiological risk factors, monitoring their neurodevelopmental progress for evidence of mild delays and deviancies in language and motor skills, and continually assessing their behavioral adaptation to their social environment. Early management concentrates on habilitation of language disorders and appropriate behavior intervention in order to optimize the child's social development and support his or her family's adjustment.

The physical exam and neurodevelopmental exam for the child with learning disability focus on the plotting of growth, visual and auditory assessment, the documentation of minor anomalies, the detection of chronic health impairments, the recording of soft neurological signs (neuromaturational assessment), and developmental assessment. Tools used by the developmental pediatrician include observations of perceptual tasks, assessment of language functioning, tests of memory, and educational instruments. Levine (1982) and colleagues have developed five standardized neurodevelopmental batteries for use by physicians in the assessment of learning and behavior problems in children. Each battery tests a specific age group within the range of 3 years to adolescence. These instruments describe areas of children's strengths and weaknesses, and subcategorize children by the processes involved (attention deficit disorder, visual-spatial disorganizing, temporal-sequential disorganization, language disability, and developmental output failure).

As for children with mental retardation, judicious use of the laboratory is in order. For the child with learning disabilities, chromosomal studies, EEGs, cranial X rays, and routine blood and urine tests are rarely definitive and may add unnecessary expense to a nonfocused search for medical etiologies.

INDICATIONS FOR REFERRAL
TO A DEVELOPMENTAL PEDIATRICIAN

The developmental pediatrician is able to provide considerable assistance in the assessment and postassessment management of a wide range of childhood disorders. The strengths of the specialty rest in its integration of pediatric medicine, developmental diagnosis, and treatment with psychosocial awareness. In order to assist the nonphysician members of a multidisciplinary team in their use of developmental pediatricians, the following parameters are presented as representing especially appropriate indicators for referral. The boundaries can be extended substantially, depending on variations in professional interests and in training focus.

A child whose history indicates an at-risk experience in conjunction with poor school performance should be referred to the developmental pediatrician. This includes the child with a history of premature birth, the child with perinatal complications that are problematic in appearance, and the child with the history of central nervous system insults or trauma.

Although mental retardation cannot be attributed to a specific cause in many cases, previously uninvestigated retardation warrants a consultation to a developmental pediatrician with access to the latest in diagnostic procedures. Also, the undiagnosed child with delayed developmental milestones should be referred. This includes a child who may be slow to walk or talk, or whose educational or psychological testing indicates substantial delay or retardation.

Hall and Jolly (1984) have developed guidelines that instruct nonmedical staff to refer a child for developmental assessment if he or she shows a strong hand preference in the first year, is unable to sit at age 10 months, or is not walking at age 18 months. Also, a child who exhibits persistent throwing of objects beyond age 2 years, is not using words at age 2 years, does not join words at age 3 years, or is unintelligible to strangers at age 4 years needs medical assessment to investigate these problem areas.

In the case of atypical language development, subsequent communication and audiology assessment is usually advised. With respect to sensory impairments, a child who has unilateral squint, crossed eyes, or a diminished response to sound at any age warrants prompt assessment.

Finally, the presence of indicators of hereditary problems or suspected dysmorphologies calls for a referral. In such cases, the developmental pediatrician can make a substantial contribution.

In conclusion, the role of the developmental pediatrician is not to see a single risk factor, a single physical exam, a single neurological sign, or a single lab test as the "gold standard" of disability. The developmental pediatrician realizes that much is unknown. Even in known conditions, the complexity of development continues to be as much an art as a science of medicine. The developmental pediatrician is aware of the humanist tradition of pediatrics: the tradition of Seguin, Montessori, and Gesell. The task of the developmental pediatrician is to integrate the biological and social in order to help children and their families reach their potential.

REFERENCES

Accardo, P.J. (1980). *A neurodevelopmental perspective on specific learning disabilities* (pp. 104–107). Baltimore: University Park Press.

Accardo, P.J., & Capute, A.J. (1978). *The pediatrician and the developmentally delayed child: A clinical textbook on mental retardation* (p. 18). Baltimore: University Park Press.

Allen, H.F. (1957). A new picture series for pre-school vision testing. *American Journal of Ophthalmology, 44,* 38.

Allen, M.L. (1984). Developmental outcome and follow-up of the small for gestational age infant. *Seminars in Perinatology, 8,* 123–156.

American Academy of Pediatrics. (1978). *Report of the task force on pediatric education: The future of pediatric education* Evanston, IL: Author.

Bayley, N. (1933). Mental growth during the first three years. *Genetic Psychology Monograph, 14* (1).

Brazelton, T. (1984). Neonatal behavioral assessment scale. *Clinical Developmental Medicine, 88.*

Capute, A., & Accardo, P.J. (1980) A fellowship program on the needs of exceptional children. In M.J. Guralnick & H.B. Richardson (Eds.), *Pediatric education and the needs of exceptional children* (pp. 137–145). Baltimore: University Park Press.

Capute, A., & Palmer, F. (1980). A pediatric overview of the spectrum of developmental disabilities. *Journal of Developmental and Behavioral Pediatrics, 1,* 66–69.

Capute, A.J., & Shapiro, B.K. (1985). The motor quotient: A method for the early detection of motor delay. *American Journal of Diseases of Children, 139,* 940–942.

Capute, A., Shapiro, B., & Palmer, F. (1981). Spectrum of developmental disabilities: Continuum of motor dysfunction. *Orthopedic Clinics of North America 12,* 3–22.

Claren, S.K., & Smith, D.W. (1978). The fetal alcohol syndrome. *New England Journal of Medicine, 298,* 1063–1067.

Crocker, A. (1983). Cerebral palsy in a spectrum of developmental disabilities. In G. Thompson, I. Rubin, & R.M. Bilenker (Eds.), *Comprehensive management of cerebral palsy.* New York: Grune & Stratton.

Drillien, C. (1979). Follow-up of low birth weight children at early school age. *Archives of Disease in Childhood, 54,* 480–481.

Drillien, C. (1980). Low birth weight children at early school age. *Developmental Medicine and Child Neurology, 22,* 26–47.

Dubowitz, L. (1981). The neurological assessment of the preterm and full-term newborn infant. *Clinics in Developmental Medicine, 79.*

Dunn, L.M., & Dunn, L.M. (1981). *Peabody Picture Vocabulary Test–Revised,* Circle Pines, MN: American Guidance Service.

Feingold, M. (1980). Genetic counseling and congenital anomalies. *Pediatrics in Review, 2,* 155–158.

Finer, N. (1981) Hypoxic-ischemia encephalopathy in term neonates: perinatal factors and outcome. *Journal of Pediatrics, 98,* 112–117.

Fitzhardinge, P. (1981). Follow-up studies of the high risk newborn. In G. Avery (Ed.), *Neonatology* (pp. 350–367). Philadelphia: J.B. Lippincott.

Frankenburg, W.K., Fondal, A.W., & Sciarillo, W. (1981). The newly abbreviated and revised Denver Developmental Screening Test. *Journal of Pediatrics, 99,* 995.

Freeman, J. (1985). *Prenatal and perinatal factors associated with brain disorders* (Report No. 85–1149). Washington, D C : NICHD and NINCDS Task Force.

Gustavson, B. (1977). Severe mental retardation in a Swedish country. Part II: Etiologic and pathogenetic aspects of children born 1959–1970. *Neuropediatrics, 8,* 293–304.

Hack, M. (1979). The low birth-weight infant: Evolution of a changing outlook. *New England Journal of Medicine, 301.* 1162–1165.

Hagerman, R.J., McBogg, P., & Hagerman, P.J. (1983). The Fragile X Syndrome: History, diagnosis and treatment. *Journal of Developmental and Behavioral Pediatrics, 4,* 122–130.

Hall, D. (1982). Developmental screening. In C. Diaz, P. Fosarelli, J. Groner, L. Grossman, D. Hall, A. Joffe, A. Lobovits, & N.A. Haltzman, Pediatric screening procedures. *Advances in Pediatrics, 29,* 411–418.

Hall, D.M.B., & Jolly, H. (1984). *The child with a handicap* (pp. 178–186). Oxford, England: Blackwell Scientific.

Hanshaw, J.B., & Dudgeon, J. (1978). *Viral disease of fetus and newborn.* Philadelphia: W.B. Saunders.

Illingworth, R.S. (1958). Dissociation as a guide to developmental assessment. *Archives of Disease in Childhood, 33,* 118.

Illingworth, R.S. (1961). The predictive value of developmental tests in the first year with specific referral to the diagnosis of mental subnormality. *Journal of Child Psychology and Psychiatry, 2,* 210–215.

Illingworth, R.S. (1971). The predictive value of developmental assessment in infancy. *Developmental Medicine and Child Neurology, 13,* 721–725.

Illingworth, R.S. (1983). *The development of the infant and young child: Normal and abnormal* (8th ed.). New York: Churchill Livingstone.

Kelly, R.I., Zackai, E.H., Emanuel, B.S., Kistenmacher, M., Greenberg, F., & Punnet, H.H. (1982). The association of the DiGeorge anomalad with partial monosomy of chromosome 22. *Journal of Pediatrics, 101,* 197.

Knoblock, H. (1974). *Gesell and Amatruda's developmental diagnosis* (3rd ed.). New York: Harper & Row.

Knoblock, H., & Pasamaniak, B. (1963). Predicting intellectual potential in infancy. *American Journal of Diseases of Children, 106,* 43–51. 1963.

Laxova, R., Ridler, M., & Bowen-Bravery, M. (1977). An etiological survey of the severely retarded Herfordshire children who were born between Jan. 1, 1965 and Dec. 31, 1967. *American Journal of Medical Genetics, 1,* 75–86.

Levine, M.D. (1982). The high prevalence-low severity developmental disorders of school children. *Advances in Pediatrics, 29,* 529–554.

Lewis, D.V., & Freeman, J.M. (1977). The EEG in pediatric practice: Its use and abuse. *Pediatrics, 60,* 324–329.

Ling, A.M., Sundara,., Read, S., & Holland, I.M. (1982). Value of computerized tomography in children with non-specific mental subnormality. *Archives of Disease in Childhood, 57,* 381–83.

Lobovits, A. (1982). Vision screening. In C. Diaz, P. Fosarelli, J. Groner, L. Grossman, D. Hall, A. Joffe, A. Lobovits, & N.A. Holtzman. Pediatric Screening Procedures. *Advances in Pediatrics, 29,* 425–433.

Mamunes, P. (1980) Neonatal screening tests. *Pediatric clinics of North America, 27,* 733–51. 1980.

Marden, P.M., Smith, D.W., & McDonald, M.J. (1964). Congenital anomalies in the newborn infant, including minor variations. *Journal of Pediatrics, 64,* 357–371.

Nelson, K.B., & Ellenberg, J.H. (1982). Children who outgrow cerebral palsy. *Pediatrics, 69,* 529–536.

Oates, R. (1984). The development of abused children. *Developmental Medicine and Child Neurology, 26,* 649–656.

Opitz, J. (1980). Mental retardation: Biologic aspects of concern to the pediatrician. *Pediatrics in Review, 2*(2), 41–50.

Penrose, L. (1963). *The biology of mental defect.* London: Sidgwick & Jackson.

Prechtl, H. (1981). The study of neural development: Biological and psychological perspectives in maturation and development. *Clinics in Developmental Medicine, 77/78,* 198–215.

Rapin, I. (1982). *Children with brain dysfunction: Neurology, cognition, language and behavior* (p. 187). New York: Raven Press.

Reynell, J. (1969). *Developmental language scales.* Slough, England: National Foundation for Educational Research.

Rubin, R. (1980). Infant neurological abnormalities as indicators of cognitive impairment. *Developmental Medicine and Child Neurology, 22,* 336–343. 1980.

Scheiner, A.P., & Moomaw, M. (1982). Care of the visually handicapped child. *Pediatrics in Review, 4,* 74–81.

Sheridan, M. (1973). The Stycar Panda Test for Children with severe Visual Handicap. *Developmental Medicine and Child Neurology, 15,* 738.

Smith, D. (1975). Rational diagnostic evaluation of the child with mental deficiency. *American Journal of Diseases of Children, 129,* 1285.

Smith, D. (1982) *Recognizable patterns of human malformation.* Philadelphia: W.B. Saunders.

Stark, R. (1984). Four-year follow-up study of language-impaired children. *Annals of Dyslexia, 34,* 49–68.

Stewart, A. (1981). Outcome for infants of very low birth weight. *Lancet, 1,* 1038–1040.

Wachtel, R. (1982). Malnutrition and the developing brain. In P. Accardo (Ed.), *Failure to thrive in infancy and childhood* (pp. 77–90). Baltimore: University Park Press.

Waldrop, M.F., Bell, R.Q., McLaughlin, B., & Halverston, C.F., Jr. (1978). Newborn minor physical anomalies predict short attention span, peer aggression, and impulsivity at age three. *Science, 199,* 563–565.

Whitt, J. (1984). Cranial irradiation in childhood acute lymphocytic leukemia: Neuropsychologic sequelae. *American Journal of Diseases of Children, 138,* 730.

Wright, G.F. (1982). The pediatrician's role in PL 94–142. *Pediatrics in Review, 4,* 191–197.

Chapter 8

Psychiatric Assessment

⁓

James E. Joy

Regardless of training orientation, child psychiatrists tend to be comfortable in team settings. Whereas other professionals who diagnose and treat children may or may not have team experience during their training, the child psychiatrist learns to function as an effective team member and thus, has a keen appreciation for the role of the multidisciplinary team and of his or her place within that team. Indeed, it is not possible today to be fully trained in child psychiatry without having worked with members of each discipline represented in this book. Given this experience, the child psychiatrist may position himself or herself as a primary or secondary resource in the evaluation and management of the child with learning disabilities or mental retardation. Whether or not the child psychiatrist practices independently or within a large or small diagnostic center depends on personal preferences, specialization interests, and regional opportunities. Each group of collaborating professions ultimately arrives at an understanding as to the role best played by each participant in the evaluation process. The final chapter in the book addresses the issues of team formation.

TRAINING FOR CHILD PSYCHIATRY

Medical schools in the United States that provide both basic physician training (leading to an M.D. degree) and postgraduate specialty training programs are regulated and standardized on a national scale. Although each training institution has substantial latitude in implementing a curriculum, the overall program must meet the evaluation and accrediting standards of the appropriate national postgraduate education committee and the American Medical Association.

All medical schools still require basic undergraduate proficiency in the sciences as a prerequisite for admission, although the stringent "premedical" undergraduate science curriculum is being abandoned in favor of more liberal courses of study. The 4-year medical school curriculum contains classroom and laboratory work in basic sciences followed by increasing amounts of patient contact and responsibility in various hospital settings. The medical student is exposed to numerous specialty services so as to develop a broad base upon which specialty training can occur. The medical school curriculum addresses a wide range of subjects so that graduates can pass standardized national licensing examinations. Successful completion of the national examinations allows a graduate physician to obtain a license to practice "medicine and surgery" within one or more states but does not confer specialty status. However, any physician holding a valid license might call himself or herself a specialist (e.g., psychiatrist, pediatrician) without violating or exceeding the limitations or conditions established by the license.

The subsequent formal specialty training, called a "residency," generally is offered in large hospital centers that are affiliated with medical schools. The emphasis is on developing proficiency in the diagnosis and treatment of disorders within a defined specialty area; the focus is on direct patient care and, in many instances, research as well. The latter, however, is not a formal stipulation during the course of such training. When a residency is completed, its program directors issue a certificate that verifies that the requirements for specialty training have been fulfilled.

The physician who has this credential may then elect to take the designated national medical specialty board examination. There are separate specialty examination boards for virtually all medical specialties (e.g., pediatrics, neurology) and subspecialties (e.g., pediatric allergy, pediatric neurology). Once a candidate has successfully completed such an examination, the designation "board certified" is conferred and the physician earns a place in the Directory of Medical Specialists (American Board of Medical Specialties, 1983). If the physician has completed appropriate specialty training in an accredited program, but has not yet passed the certification exam, he or she may be designated as "board eligible."

To fulfill the requirements for specialty training in child psychiatry, the physician must complete 3 years of training in an accredited adult psychiatry residency program and an additional 2 years in an accredited child psychiatry program (called either child residency or child fellowship). To be board eligible in child psychiatry, the physician must first be board certified in general psychiatry. He or she may then sit for the child psychiatry examination offered by the American Board of Psychiatry and Neurology. This specialty examination is a 3-day process that involves extensive written and oral interrogation. The reader should be aware that the governing bodies of the various specialty boards, including child psychiatry, indicate that board certification cannot guarantee competence. The designation, however, does denote in-depth training in an accredited setting followed by successful completion of a national examination.

As part of residency training, the child psychiatrist studies both normal and abnormal childhood development and has experience in both hospital and outpatient settings with a full spectrum of disorders that occur from infancy through adolescence. He or she also gains experience in the community as a consultant and an observer, in settings such as courts, foster care systems, public agencies, and school programs. Liaison with pediatric training programs is considered to be a very important experience as well and the child psychiatrist has substantial opportunity to communicate with pediatricians in this portion of the training. Despite the wide range of uniform experiences from one program to the next, there still remain some differences in philosophical orientation. For example, all trainees have experience in the appropriate use of medication in children, but some programs emphasize the biological component over the interactional or intrapsychic origins of mental disturbance. The trend today, however, is for programs to present a clinically balanced curriculum that will serve the child psychiatrist well in any practice setting.

THE ROLE OF THE CHILD PSYCHIATRIST

As both awareness and understanding of the interrelationship between biology, behavior, and emotions have become more sophisticated, the purview of the psychiatrist has become more biologically precise and diagnosis has become more clearly focused. Yet because psychiatry has historically focused on intrapsychic conflict as the primary origin of psychiatric disturbance, referral for psychiatric consultation may still occur out of desperation or by exclusion, that is to say a final effort at diagnosis for treatment when "real medicine" has exhausted its options. Indeed there are those today who continue to perceive psychiatry in this light but their numbers seem to be diminishing.

Similarly, there are a declining number of psychiatric practitioners who continue to espouse outdated, extravagant, or unproven approaches to diagnosis and treatment. The majority of contemporary child psychiatrists practice in ways that acknowledge the gains made in the years since 1960, a time of dramatic increases in the awareness of neurophysiological underpinnings of behavior and emotion. Research continues to bring psychiatrists closer to an understanding of the brain mechanisms which utilize centrally acting chemicals, called neurotransmitters and neuroregulators, and how they affect behavior and development (Greenhill & Shopson, 1984). Concurrent with these advances is the emergence of psychopharmacology as a valuable treatment modality that offers symptomatic relief or control, if not cure, in many problematic conditions. For example, medications have been found appropriate for treating certain aspects of psychotic disorders such as hallucinations, behavior excesses, and disordered thinking. Anxiety disorders are also responsive to medication, as are disturbances in mood regulation, including depression and varying degrees of mania (Hollister, 1983). Also, a large percentage of children with the behavioral/attentional syndrome known as attention deficit disorder (ADD) has shown improvement if appropriate medication is prescribed (Barkley, 1981).

Despite these remarkable achievements, and even in light of research in progress, there are still complex and as yet undefined combinations of psychological, social, and biological factors operating in what may at first seem to be a nearly "pure" biological disorder. It is in disorders with complex "biopsychosocial" foundations that the psychiatrist has exceptional expertise. The contemporary child psychiatrist has the ability to synthesize multiple system variables in such a way as to produce a reasonable and coherent diagnostic impression that has substantial implications for treatment. Indeed, it is this biopsychosocial orientation that is leading psychiatry back to the mainstream of medicine.

PSYCHIATRIC CLASSIFICATION

The increasing complexity of psychiatry and the emergence of child psychiatry as a subspecialty is nowhere more apparent than in the pages of the *Diagnostic and Statistical Manual of Mental Disorders* of the American Psychiatric Association (APA); now in its third edition, it is referred to as *DSM-III* (American Psychiatric Association, 1980). This volume has both facilitated and standardized communication about psychiatric disorders among professionals, and it provides a reference for research that will ultimately allow greater diagnostic specificity and improved treatment efficacy. The reader should be aware that nonpsychiatric medical specialists assign diagnoses according to the system used in the International Classification of Diseases; now in its ninth edition, it is referred to as *ICD-9* (U.S. Department of Health and Human Services, 1980). These two systems are not completely integrated and it is helpful for nonmedical professionals to have some familiarity with both, at least as they relate to their own specialty of interest and expertise. Both volumes are generally available for review in medical centers or university libraries.

Historically, the APA manual was revised twice in a span of 28 years. *DSM-III*, however, will abbreviate this time line and an interim revised edition (*DSM-III–R*) is anticipated in 1987. The first edition, called *DSM-I* (American Psychiatric Association, 1952), was a scant volume that was replaced in 1970 by *DSM-II* (American Psychiatric Association, 1970). In fact, *DSM-II* was the first edition in which childhood disorders were specifically identified. In 1980, the publication of *DSM-III* greatly expanded the space allocated to childhood disorders and, although imperfect, represents a tremendous step forward.

The increasing size of each new edition of the manual reflects to a large extent the identification of an increasing number of discrete psychiatric disorders. In addition, there is much greater narrative description of the conditions listed. By specifically identifying the criteria that establish a given diagnosis, there is a greater likelihood of increased interrator reliability. However, a discussion as to whether each identified disorder represents a truly valid diagnostic entity is beyond the scope of this chapter. Suffice it to say that there is substantial heterogeneity within certain conditions that is not conveyed by *DSM-III* to the reader.

CONDITIONS ASSESSED BY THE CHILD PSYCHIATRIST

Children who are identified as candidates for multidisciplinary assessment that includes psychiatric consultation are most likely to cluster in one of several groups of conditions assessed by child psychiatrists. These are attention deficit disorders (ADD), pervasive developmental disorders (PDD), affective (mood) disorders, anxiety disorders, and psychotic disturbances. Some children may also reflect family disturbances. Each of these groups may include a substantial proportion of children who have learning problems that are either primary or secondary in terms of the reason for multidisciplinary assessment. (The role of the child psychiatrist when dealing with mentally retarded children is noted later in this chapter.)

Another condition frequently assessed by the child psychiatrist is hyperactivity, but it is no longer felt to be a diagnostic entity in and of itself. Hyperactivity, exhibited as either an increased level of motor activity or a decreased ability to inhibit motor activity (i.e., no "brakes"), is variously associated with ADD, PDD, affective disorder, anxiety, mental retardation, and neurological impairment. The child psychiatrist should attempt to identify the substrate within which the hyperactivity occurs and indicate the primary nature of that problem.

Attention Deficit Disorder (ADD)

Certain psychiatric conditions have been identified as more attributable to neurophysiological dysfunction than others, and have been found to have other prominent components that can impair learning and the function of a family system. ADD is such a condition (Barkley, 1981). ADD was first presented as a specific diagnosis in *DSM-III*, defined as "developmentally inappropriate inattention and impulsivity with or without hyperactivity" (American Psychiatric Association, 1980, p. 41). In *DSM-II*, ADD was included under the parallel diagnosis of "hyperkinetic reaction of childhood." Both diagnoses, however, include the same group of children.

Behavioral Manifestations ADD is a disorder recognized by behavioral manifestations but also assumed to reflect neurological dysfunction that is not yet fully understood (Ross & Ross, 1976). By virtue of training and orientation, the child psychiatrist is especially qualified to assess children in whom this diagnosis is being considered. Although future research will no doubt identify some groups of children with ADD who, for example, differ from "normal" children in the degrees of coexisting aggression or affective components, current understanding postulates only an underlying deficit in those functions that define "attention." These parameters include selection of an incoming stimulus, the ability to remain focused on a stimulus with the effective exclusion of competing stimuli, and, finally, the ability to withdraw attention so as to select a new stimulus or focus when appropriate. Children with ADD are deficient to varying degrees in one or more of these functions. It is not difficult then to see how such deficits can compromise a child's learning processes. For reasons that are not yet understood, some children with ADD have associated problems with control of impulses, excessive excitability, and motoric overactivity (hyperactivity). These behavioral manifestations can set apart such children from their peers and thus invite the designation of "disturbed," either behaviorally or emotionally.

Whether identified by the contemporary term "ADD" or the outdated designations "minimal brain dysfunction" or "hyperkinetic reaction," the percentage of children who show the disorder is significant. The incidence of ADD is reported to be approximately 3% of the school-age population, with boys outnumbering girls in a ratio of 10 to 1 (American Psychiatric Association, 1980; Barkley, 1981).

The exact nature of the relationship between ADD and learning disability is not yet fully delineated. It is known, however, that children with learning disabilities may be free of the attention deficit that is central to ADD. It is also known that some children with ADD have a coexisting learning disability. Finally, it is also clear that children with ADD and learning disabilities may be behaviorally or emotionally at variance with their peers. The task of the child psychiatrist is to establish the proper diagnosis, and also to help parents understand the nature of ADD in general and as it relates specifically to their child. Parents need this help because establishment of the ADD diagnosis often requires a revision in parent expectations and interpretation of a child's academics, behaviors, and emotional states. Also, parents frequently need reassurance that ADD is not a product of their parenting style or child-rearing philosophy.

Role of Medication in Intervention　In recent years, parents and educators have received much information focusing on the uses and abuses of medication in the management of childhood disorders, with ADD and hyperactivity being the most notable examples. The media have compounded issues in this area with reporting that has often ranged in tone and content from rational and informative to hysterical and misleading. Topics of discussion ranging from issues of physiology to morality have emerged, some of which have more merit than others. When it is necessary to make an intervention decision that affects one particular child, those participating are entitled to guidance from a specialist who is versed in the benefits and risks of medication. The child psychiatrist can answer questions as to the appropriateness of medication and can also address other concerns (e.g., the effect of medication on growth and appetite, or concerns related to the risk of habituation or dependency).

Although the role of medication in the management of children with ADD continues to generate controversy, there are a number of medications that can be tremendously beneficial. Such benefits are seen in the enhancement of a child's classroom performance, both academically and socially. Stimulants such as Ritalin and Dexedrine are recognized as producing improved attention span, diminished impulsivity, less excitability, and reduced purposeless motor activity. It is less widely known, however, that the optimum dose of these medications for behavior improvement may exceed the dose that produces enhanced attending. Overall, it is important to note that the parameters of improvement as a result of medication lie within the performance deficit area rather than in the child's skill deficit area (see Chapter 2).

An overlap between ADD and learning disability, and the fact that behavior problems, by virtue of their visibility, usually elicit a referral before academic difficulties, mean that the child psychiatrist may be the first to suspect the existence of a learning disability. In such cases, however, little time passes before psychological consultation is requested to determine the degree to which a learning disability may be present. Indeed, most child psychiatrists work hand-in-hand with psychologists so as to facilitate the prompt and accurate diagnosis of learning disability in those children with school problems. Such a partnership is mutually beneficial for intervention purposes as well.

Pervasive Developmental Disorders (PDD)

Autism and other nosologically related developmental disorders are felt to be manifestations of serious yet undefined central nervous system impairment with essentially no experiential or interpersonal factors being etiological (Ritvo, 1976). Although clinically recognized in various forms since the mid-1940s, these disorders were not defined in any standardized system of classification until 1980 when they were incorporated in *DSM-III* (American

Psychiatric Association, 1980). Before then, children with such disorders were variously called atypical, borderline, or possibly schizophrenic. With our current classification of diseases, there are criteria that, to a certain extent, operationally define autism and other related disorders.

Before professional consensus developed regarding the neurological basis of autism, parents were painfully implicated in the genesis of this group of disorders. Blame for a child's "turning to self" (autism) was placed upon the parents, who were erroneously called cold, aloof, unresponsive, and ineffective. It is inevitable that parents will struggle with issues of guilt and question their role in the development of their child's problems and disabilities. To minimize such suffering, however, parents deserve explanations that are accurate and based on methods of assessment that are valid and contemporary.

Even with advances in the understanding of developmental disorders such as autism, the agreed upon conditions which, when present, establish the diagnosis are probably overinclusive. That is, the group is more heterogeneous than a single diagnostic label implies. According to *DSM-III*, in infantile autism "the essential features are a lack of responsiveness to other people (autism), gross impairment in communicative skills, and bizarre responses to various aspects of the environment, all developing within the first thirty months of age" (American Psychiatric Association, 1980, p. 87). Autism has been associated with several central nervous system (CNS) viral infections, a metabolic disorder known as phenylketonuria (PKU), and the chromosomal abnormalities producing Down syndrome and the fragile-X syndrome (Shaffer, 1985).

It is also known that the behaviors and diagnostic features have developmental determinants and that they may change over time. The several coexisting behaviors and diagnostic features vary in the manner in which they exhibit themselves, so great care must be taken to review the child's development longitudinally in order to establish the correct diagnosis. In fact, this group of children can show problems that might justify referral to any of the specialties represented in this book. For example, the first report of developmental variation in an autistic child is often related to language delay. The child may be referred for audiological consultation and subsequent speech and language assessment. Concurrently, observation of abnormal body posturing or eye movements can lead to neurological consultation. The child can be placed in an early infant or preschool stimulation program that involves the services of an occupational therapist or a special educator. A developmental pediatrician may be consulted for evaluation of developmental delay and a psychologist may be asked to see the child regarding possible mental retardation. At some point the child's aloofness and disordered socially related behavior becomes apparent and a child psychiatrist is consulted. The point is to emphasize that much of the practice of child psychiatry is in the diagnosis of children with such multiple delays, especially delays in language and social abilities. In addition, long-term management of such children is often coordinated effectively through the child psychiatrist.

There is a related group of children who exhibit "autistic-like" symptoms without the full complement of qualifiers needed to establish the diagnosis of autism. These children are considered to have childhood onset pervasive developmental disorder or atypical PDD. In addition to the major disturbances in their ability to relate to others, these children have problems with inordinate anxiety, rapid and unpredictable mood changes, peculiarities of movement, speech abnormalities, self-mutilating behaviors, and marked variability to sensory stimuli (American Psychiatric Association, 1980, p. 90). This combination of symptoms may escape classification by the professional unfamiliar with or inexperienced in diagnoses of such children. Although the incidence of such disorders is quite low, the child psychiatrist is the one who, among the professionals who may be asked to evaluate these children, is likely to have seen the greatest number and will therefore have the broadest experience in establishing the diagnoses.

The author has found that many children in whom he diagnoses childhood onset pervasive developmental disorder or autism have been previously misclassified by less experienced evaluators as primarily learning disabled or mentally retarded. This is no doubt due in part to the difficulties in testing these children. He also notes that some evaluators are prone to structure interventions without establishing a diagnosis. This is problematic because parents focus incompletely on such interventions if their child has not had a diagnosis determined. As there seems to be a perpetual quest for answers undertaken by these parents, making a clear diagnostic statement can bring this needless search to an end. In fact, once the diagnosis is determined, parents most often accept the lack of a proven treatment for the condition. Thus, it can be seen that, regardless of other problems that may be present, the peculiarities in emotional states and interpersonal deficiencies cause this group of children to be identified as "seriously disturbed" and that the child psychiatrist is often the key to appropriate assessment.

Affective Disorders

Affective disorders refer to that group of emotional disturbances that can result in defects in the regulation of mood. Such disregulation can be downward (depression), upward (mania or driven overactivity), or a range between the poles, at varying rates. The rationale for including such disorders in this chapter stems from the fact that often the first indicator of such a problem is difficulty in school. Overall, however, exhibition of these conditions in children is extremely variable in both intensity and duration of symptomatology. Consider, for instance, that depression on the one hand can cause a child to become inattentive, preoccupied, listless, lacking motivation, forgetful, and isolated. On the other hand, a child so afflicted may be quite hyperactive, volatile, and irritable. Inasmuch as the natural (untreated) course of depression and related affective disturbances is on the order of months rather than days or weeks, it is not difficult to imagine how such disorders might be suspected initially to be learning disabilities.

As in other areas of child psychiatry, problems that relate to the diagnosis of affective disorder are receiving much attention and research is ongoing (Cantwell & Carlson, 1983). To put this in perspective, consider how the awareness of the nature of depression in childhood has changed substantially since the mid-1970s. Prior to the elucidation of the role of neurotransmitters and central nervous system function, theories of depression were based on psychoanalytical premises. Analysts purported that depression followed loss of a "love object," with resulting anger being directed at the lost object. This was followed by the development of guilt or repressed aggression. Theory stated that guilt could only occur in the presence of a *super ego* (conscience) but since this particular function was not developed in children, depression, therefore, did not exist as a childhood disorder. Fortunately, times change.

Depression is now recognized as a disease that can result from neurochemical malfunction rather than as solely an interpersonal or intrapsychic phenomenon. Medications have been identified that alter central levels of neurotransmitters and affect regulation of mood. For example, enhancement of noradrenaline and serotonin (two widely studied neurotransmitters) within the central nervous system can produce remission of a depressive disorder (Hollister, 1983). Medical intervention for school-age children as well as adults can be most beneficial, particularly when combined with other approaches that involve adjustment of the environment and focus on family issues.

Concurrent with advances in understanding the neurophysiology of depression, there has developed an awareness of a hereditary component to the affective disorders. Questions that examine extended family history can be tremendously enlightening, and should be routine in child assessment. The extended family of a child being evaluated for depression may reveal strong evidence of familial affective disorder. Nonpsychiatrists seldom obtain such a history, perhaps because behavior or learning problems are not usually considered indicators of a more fundamental or underlying pathology with familial transmission. If the long range outcome of depression is to be favorably influenced by intervention, however, correct diagnosis is essential. The child psychiatrist conducts a close investigation of both individual factors and the family history. He or she looks for indicators of change in the child's energy level, esteem, productivity, social interaction, capacity for enjoyment, overall outlook, and subjective sense of happiness. Inasmuch as these parameters shift over time in both prominence and quantity, it is the psychiatrist's task to integrate a longitudinal view with the current level of function.

An Illustrative Case   Monica, age 8 years, was referred to her school psychologist because of academic underachievement. She was an articulate child who expressed an increasing dislike for school. Attempts to encourage her brought tears and tantrums. A list was found in her desk that began with "I hate Mark, I hate Alan." Psychological testing was obtained and was more notable for observations regarding the child's oppositional behavior and tearfulness than any other aspect. She also had a marked "I can't do this" attitude. An incentive program was suggested and put in place with no substantial change in Monica's behavior over the next several weeks. Consultation was then obtained with the child psychiatrist, and this led to a parent conference during which the family history was closely examined for evidence of affective disorder. Monica's parents verified that one of them had had two hospitalizations for depression, and that there were two uncles who had committed suicide and an aunt who was taking lithium and an antidepressant. Further inquiry as to the child's behavior at home corroborated the suspected diagnosis of depressive disorder beginning in childhood.

Major depression, which is the most severe form of affective disorder, is often characterized by notable biological changes that include sleep disruption, appetite change, slowing of thought processes, and emergence of thought content that reflects poor self-esteem, despair, or futility. Clearly if such a child is doing poorly in school, remedial efforts will be less than optimally successful until the affective component is appreciated and appropriate intervention is begun.

Anxiety Disorders

Children who are chronically fearful or apprehensive, either because of performance factors or perceived environmental dangers, do not do well in school. Whereas the child with pervasive developmental disorder may represent a diagnostic puzzle, the overanxious child can be more easily identified. Referral to a school diagnostic team should lead to identification of anxiety as the source of difficulty. It then becomes appropriate to refer the child to an expert diagnostician capable of identifying the source of the child's anxiety. Often the child psychiatrist is such a diagnostician. There is substantial constitutional or temperamental variability in children's tolerance to stress and anxiety, and the child psychiatrist can be a great help in sorting out these factors.

An Illustrative Case   Brad, age 6 years, was rather quickly identified as "different" from his first-grade classmates. He avoided all group participation, rarely answered direct questions, and seemed not to understand what was asked of him. Because of his inability to answer or contribute at school, his teacher expressed concern that he might have mental retardation. Appropriate consultation was obtained within the school district, and psychological testing ruled out mental retardation as a primary diagnosis. Substantial anxiety was noted during test administration, and consultation and case review with a child psychiatrist established a diagnosis of an overanxious disorder of substantial proportions. The history revealed that Brad was temperamentally shy, as were several other members of his family. The father had overcome his high anxiety and viewed Brad's problems as representing a lack of will power. By stressing the constitutional nature of Brad's difficulties, it was possible to help his parents avoid placing undue pressure on him and become better able to match their demands to their child's temperament.

Psychotic Disorders

Psychoses are identified as major disruptions in a child's ability to test reality and respond accordingly. Although psychotic children are not many in number, their disordered thinking usually makes them quite visible. Occasionally, however, a psychotic child will passively attend school without any overt manifestations of the underlying disorder. In these cases, referral and assessment within the school may focus on diagnosing a learning disability as a possible cause for poor achievement. If thought content and processes are not closely examined, the psychotic disorder itself may escape diagnosis.

An Illustrative Case   Twelve-year-old Carl was a new placement in his school's sixth grade. His adjustment to the new class was tenuous, marked by passivity; he had apparent comprehension problems but lacked any substantial disorder in conduct. After waiting several weeks for the social adjustment that did not occur, Carl's teacher initiated referral to the school psychologist. Several more weeks passed before testing was accomplished. The psychologist identified problems in reading but also noted that the boy had made some references to some unusual physical symptoms, including "funny feelings" in his arms. Consultation regarding this with a child psychiatrist known to the school psychologist led to an evaluation that established the diagnosis of a schizophrenic disorder of psychotic proportions. The child believed that worms were moving within his blood vessels, and much of the time he was preoccupied with this delusion. Short-term hospitalization was recommended. Carl's condition improved notably after the initiation of antipsychotic medication, family counseling, reduced educational demands, and ongoing supportive therapy.

Cases such as Carl's are often "tough calls" for other professionals whose work does not usually bring them into close contact with such serious pathology. When a schizophrenic child is evaluated for school problems, the nonpsychiatrist can at times perceive that something is wrong but can be unaware of the true diagnosis. Referral to the child psychiatrist when one senses that something is wrong helps determine a diagnosis, address its impact on learning, identify therapeutic needs, and make prognostic statements.

Family System Disorders

A child functions within the context of his family as a member of the family system. As used here, the term "system" defines a network of reciprocal interactions that can be mutually influential. Major disruption of the family system such as occurs during the process of separation, divorce, or alcohol abuse are of substantial duration and the child who is in the midst of such conflict can be academically compromised for months. In fact, any type of recurrent or ongoing adult mental disorder, especially mood disorders, can thwart the anticipated developmental course of a child and his or her school performance will be far off the mark. Of all the members of the multidisciplinary team, the child psychiatrist is often in the strongest position to uncover covert forces originating within the family system and to intervene in such a system on the child's behalf.

Familial Disorders and Disturbances While psychotic disorders and pervasive developmental disturbances do not of themselves originate as a result of family system interaction, the disturbance certainly affects the entire family system and ultimately affects the child as well. This interaction, of course, has implications for intervention. Disorders of mood regulation and anxiety may originate or emerge in a genetically vulnerable child who is subject to elements of stress either from family members or from within himself or herself. Any assessment that focuses on the child alone will likely fail to uncover the path by which the child's symptoms develop and those forces that are in place to maintain the symptoms.

Varying degrees of psychiatric disturbances in adults also affect the child in the family system. As can be imagined, these interactive patterns are often quite complex. By having specialty training in adult psychiatry, the child psychiatrist can identify dysfunction occurring in parents or other adult members of the family. The initial manifestation of such disturbances, however, may be noted by school officials who are thwarted in their efforts to discuss a child's school problems with his or her parents.

An Illustrative Case Brian, age 6 years, was noted by his first-grade teacher to be having difficulty keeping up with his classmates' performance. Reasons for this difficulty were not immediately apparent. When Brian's teacher contacted the child's father by phone, the teacher was abruptly told to use her time working with her students rather than interrupting fathers' work with phone calls. This response led the teacher to discuss the case with her district school psychologist and because of the parents' antagonism, Brian's case was presented to the school district's consulting child psychiatrist. A staffing was arranged to include the parents, and the psychiatrist was of much assistance in identifying a paranoid personality style in Brian's father. In order to initiate and complete Brian's assessment, the psychiatrist provided clear guidelines to the school personnel for maximizing the chances for parent cooperation in the face of substantial pathology.

Problems of Separation Another area of concern arises in particular during the first few years of school when children may struggle with separation issues. The changes in the parent-child relationship that follow mandatory school attendance are most often not cause for concern and most of the difficulties are overcome during the course of normal development. There are, however, parents and children for whom separation is not easily accomplished. In these cases, the child's attendance at school produces tremendous tension in both the child and the parents. Although there are often social indicators of such difficulty, in many cases impaired learning is the primary symptom. The forces that operate to sustain separation anxiety are so complex and powerful that they are very resistive to change. The child psychiatrist is well equipped to deal with the parents and the child as assessment is undertaken.

High Parent Expectations   There are also situations in which parent expectations relative to a child's academics are inordinately high with no realistic recognition of the child's achievement potential. Such pressure may be extremely covert but it is nearly always perceived by the child and school performance may suffer substantially as anxiety is generated by this conflict. Not all children respond to this pressure with behaviors that are obviously related to anxiety. Some who are temperamentally so disposed adopt a passive resistive or nonperforming mode, that is again shown as impaired learning. All children, however, act-out when anxious, with resultant behaviors that look most like disordered conduct.

Mental Retardation

Assessment of mental retardation can frequently be undertaken and completed without the participation of a child psychiatrist. Those who evaluate these children should keep in mind, however, that the coexistence of psychiatric disturbance in the child with mental retardation is well recognized and psychiatric consultation can be beneficial. Studies of populations of children with mental retardation have identified the incidence of psychiatric disturbance as being higher than that found in "normal" child populations; the likelihood of coexisting psychiatric illness increases with the severity of the degree of retardation (Corbett, 1985). The types of coexisting psychiatric disturbances include the full range of disorders mentioned above, such as psychotic states, attention deficit disorder, affective disorders, and anxiety states.

Specific interest in mental retardation is being encouraged in child psychiatry training programs in an effort to create a population of psychiatrists who will attend to the assessment and treatment needs of children with mental retardation. With increasing biobehavioral technology, coexisting mental pathology is being identified more frequently and with greater accuracy. However, the overall number of child psychiatrists who welcome the opportunity to help in the assessment of children with mental retardation needs to increase substantially. At least part of this apparent and unfortunate bias derives from the earlier days of child psychiatry when theoretical constructs of psychological development excluded the child with mental retardation. Such children were further excluded from psychiatric intervention because they lack the cognitive mechanisms necessary to benefit from "talk" psychotherapies.

THE PROCESS OF PSYCHIATRIC ASSESSMENT

The emotional and behavior variations that children exhibit make the psychiatric assessment somewhat different from the medical or neurological evaluation. In the latter specialty areas, disturbance or pathology tends to be fixed or relatively stable and reproducible. For example, children rarely lose neurological signs in the presence of an examining neurologist and physical signs tend to remain constant before the developmental pediatrician. In contrast, an overactive child or one with "masked" depressive symptomatology may look quite "normal" when he or she is seen by the psychiatrist, and, in fact, may seem different from one appointment to the next. In the case of the child with ADD and hyperactivity, it is not widely recognized that the stress associated with visiting a physician can exert a substantial neuroinhibitory effect on the child's motor behavior that can cause the overactivity to disappear temporarily. Such inhibition is rarely maintained over multiple visits, but unfortunately, costs and time availability often preclude multiple office appointments simply to identify a problem.

In order to maximize the likelihood of a productive interview, most psychiatrists request that a substantial data base be prepared prior to an appointment for an interview. To this end, multiple sources are tapped for information including, in particular, the primary care physician and school personnel as well as previously consulted professionals, if accessible. Requests are made for laboratory data, summaries of hospitalization, and prior evaluations. Parents are asked to provide developmental, medical, and behavioral data as well. In the interest of focus and data collection, many practitioners provide specific rating forms, checklists, and questionnaires so that essential data is not overlooked. If all information is provided as requested, the psychiatrist has at hand sufficient data to construct a longitudinal portrayal of the child's development.

Review of Biological Factors

Biological factors to be reviewed include data regarding the child's mother's pregnancy, labor, and delivery. The clinician notes the history of childhood illnesses as well as any significant medical problems in family members. Particular attention to a history of allergic difficulties often reveals a seasonal component to the child's school problems that may not be revealed unless specifically pursued. Although learning problems and upper respiratory allergies are not causally related, a child with chronic discomfort due to histamine release (a cellular response to allergic stimulation) can be quite "foggy," inattentive, and variably irritable or sleepy over a period of several months. Identification of the offending allergens and appropriate medical therapy can produce marked improvement in the child's mental status and classroom performance.

It is also important to note if certain medications are taken over long periods of time. If not properly monitored while on such medications, the child can show notable difficulties in school achievement. Anticonvulsant medications in particular are potential sources of difficulty. On the one hand, insufficient dosage of an anticonvulsant produces poor control of seizure activity and this is almost always reported to the prescribing neurologist or pediatrician. Toxic or subtoxic elevations of medication blood levels, on the other hand, may produce attention and behavior difficulties that do not immediately give clues as to their origin. If the nonphysician has a working relationship with a child psychiatrist, informal consultation around these observations can occur and unnecessary multidisciplinary evaluation may be avoided. Such problems with medication may occur when parents, despite admonitions by the prescribing physician, attempt to adjust a child's medication on their own.

An Illustrative Case Jenny, age 8 years, was recently enrolled in third grade after moving to a new state. Her teachers observed her to be slow to respond and somewhat clumsy. Prior school records indicated modest achievement but no history of special education or psychological evaluation, and no mention of medical problems. The staff wondered if a processing problem had been overlooked. Before seeing Jenny for evaluation, the case was casually discussed between the school psychologist and a child psychiatric consultant. The clumsiness, as described to the psychiatrist, fit the description of ataxia (loss of muscle coordination) rather than the "soft" neurological dysfunction or maladroitness of the type that might be associated with a child with learning disability. As a result of this conversation, the child's parent was contacted and it was learned that Jenny was taking medication for seizures. Jenny's mother had anticipated increasing stress around the relocation and she had misinterpreted her discussion with the child's previous neurologist regarding stress and the occurrence of seizures. Thinking she would be helping her daughter, the mother increased the medication. She had also delayed in following through on recommendations to seek neurological consultation on arrival in the new city. Appropriate neurological referral was made by the child psychiatrist and it was determined that Dilantin toxicity had developed. Regulation of dosage improved Jenny's coordination and resulted in much brighter participation in class.

Review of Child Development

In addition to a review of past medication history, child development is considered along the lines of gross and fine motor skills, language acquisition, and socialization. Specific attention is directed toward the assessment of a child's temperament and of parent-child compatibility. The reciprocal relationships between the child and other family members must be examined if one is to detect family factors that would adversely affect learning. Theories of such interaction and strategies for assessment can be found in French (1977), among others.

To practice with increased efficiency, many child psychiatrists work with a psychiatric social worker. They constitute a "mini" team with combined experience in the diagnosis and treatment of child and adult disorders as well as family dysfunction, and they may share in data collection and the assessment process. Such a combination makes a particularly strong unit for the synthesis of biological factors with social and family systems parameters.

If the psychiatrist is satisfied that the child has had an adequate pediatric physical examination recently, he or she may elect to report that exam in his or her own findings. If the child has not had a recent examination, the psychiatrist may appropriately elect to examine the child according to personal preferences and previous training. There are, in fact, a number of child psychiatrists practicing who are fully trained pediatricians and who re-entered training to become child psychiatrists.

Because parents often view psychiatrists as possessing broad knowledge about the medical aspects of behavior, they often ask about popular theories or fads that purport to explain hyperactivity or learning disabilities. Many of these fads rest on marginal, uncertain, or, frankly, contrived data. Parents question issues regarding hair analysis, vitamins, hypoglycemia, eye muscle exercises, food additives, etc. and it is well within the province of the child psychiatrist to discuss what has been scientifically determined thus far in these areas.

Laboratory Testing

The child psychiatrist is a physician, so he or she can indeed assess the medical causes of delayed or unusual development. He or she can also order those laboratory studies that may prove useful in the evaluation process.

Metabolic tests may disclose thyroid abnormalities in a small number of children. Also, examination for amino acid breakdown products may yield an understanding of certain causes of mental retardation. In the absence of a developmental pediatrician, it is within the spectrum of psychiatric practice to order genetic studies such as karyotyping (chromosome analysis).

Inasmuch as each of the medical specialists (pediatrician, neurologist, and psychiatrist) may at times want the same laboratory data, their collaboration is essential to avoid needless duplication and expense. These three specialists do not, however, always agree regarding the need for an EEG or the relevance of the data obtained. The relationship between EEG findings and the results of clinical observation is incompletely understood. While it is clear that valuable data may be obtained from the EEG and other neurodiagnostic studies (see Chapter 9), the nonmedical profession should temper expectations regarding the results from such procedures. Children should be referred in anticipation of a specialist's overall clinical opinion rather than in anticipation of results from a test.

The Interview

In addition to compilation of history, the medical examination, and decisions regarding laboratory testing, the psychiatrist relies on interview techniques that utilize observational and comparative skills developed through formal training and experience. The exact strategies used may vary according to the demands of the diagnostic situation. At the time of evaluation, the psychiatrist notes the child's appearance, size, and physical features in relation to comparable age-appropriate factors. He or she also examines for the presence or absence of dysmorphic features and considers if referral to a developmental pediatrician is indicated.

Depending on the age of the child, at least part, if not all, of the evaluation process should occur with the parents present. This allows the psychiatrist to assess parent factors and the parents' patterns of relating to each other and to the child. The examiner also forms an opinion about the child's cognitive style and thought content (i.e., how the child organizes and relates experiences, and which experiences seem to command most of the child's attention). He or she notes the child's communication style, language development, and speech so as to identify deficits or suspected weaknesses that need appropriate referral for in-depth evaluation by the communication specialists. The psychiatrist identifies tendencies toward or the presence of distractibility, disorganization, and impaired thought processes. He or she may perform a number of screening examinations in order to make a specific referral for additional consultation. It is not, however, within the province of the child psychiatrist to administer formal psychometric assessment.

Throughout the evaluation, the psychiatrist observes the child's affect and notes the predominant mood. At some point the psychiatrist also assesses the child's motor skills and coordination through a neurological screening evaluation. If there is evidence of neurological disease, through history or direct observation, referral to a neurologist follows.

The vehicle for interchange between the child and the psychiatrist is determined by the developmental level of the child. Interviews with younger children incorporate various play techniques because direct expression is not possible. Examples of such play strategies include puppet play, use of family doll figures, and pretend phone conversations. The psychiatrist has a repertoire of diagnostic and therapeutic play skills that allow considerable flexibility when working with a child. Formal interaction with children must be conducted in such a way as to facilitate a child's expression of difficulties. The psychiatrist must be adept at transforming a stressful, uncertain initial encounter into an experience that the child perceives as supportive and encouraging. Although individual practices and styles vary, one can say that the child psychiatrist is an expert in developing special relationships with children and can use the process occurring within the context of that relationship for both diagnosis and treatment.

INDICATIONS FOR REFERRAL TO A CHILD PSYCHIATRIST

This chapter has presented the child psychiatrist as a team member with a broad range of competencies. He or she does not, however, replace or subsume the developmental pediatrician or child neurologist, but functions as a valuable central contact or resource who is able to determine the need for other medical consultations. If a core assessment team is to be assembled, consideration should be given to identifying a child psychiatrist as the medical representative. If there is no core team, a child psychiatrist should be located to serve as a resource. It is then appropriate to confer informally with this specialist as needs arise, without the psychiatrist having direct patient contact. For example, a school psychologist who has such a resource may call informally with questions about disorders ranging from epilepsy to hypoglycemia, concerns regarding medications, and inquiries as to whether a particular developmental pediatrician might be a good resource for a child with mental retardation.

Specific case referrals for the child psychiatrist's direct evaluation should be considered if ADD appears to be a likely diagnosis (i.e., a child with substantial impairment in concentration, and coexisting impulsivity, excitability, and hyperactivity). Another appropriate referral is the child who seems unhappy, dysphoric, discouraged, isolated, or irritable. These conditions may presage a significant disturbance in affect regulation or may predict depression. Also in line for consultation is the child who has substantial disordering of interpersonal relationships, aloofness, or atypical and extraordinary emotional responses to ordinary situations. Children displaying idiosyncratic thought processes and bizarre behaviors of any sort that defy interpretation should also be referred.

Autism and other pervasive developmental disorders are extremely difficult for parents to understand. Referral to a child psychiatrist allows the parents to discuss these conditions and increase their understanding, at least to the extent that medical science can offer explanations.

Educators and other school professionals who find the child's development or achievement thwarted by family dynamics should initiate a referral on that basis, as it is often easier for professionals outside the school to pursue sensitive information regarding a family. Cases of marked overprotection, symbiotic dependencies, emotional maltreatment, or neglect of various types should also be referred. Cases in which parents seem to be displaying denial of their child's apparent problems profit from a referral as well. Finally, since children with mental retardation experience psychiatric disturbances as coexistent but possibly unrelated conditions, if such a child shows the same indicators as those just mentioned, referral is appropriate.

REFERENCES

American Board of Medical Specialties. (1983). *Directory of Medical Specialists* (21st ed.). Chicago: Marquis Who's Who.

American Psychiatric Association. (1952). *Diagnostic and statistical manual of mental disorders*. Washington, DC: Author.

American Psychiatric Association. (1970). *Diagnostic and statistical manual of mental disorders* (2nd ed.). Washington, DC: Author.

American Psychiatric Association. (1980). *Diagnostic and statistical manual of mental disorders* (3rd ed.). Washington, DC: Author.

Barkley, R. A. (1981). *Hyperactive children: A handbook for diagnosis and treatment*. New York: Guilford Press.

Cantwell, D. P., & Carlson, G. A. (Eds.). (1983). *Affective disorders in childhood and adolescence—An update*. Jamaica, NY: SP Medical & Scientific Books.

Corbett, J. A. (1985). Mental retardation: Psychiatric aspects. In M. Rutter & L. Herson (Eds.), *Child and adolescent psychiatry—Modern approaches* (pp. 661–678). St. Louis: Blackwell Mosby.

French, A. P. (1977). *Disturbed children and their families*. New York: Human Sciences Press.

Greenhill, L. L., & Shopson, B. (Eds.). (1984). *The psychobiology of childhood*. Jamaica, NY: SP Medical & Scientific Books.

Hollister, L. E. (1983). *Clinical pharmacology of psychotherapeutic drugs*. New York: Churchill Livingstone.

Ritvo, E. R. (Ed.). (1976). *Autism—Diagnosis, current research and management*. New York: Spectrum Publications.

Ross, D. M., & Ross, S. A. (1976). *Hyperactivity: Research, theory, and action*. New York: John Wiley & Sons.

Shaffer, D. (1985). Brain damage. In M. Rutter & L. Herson (Eds.), *Child and adolescent psychiatry—Modern approaches* (pp. 129–151). St. Louis: Blackwell Mosby.

U.S. Department of Health and Human Services, Public Health Service, Health Care Financing Administration. (1980). *International classification of diseases* (9th ed.). Washington, DC: Author.

Chapter 9

Neurological Assessment

~

Peter Rosenberger

The earliest descriptions of the functional deficits to which we now refer as learning disabilities or mental retardation usually included reference to hypothesized organic or physiological mechanisms. This historical precedence in itself does not establish the legitimacy of the physiological approach; after all, the historically preeminent pathophysiology of epilepsy was witchcraft. However, as this chapter attempts to convince the reader, physiological and neurological explanations have, for the most part, stood the test of time. Recent research promises real advances in the application of these principles to real-life problems of diagnosis and management of learning disabilities and mental retardation.

THE ROLE OF THE BRAIN IN LEARNING

What is the role of the brain in learning? Learning requires interaction of the organism with the environment, and this interaction is mediated almost entirely by the nervous system. What in the nature of the nervous system allows it to function in this way?

Irritability is the basic physiological property of all living cells that allows interaction with the outside world. Nervous tissue is especially adapted for irritability, a property known to consist of a change in the resting difference in electrical potential across the membrane of the neuron (nerve cell).

This potential in turn is the result of the *semi-permeability* of the cell membrane, which allows certain electrically charged ions to cross more readily than others. Once a change in electrical potential has occurred, *cable properties* of the neuron allow propagation of this potential difference along a distance, thus enabling the transmission of information more rapidly and specifically than was possible through the secretion of humors (extracellular fluids of the body) in more primitive organisms.

While it is well known that organisms without highly developed brains can learn, how much of a nervous system is required? Eisenstein and Cohen (1967) convincingly demonstrate learning, albeit of the avoidance type, in the isolated thoracic ganglion of the cockroach. As Geschwind (1965) and others suggest, positive or appetitive learning probably requires, in addition to the basic reflex arc, some input from motivation, that is, some appreciation of pleasure as well as pain. The anatomic substrate of such input, according to present evidence, is the limbic system (a set of phylogenetically primitive structures, deep within the brain, that are importantly involved with both memory and emotional responses). Thus, the operational question is: Can any organism or part thereof without any evidence of a limbic system demonstrate true appetitive learning?

On the clinical level, students of mental disorders have long appreciated that those persons with generalized or nonspecific incapacity for learning do not constitute a homogeneous group. Moser and Wolf (1971) review evidence that states that as the severity of mental retardation increases, the likelihood of identifiable brain defect becomes greater. The point is not that there is no important role for nonorganic factors in the determination of learning ability, but simply that proper brain function is one essential factor, perhaps a necessary prerequisite, for intact learning ability.

TRAINING OF THE PEDIATRIC NEUROLOGIST

The pediatric neurologist is first and foremost a physician (i.e., an applied biological scientist or biological engineer). His or her knowledge and skills relate to the biological sciences in precisely the same manner as do those of the mechanical or chemical engineer to their respective basic sciences. Like any engineering trade, medicine demands a hands-on personality, a passion for not only understanding nature but manipulating it to suit mankind's purposes. In common with the basic biological sciences, medicine requires a commitment to the scientific method, a basic respect for data and inductive reasoning.

To a greater extent than the basic sciences, however, medicine requires the empiricist rather than the rationalist; one must possess a willingness to deal with things as they are, not as the equations say they should be. It is probably for this reason that the 4-year medical school grind is basically an undergraduate experience, providing the survivors with what amounts to a second baccalaureate degree. A foundation in anatomy, physiology, biochemistry, bacteriology, and pharmacology is combined with training in techniques of diagnosis and therapy. With few exceptions, however, original research is not performed, and concentration on individual problems is not encouraged.

Graduate medical training (postmedical school) is in a process of evolution. The trend is toward both longer training and earlier specialization. Traditionally, the first year, or internship, was essentially the same for all physicians. In the period since the 1930s, internship training has been offered in adult medicine, pediatric medicine, or surgery, or, in a few cases, "rotating" among these three plus obstetrics/gynecology. Very recently, psychiatry and some of the surgical subspecialties have encouraged specialization during the internship year. For the most part, however, specialty training is accomplished in subsequent residency years—as many as five in some cases.

Although different training programs variously view pediatric neurology as a subspecialty of pediatrics or neurology, all involve both separate and combined training in the two specialties. To qualify for certification in Neurology with Special Competence in Child Neurology, the American Board of Psychiatry and Neurology requires a minimum of a 2-year residency training in pediatrics, along with a 1-year residency in adult neurology, a 1-year residency in clinical child neurology, and an elective year that may include basic neurological sciences or diagnostic subspecialties such as neuroradiology, neuropathology, neurochemistry, or electrophysiology. Although various sections of the training may be taken in nearly any order, the usual procedure is to take the pediatric training first, beginning with the internship. Once an approved training program has been successfully completed, certification in child neurology then requires passing a half-day written examination and, on a different occasion, five separate hours of oral examination, two of which involve actual patients. Those child neurologists whose pediatric training has qualified them for certification by the American Board of Pediatrics usually take that board's examination as well.

THE ROLE OF THE NEUROLOGIST IN THE MANAGEMENT OF LEARNING DISABILITIES AND MENTAL RETARDATION

The question of the neurologist's role in the management of any problem is often discussed among neurologists themselves. Historically, neurology has been viewed as a consultative specialty and, partly by virtue of the nature of the diseases it treats, primarily diagnostic in function. However, a number of large and influential residency programs have trained neurologists to be primary caretakers of patients with disease of the nervous system. Physicians with such training are usually specialists who will function in either capacity as the market demands. An example of the interspecialty relationships thus engendered is that in the emergency room of the Massachusetts General Hospital, patients with strokes (cerebral vascular accidents) are assigned to the medical and neurology services on a rotating basis, while head trauma patients are assigned to neurology and neurosurgery services in similar fashion. (This, of course, holds true only with patients for whom no primary physician is available to specify the nature of the consultation desired.)

Along with headaches and behavior problems, learning disabilities and mental retardation constitute the ''bread and butter'' of most child neurology practices. In dealing with the latter three, the neurologist encounters several closely overlapping specialties, including psychiatry, developmental pediatrics, clinical psychology, and special education. The Learning Disorders Unit at the Massachusetts General Hospital functions as a neurological subspecialty clinic; however, there are excellent units in the Boston area administered by practitioners of each of the other above-mentioned disciplines. The author believes that the patient or referral source should be free to specify the nature of the service desired in the individual case, much as a choice is made among plastic surgery, oral surgery, and ENT surgery for care of a patient with cleft palate. At Massachusetts General, the neurologist, psychologist, and special educator work as a team, but the author is skeptical of the value of multidisciplinary evaluations that leave the patient ''locked in'' to a predetermined sequence of specialty interventions.

Medical diagnosis and treatment are practiced with the aid of diagnostic labels, or nosological categories. A brief review of these entities as they relate to learning disabilities and mental retardation is appropriate to a description of the neurologist's role. However, simply providing a list of these categories misconstrues the doctor-patient interaction. The patient does not come to the doctor with the name of a disease or disorder stamped across his or her forehead; the patient comes with a complaint. He or she is not necessarily interested in having the disease or disorder ''cured.'' What the patient really wants is to have the suffering relieved.

FUNCTIONAL DEFICITS ASSESSED BY THE NEUROLOGIST

A preliminary word is in order concerning the author's use of the term ''functional.'' It has become fashionable in medicine to designate as ''functional'' those complaints that do not add up to a known organic disease entity, and must, therefore, have a psychodynamic or environmental origin. The author suggests a slightly different approach. *All* patient complaints are functional, inasmuch as they refer to disorders of function. The physician's first task is usually to assign a pathophysiological correlate to the complaint. This correlate may involve a chemical, electrical, or even environmental change just as readily as a change in tissue morphology. Whether psychodynamic etiologies of complaints can be proven is a separate question from whether those complaints are functional.

Motor Deficits

Of the functional deficits commonly encountered by the neurologist, perhaps the least relevant to learning disorders are the very common deficits of motor function. Motor weakness, generalized or focal, can result from many of the diseases that cause learning disability, but is not commonly a factor in the disability itself. Common alterations of motor tone include spasticity (increased muscular tone with exaggerated tendon reflexes), rigidity, hypotonia ("floppiness"), and dystonia (irregularity in tone). Coordination deficits include ataxia (unsteadiness of balance), dyssynergia (disruption of the complex programming of contractions of various muscle groups constituting a single smooth movement), tremor, and dysmetria (failure of the servomechanism that arrests muscular movements at the desired point).

Speaking and writing are the learning behaviors most frequently affected by motor deficit. When they are disturbed in isolation, simple prosthetic or compensatory strategies can sometimes make a dramatic difference in the learning progress. Rapid fine motor manipulations for nonverbal problem solving, especially under time constraints (e.g., the Coding subtest of the Wechsler Intelligence Scale for Children–Revised), can also be impaired by motor dysfunction.

The mild, diffuse, and usually nonspecific clumsiness seen in some children with learning disabilities has often been cited as a feature of the syndrome of "minimal brain dysfunction." While there is no question that motor dexterity is relevant to learning, the author agrees with Rutter (1982) that to postulate a syndrome of learning disability that includes clumsiness is to ignore the extreme heterogeneity of motor dexterity among groups of both "normal" children and children with learning disabilities.

An Illustrative Case   A 5-year-old boy was referred to the child neurologist because of his failure to speak. His mother had experienced an uncomplicated 43-week pregnancy with a difficult 22-hour labor; the child was limp and cyanotic (blue, due to an oxygen deficiency) at birth, and did not cry or breathe for the first 5 minutes. Early motor development was delayed; he was not sitting by age 15 months, but he appeared alert. At age 4 years, he still had an expressive vocabulary of less than 6 words. At age 5 years, he was brought to the neurologist because his mother realized that he was attempting, but failing, to communicate a complex thought (he was trying to ask her why the leaves change color in the fall).

Neurological examination showed normal language comprehension and perceptual abilities. Multiple severe cranial nerve deficits were noted, as well as spastic tetraplegia (weakness of all four extremities, with increase in tone), which was worse on the child's right side. Appropriate psychometric tests confirmed average nonverbal intelligence and receptive language.

The child's problem was managed with alternative communication training. Ten years later at age 15, he was a sophomore in regular classes at a parochial high school.

Sensory Deficits

The most common sensory complaint, pain, is seldom directly relevant to learning disability. Persistent or intractable pain can, of course, make concentration difficult. Alterations of pain perception by affective disorder, that are so troublesome to the neurologist who treats adults, are not common in children, who, for the most part, "only cry when it hurts."

The integrity of the primary senses, including vision, hearing, and touch, is critical to learning, especially in the academic sense. However, it is highly uncommon for a primary sensory deficit of sufficient proportions to affect learning to escape detection by the school screening programs. A possible exception is the effect of hearing loss that is secondary to chronic serous otitis media (middle ear infection) on language development. Traditionally, it has been thought that mild hearing loss, especially if episodic and/or unilateral, does not impair language. Recent evidence, however (see Chapter 4), suggests at least a statistical correlation between the two.

Of greater interest to the study of learning disorders are certain aberrations of sensory function. For example, homonymous hemianopia (blindness affecting half the visual field as seen by both eyes) can result from disease of either the visual cortex of one hemisphere or the incoming pathways serving it. This can be diagnosed in a child with otherwise normal visual acuity who had been unaware of the deficit. Atypical responses to sensory input may be seen in children with certain learning disabilities in the absence of measurable threshold elevation. Thus, the child with autism appears to be deaf in some contexts but shows excellent auditory discrimination in others. Children with certain other handicaps appear "sensorially defensive"; that is, they avert their gaze or hold their hands over their ears.

An Illustrative Case A kindergartner was found to be paying poor attention in class and having difficulty with hopping and skipping games. Neurological examination revealed a child of otherwise normal intelligence who had difficulty reporting double simultaneous stimuli, both tactile and visual. CT scan revealed a left parieto-occipital congenital cyst. Careful perimetry (testing of the limits of the visual field) confirmed a right homonymous extinction hemianopia (failure to respond in one visual hemifield when both are tested simultaneously). Being seated on the extreme right side of the classroom improved the child's attention and participation.

Communication Deficits

Functional deficits involving communication are the most relevant of all to learning performance. Chief among these are deficits of language. For a detailed review of the neurology of these deficits as it relates to disorders of learning, see Rosenberger (1980). Only the broad outlines are touched upon here.

The delineation of the syndromes of spoken language deficit in children is still in the early stages (Aram & Nation, 1982; Rapin & Allen, 1983). However, it is clear, from the author's clinical experience, that classical neurological categories of spoken language deficit are at least partially relevant to children with learning disabilities or mental retardation. Among children who fail to acquire spoken language at the expected rate, a distinction can be made between those for whom comprehension is relatively intact (expressive dysphasia) and those for whom it is delayed as well (receptive dysphasia). For reasons too complex to review here, children with acquired dysphasia nearly always stop talking; the jargon and paraphasias (jumbling of words and sentences) of receptive dysphasia in the adult are a rarity in childhood.

Some of the more complex syndromes known to the aphasiologist also appear to have developmental correlates. Verbal auditory agnosia (pure word deafness) is the language deficit exhibited by children with the syndrome of acquired epileptic aphasia (Gascon, Victor, & Lombroso, 1973; Landau & Kleffner, 1957). These children are not deaf, but act as though what is being said to them is gibberish. The transcortical sensory dysphasia of Henschen, or "isolated speech area" syndrome of Geschwind, features severely impaired comprehension with preserved repetition. It may be of some relevance to the language deficit of children with hydrocephalus or others with prominent echolalia (Rosenberger, Cowgill, & Heiman, 1977).

The neurological syndromes of dyslexia and dysgraphia have been invoked to account for developmental delay in the acquisition of the skills of reading and writing for nearly as long as deficits in the area of written language have been recognized in children. Association of the two deficits in the same case has been well documented, both in earlier case descriptions (Orton, 1937) and in more recent formal studies (Rosenberger, 1970). Nosological classifications for subtyping of dyslexias (Boder, 1973; Mattis, French, & Rapin, 1975) borrow heavily from classic neuropsychology for their distinctions, notably between dyslexia with other language deficits (dysphasic, dysphonetic) and dyslexia with other perceptual deficits (dysgnostic, dyseidetic). A case may be made for application of a similar concept to the subtyping of dysgraphia, to distinguish between "linguistic" and "orthographic" writing deficit (Rosenberger, 1981).

An Illustrative Case (Hier & Rosenberger, 1980) A 5-year-old right-handed boy was referred for neurological examination. He had been delivered by cesarean section because of a small birth canal, and his birth weight was 2,800 grams. There were no neonatal complications. He sat at 7 months of age and walked at age 16 months. Babbling began at age 6 months, but he did not utter his first words until age 30 months. His speech then regressed into unintelligible sounds. At age 5.8 years (5 years, 8 months), his language equivalent score was 2.1 years. Receptive vocabulary was at the 2.5 year level, giving an extrapolated verbal IQ of 32. His nonverbal IQ by the Leiter scale was 74.

Neurological examination was unremarkable. An electroencephalogram showed repetitive spike and slow wave activity over the left central and midtemporal regions. A CT scan demonstrated an area of tissue destruction in the anterior left temporal lobe (the speech area of the major cerebral hemisphere).

Memory Deficits

The identification of memory deficits in childhood learning disorders is complex and problematic. Amnestic syndromes (amnesia) identical to those seen in Wernicke-Korsakoff disease or posterior cerebral artery infarction in adults are well-recognized features of certain brain diseases in children, notably herpes encephalitis and midline tumors (see following case). However, these syndromes are rarely seen in children with learning disabilities despite the obvious central role of memory in learning.

Resolution of this paradox is probably to be found in the suggested distinction between procedural or skill memory and informational or content memory (Squire, 1982). The childhood learning disorders for the most part involve delayed acquisition of necessary academic skills, and only secondarily affect assimilation of information. Thus, of the child with dyslexia who gets perfect scores on spelling tests and makes numerous spelling errors on written compositions, it may be complained that he or she "learns but can't remember"; in fact, what the child is doing is memorizing the spelling word lists rather than learning the spelling rules.

A disorder frequently confused with memory disorder is attention deficit disorder. A rule well known to the emergency room neurologist is that memory cannot be tested if the patient is too confused or disoriented to register and retrieve information. Thus, the patient with Korsakoff's syndrome (acute amnesia due to brain degeneration) may show a normal digit span despite a devastating overall memory deficit.

An Illustrative Case A 20-year-old male high school graduate complained of an inability to hold a job. Further history established that although diligent and cooperative, he was simply unable to master the routines and simple information of a new task. He had been operated on successfully at age 14 years for removal of a tumor in the pituitary fossa. He required only modest pituitary replacement therapy, but had much difficulty readjusting to high school, graduating only with the help of much resource room teacher support.

On neurological examination, he showed a digit span of 7 numerals forward and 5 backward. He required only two rehearsals of a 9-element story for perfect repetition, but could recall none of the 9 elements after 10 minutes. Psychometric testing showed a full scale IQ of 86, but revealed a score at the first stanine on several subtests of the Goldman-Fristoe-Woodcock Memory Scale.

Social Deficits

Whether deficits of social interaction should be included among learning disorders entails, of course, the question of whether sociability is a learned skill. The frequency with which these deficits are found among children with learning disabilities, however, justifies their consideration.

Autistic withdrawal is the most striking of these, and is frequently found as part of a syndrome that also includes receptive (and sometimes expressive) language disorder, motor automatisms, intolerance for change or novelty, and atypical responses to sensory input. The disorder may be apparent from infancy, but generally the parent reports some degree of normal development with subsequent regression. More careful analysis may reveal that early normalcy was more apparent than real—that spoken language, for instance, never progressed beyond the echolalic stage. Rutter (1978) and others suggest that only cases in which onset was apparent before age 30 months be included in the syndrome.

To be distinguished from autistic withdrawal is the social regression and isolation associated with major depressive disease. In children, this can take the form of what is referred to as the oppositional facet of the hyperkinetic behavior syndrome (attention deficit disorder), which is distinguishable by certain clinical and psychometric features (DeLong & Nieman, 1983). Mood instability; sociopathic tendencies, such as lying, stealing, and pyromania; neurovegetative disturbances; and hatefulness all contribute to a syndrome that has been shown to have a strong familial association with major depressive disease and to respond favorably to certain neurotropic medications.

Far more frequently encountered than the above-mentioned is the conduct disorder commonly associated with the hyperkinetic behavior syndrome. This produces a social maladjustment that as often as not takes the child by surprise, as it were, leaving him or her wondering what he or she did to arouse such negative reactions in his or her peers. Seen from the other side, what appears is social maladroitness; that is, a talent for saying the wrong thing at the wrong time, an inability to "take a hint" or read a social message, an inability to engage in competition without taking the matter to heart, etc.

Attention Deficits

The question of whether attention deficits are to be classified separately from learning disabilities is at least partly one of semantics. The two are certainly seen together in the same child far more frequently than chance would predict. However, in the author's experience, more than half of all children with learning disabilities are free of attention deficits, and nearly a quarter of those with attention deficits show no other learning disorder. One reasonable suggestion for how the two might relate is made by Kinsbourne and Caplan (1979), who refer to learning disabilities as "cognitive power" deficits and attention disorders as "cognitive style" deficits.

It has been apparent for some years to clinicians dealing with children with learning disabilities that: 1) an inability to focus attention is what is chiefly wrong with the learning ability of the "hyperkinetic child"; and 2) a substantial portion of children with attention deficits are not hyperkinetic. These insights gained official recognition when the authors of *DSM-III* (American Psychiatric Association, 1980) renamed the hyperkinetic behavior syndrome "attention deficit disorder." From the author's standpoint, this change merely shifts the focus from one symptom to another, and ignores the disintegrity of the syndrome of "minimal brain dysfunction" and substantial independence of the various deficits. Change for the better is promised by the forthcoming *DSM-III-R,* scheduled for publication by the American Psychiatric Association in 1987, which proposes to recognize the distinctions made by Shaywitz and Shaywitz (1984) and others among attention deficit disorder, conduct disorder, and oppositional disorder in the "hyperkinetic child."

Ability to focus attention is partly a developmental talent; that is, to some extent both inattentiveness and hyperactivity are the norm for the preschooler.

Table 9.1. Physiological correlates of functional neurological deficits relevant to learning

	Developmental	Acquired
Structural-anatomical	Neuronal migration deficits Genetically determined errors of neuronal architecture	Birth trauma Congenital infections Damage from abnormal metabolites Damage from neonatal hy- poxia or hypoglycemia Damage from toxins
Chemical	Inborn errors of metabolism Deficits of neurotransmitters	Hypoxia Hypoglycemia Toxins
Electrical	Epilepsy of hereditary origin Light-induced and other re- flex dysrhythmia	Epilepsy secondary to brain damage

Furthermore, the development of attention skills is probably part of the essential task of nursery school and kindergarten. The need for such development appears to be highly variable among "normal" children. Thus, it may be unwise to make a diagnosis of attention deficit disorder in the child who has not yet had the opportunity for such instruction.

The developmental nature of attention skills is probably responsible for earlier notions that attention deficit disorder is a purely "maturational" problem. Presently, it is rather widely accepted that attention deficit disorder is a lifelong problem, however well the individual learns to cope with it, and however less relevant attention skills become with departure from formal schooling. The conventional wisdom that stimulant medications are no longer effective for attention deficit disorder after the child reaches puberty is not confirmed by the author's experience.

PHYSIOLOGICAL CORRELATES
OF NEUROLOGICAL FUNCTIONAL DEFICITS

For purposes of classification, the physiological deficits underlying developmental disabilities may be distinguished along two axes: first, whether the deficit is primarily structural, chemical, or electrical; and second, whether the lesion is developmental or acquired (see Table 9.1). A preliminary comment is in order concerning the latter distinction. In common parlance, "developmental" usually means "programmed into the way the organism was put together to begin with," while "acquired" refers to an insult to a previously "normal" organism. As knowledge of pathophysiology progresses, many lesions once thought developmental become recognized as having been acquired early in life. For example, it has become known that the fetus once thought to be derailed in development by maternal rubella is actually infected with the virus itself; thus, the condition is now referred to as "congenital rubella." The situation may be even more complex, as in the case of phenylketonuria (PKU). The biochemical lesion in this disease was once thought to be directly responsible for the resultant learning disability. However, the observation that infants born to mothers with PKU may have mental retardation but not PKU themselves has suggested that a structural lesion due to phenylalanine poisoning may be responsible; recent experimental evidence (Nigam & Labar, 1979; Rosenberger & Ferraro, 1984) supports this hypothesis.

Structural Correlates

Structural correlates to functional deficits are not necessarily lesions. They may consist of atypical, although not necessarily abnormal, development, as in atypical asymmetry (Rosenberger & Hier, 1980). Of the structural lesions that are unquestionably developmental, probably the most clearcut are the genetic errors. The structural lesions cover a spectrum, at one end of which is a blatant dearth of neurons and synaptic connections, as in familial microencephaly (small head). Farther along the spectrum are such disorders as Down syndrome, in which the gross anomaly of brain structure is definite although mild, but the microscopic lesion is still controversial.

At the other end of the spectrum are the specific learning disabilities, clearly constitutional and in some cases hereditary. What is the evidence for developmental brain abnormalities in learning disabilities? This important topic is reviewed by Golden (1982), and only selected highlights are mentioned here. A varied and potentially fruitful group of studies have proceeded from the observations of Geschwind and Levitsky (1968) regarding anatomical asymmetries in the language areas of the normal human brain. Galaburda and Kemper (1979) show cellular abnormalities, possibly related to a failure of migration of neurons during development, in the brain of a man with dyslexia; and clinical studies of Geschwind and Behan (1982), relating dyslexia to lefthandedness and immune disorders, provide a hypothesis for the mechanism of these abnormalities of cell architecture. Using measurements from CT scans first described by LeMay (1976), Hier, LeMay, Rosenberger, and Perlo (1978) show an increased incidence of atypical gross asymmetry of the brain in persons with dyslexia, with a larger parietal cortex (speech association area) on the right rather than the left. Rosenberger and Hier (1980) relate this finding specifically to verbal intellectual deficits. Relevant to the nondominant hemisphere, Alexander and Money (1966) relate a specific dyscalculia to the genetic anomaly of Turner's syndrome, and further show it to be different from that found in the major hemisphere disorder of Gerstmann's syndrome.

Acquired structural lesions responsible for learning disorders or mental retardation are usually sustained very early in life. Moser and Wolf (1971) classify these lesions in respect to one group of individuals with mental retardation. They may be physical (i.e., a direct result of trauma to the fetus or newborn child, or cerebrovascular accidents such as occlusion or hemorrhage). They may be infectious, as in the encephalopathies (diseases of the brain) of measles, rubella, toxoplasmosis, cytomegalovirus, or herpes. They may be metabolic, the result of an early deprivation of oxygen or essential nutrients; or toxic, from exposure of the fetus to maternal alcohol ingestion or of the young child to lead. They may be neoplastic (an enlarging new growth of abnormal tissue), as in tuberous sclerosis, congenital gliomas (nerve cell neoplasms), hamartomas (neoplasms of multiple cell types), or other tumors.

Most acquired structural lesions in early life are relatively diffuse, and as such obey the rule of adult neuropsychology that diffuse lesions tend to lead to perceptual handicaps or attention deficit disorders rather than to language disorders. This is demonstrated in childhood learning disorders with regard to hypoxia (O'Dougherty, Wright, Loewensen, & Torres, 1985), trauma (Chadwick, Rutter, Shaffer, & Shrout, 1981), and lead intoxication (David, Clark, & Voeller, 1972; Landrigen et al., 1975). Conversely, developmental language disorders are usually not syndromes of recognizable brain damage. Notable exceptions include delayed language development related to temporal lobe lesions (Hier & Rosenberger, 1980), the syndrome of acquired epileptic aphasia (Landau & Kleffner, 1957), and the autism syndrome (Knobloch & Pasamanick, 1962).

Chemical Correlates

The chemical correlates of neurological deficits are to be distinguished from the chemical causes of structural lesions, just described. Ongoing chemical imbalance, in the absence of structural disintegrity, can interfere with nervous function in general and learning in particular. Chronic hypoxia (lack of oxygen) has been suspected (although less well documented than the acute form) as an impediment to learning, and may be responsible in part for the learning disability known to accompany cyanotic congenital heart disease.

The ongoing effect of a lack of essential nutrients on learning is poorly understood. Acute hypoglycemia (low blood glucose) can have a profound effect on consciousness and motor function. Anyone who has tried to teach a hungry child agrees that lesser degrees of hypoglycemia interfere with learning, although popular theories of hypoglycemia as a cause of specific learning disability have failed to achieve scientific respectability. Other nutrient substances have been claimed to have direct action on intelligence (see Wolfensberger & Menolascino, 1970). Of these, only glutamic acid has shown enough promise to warrant further study.

Of the toxic substances that have a negative effect on learning, ethanol is perhaps the most notorious and frequent offender, followed closely by narcotic drugs and marijuana. The major tranquilizers or antipsychotics, even the milder ones in acceptable therapeutic doses, increase reaction time and reduce accuracy in experimental discrimination tasks (Sprague, Barnes, & Werry, 1970). Certain mild sedatives are well known to pediatric clinicians to have a harmful effect on attention span, especially in younger children. Frequently prescribed drugs in this category include the barbiturates (phenobarbital, Seconal, Nembutal, etc.) and the antihistamines (common ingredients in cold remedies).

Although understanding of the role of neurotransmitters (chemicals that mediate nerve conduction) is in its infancy, this is the most promising area at present for research in the chemistry of learning. Shaywitz, Yager, and Klopper (1976) show that increasing dopamine turnover in the brains of rat pups can produce a syndrome with some features of attention deficit disorder; Shaywitz, Cohen, and Bowers (1977) demonstrate altered levels, under certain conditions, of homovanillic acid, a principal metabolite of dopamine, in the cerebrospinal fluid of children with attention deficit disorder. Deutsch,

Swanson, Warsh, and Fargas (1984) note a correlation between minor physical anomalies and levels of a norepinephrine metabolite in children with attention deficit disorder. Zametkin et al. (1985) take this work a step further to show differential effects of methylphenidate and dextroamphetamine on urinary catecholamines in children with attention deficit disorder. Finally, initial results obtained with the administration of piracetam, or gamma hydroxybutyric acid (closely related to a naturally occurring neurotransmitter), to persons with dyslexia show sufficient effect on reading rate to warrant further research (Chase et al., 1984).

Electrical Correlates

Since the late 19th century, electrical correlates of neurological deficits in general have been the principal concern of the discipline of neurophysiology. The study of electrical events in the central nervous system as they affect learning had to await the development in the 1930s of the electroencephalograph, which, although it employs essentially the same principle as the electrocardiograph perfected twenty years earlier, requires the additional amplification afforded by the vacuum tube. The electroencephalograph measures ongoing electrical activity in the brain by recording the potential difference between two adjacent points on the scalp, or between one of these points and an electrically neutral or reference point elsewhere on the body.

Convulsive or epileptic disorders cause the most dramatic alterations of brain electrical activity, and disturbances of learning are a well-recognized clinical feature of these disorders. Three types of such disturbance can be distinguished according to their temporal relation to the seizure.

The first is the ictus, or seizure, itself, which nearly always produces some disturbance of cognitive function. The major motor seizure characteristically produces complete loss of consciousness. The absence, or "petit mal," seizure features transient inattention and unresponsiveness, usually with total amnesia for events during the spell, and often an unawareness of the spell itself. The complex partial, or "psychomotor," seizure can leave sensory awareness, motor responsiveness, and/or memory for events during the episode relatively unimpaired, but usually produces some degree of confusion, disorientation, or sensory distortion. A classic example of the latter from popular literature is the changes in size of self or the environment as described in Lewis Carroll's *Alice's Adventures in Wonderland.*

Second, cognitive disturbance can occur during the "aura," or time immediately preceding the seizure. This altered state of mind typically occupies seconds or minutes but can last as long as days for some children.

Third, the postictal state, during which the body behaves as though part of the brain were exhausted, can feature cognitive deficit along with focal paralysis, sensory loss, language disturbance, or virtually any functional sign of focal brain deficit. Again, this state lasts from minutes to hours typically, to as long as two weeks in the rare case.

At the experimental level, electroencephalographic correlates of learning have been studied both through spontaneous or ongoing activity, and through evoked potentials, or electrical responses to external stimuli. Because of the problem of sorting out relevant potentials from background "noise," the considerable early promise of studies of the latter type went largely unrealized until the advent of the digital computer. The first major contribution of this technological revolution was the computer-averaging technique, which allowed evoked responses to multiple stimuli to be electrically averaged, thus reducing random background noise to zero. Early studies of occipital responses in persons with dyslexia (Conners, 1971) were promising, but more potentially fruitful electrical events to be identified experimentally are the contingent negative variation, or "expectancy wave," (Rohrbaugh, Syndulko, & Lindsley, 1976), and the long-latency, or P300 potential (Finley, Faux, Hutcheson, & Amstutz, 1985). A second major contribution of computer technology is computer-assisted topography of brain electrical activity (Duffy, Burchfiel, & Lombroso, 1979), which makes use of information from all nearby electrodes in assessing electrical events at any given spot. Initial studies show differences in both spontaneous activity and evoked potentials in neuropsychologically relevant areas of the brain in persons with learning disabilities as compared to control individuals, and have even promised a contribution to the diagnosis of dyslexia (Duffy, Denckla, Bartels, & Sandini, 1980).

TECHNIQUES OF NEUROLOGICAL ASSESSMENT AND THEIR SCIENTIFIC BASIS

To understand how the contemporary American physician thinks in approaching a clinical problem, one must understand that for the better part of the past 100 years, American medicine has lived under the tyranny of pathology. The basic diagnostic exercise consists of: 1) constructing a history or "necrography" of the illness through information from the patient or other sources; 2) describing the diseased organism through physical examination; 3) arriving at a diagnosis through application of constructs from established nosologies; 4) seeking to confirm that diagnosis by means of relevant laboratory studies; and 5) when possible, validating the diagnosis by direct examination of diseased tissue, at biopsy or necropsy. The resulting passion for diagnostic accuracy (occasionally, some claim, at the expense of therapeutic efficacy) is rather different from what one might expect of the physician trained elsewhere. It may also help explain what at times comes across to colleagues in related professions as a lack of enthusiasm for multidisciplinary involvement. The physician seems, at times, obsessed with the notion that a parent expects the same sort of attention to be given to his or her child's learning disability that the founders of the Mayo Clinic gave to his or her father's gall bladder.

Construction of a History

History is sometimes described as the cornerstone of medical diagnosis. It might be thought of as the whole foundation of neurology. A case can be made for the proposition that the history usually tells the neurologist *what* the illness is, the examination mainly *where* it is.

Certain elements of the history are of particular value to the diagnosis of learning disorder. Appendix A at the end of this chapter shows a copy of the case history form mailed from Massachusetts General's Learning Disorders Unit to the parents of prospective patients prior to the first visit. They are encouraged to fill out the form thoughtfully at their leisure, with reference to baby books and other documents available at home. It is then reviewed with them at the time of the initial clinic visit. Careful attention is given to the pregnancy and perinatal history. The developmental history is purposely selective, for it could easily be two to three times as long. The educational history is crucial, as basic skills achievement must be assessed relative to educational opportunity and exposure. Family history is always helpful when the question arises as to whether one is dealing with an individual with an inherited lack of talent or a damaged brain. Behavior history helps sort out whether maladaptive behaviors are the cause or result of school underachievement.

Appendix B represents the form for recording initial patient contact in the clinic. Those parts of the history detailed in the Case History Form are amplified on this form when they contribute importantly to the diagnosis; otherwise, they are noted as normal or abnormal for reference. All information that would be relevant to a complete narrative summary of the case is included.

Physical Examination

The physical examination section in Appendix B includes a standard neurological examination, not because it is always relevant to the learning disorder, but because the patient who has consulted a neurologist for any reason has a right to conclude that he or she is free of frank nervous disease except as otherwise noted. This examination typically includes attention to the cranial nerves (including clinical assessment of visual and auditory acuity), tendon reflexes, motor strength and tone, coordination, and sensory responses.

Of greater interest are the special examinations for learning disorder. These should not be thought of merely as screening tests for formal psychometry, since they can be definitively diagnostic in themselves and since there is increasing economic pressure to spare the patient expensive laboratory testing when possible.

The physician involved with children with developmental disabilities should build a small repertoire of tests for developmental assessment across a broad age-span. The precise materials used are of secondary importance; they are only as good as the observer's experience with them. The following items cover the range from infancy to junior high school: a bright red ball to excite visual attention; a small tinkling bell; a half dozen blocks to stack or count; ten small pictures of common objects to name or to point to in response to their spoken names or described functions; two sets each of five primary color cards to name, pick out, or match; a simple action picture to describe; ten flash cards each of capital and lower case letters; some paragraphs graded according to readability levels; a list of spelling words arranged according to grade-levels; and a pencil and paper.

For comparing performance with the norms, a plethora of schedules are available, nearly all of which are derived from the work of Gesell and co-workers (Knobloch & Pasamanick, 1974) or from Illingworth (1960). For the child less than 5 years old, the Denver Developmental Screening Test (Frankenburg & Dodds, 1969) provides an especially useful distillation of these norms for the physician's purposes. A thoughtful modification of the Gesell and Illingworth data for the clinician is provided by Dodge (1964).

The neurologist needs to develop some skill in generating verbal output from the patient for assessment. The upshot of the initial interchange may be: "Where did you go?" *Out.* "What did you do?" *Nothing.* It is sometimes best to suspend judgment in this area until later in the examination, when the patient is more adjusted to the setting. One helpful trick is to ask the child to name his or her favorite game and then to describe the rules of play. One can also ask the name of a best friend, with a description of favorite activities with that person.

Writing, reading, and calculation tasks must obviously be selected within an initially estimated range of performance. Materials should be used that do not duplicate or conflict with those employed locally for formal psychometric testing. Also, in office testing of basic academic skills, achievement norms should be checked with the local school system. In some Boston area schools, for example, regrouping in double integer calculations may be expected of the average second grader, while in other schools these skills are not firmly established until the third grade.

Tests for assessing writing, reading, and arithmetic are readily available. However, the author is troubled by a dearth of available standard reading paragraphs that present one or two easily accessible "main points" for the testing of comprehension. Counting skills and number concepts may be accurately assessed well in advance of the acquisition of formal arithmetic operations. A simple procedure for a child aged 4–6 years is as follows: 1) the examiner lays six coins on the table; 2) the examiner asks the child to count them; 3) the examiner asks the child to hand three coins to him or her, then asks how many are left on the table; 4) the examiner gives back one coin, then asks how many are on the table; and finally, 5) the examiner asks how many coins remain in the examiner's closed hand.

The remainder of the examination for learning disabilities is straightforward, except that eye preference must be tested with an object held by the child with both hands equidistant—a piece of paper punctured at the center will do.

Laboratory Testing

Many standard medical laboratory studies can be relevant to the diagnosis of learning disorder, although none is routinely ordered in the Massachusetts General clinic. Of the cytological (cell structure) studies, the blood count is indicated when anemia is suspected in the inattentive child. The karyotype (examination of the cell's chromosomes) aids in the diagnosis of syndromes such as Down, fragile-X, or Turner's, when characteristic physical anomalies are present. Of the available chemical studies, blood glucose and blood oxygen tests establish levels of these essential nutrients. Blood and urine amino acids tests are indicated whenever mental retardation is suspected but undiagnosed, since most disorders of amino acid metabolism do not reliably produce characteristic physical signs. In the rare cases in which progressive deterioration of learning capacity is evident, assays of lysosomal enzymes or brain lipid metabolites may enable diagnosis of metabolic diseases (usually hereditary) causing the degeneration of brain substance. Blood levels of toxins such as lead or abused substances should be ordered whenever clinically indicated. Children on anticonvulsant or tranquilizing drugs should have those levels carefully monitored whenever academic performance is a matter of concern.

Standard electroencephalography should be ordered whenever: 1) learning disability or inattention appears paroxysmal (characterized by abrupt onset and cessation), 2) a destructive brain lesion is suspected, or 3) there is reason to believe that hemispheric activity is asymmetrical. Evoked potential studies are of use mainly for the assessment of visual function or auditory function (see Chapter 4) when the subject's response is unreliable. The use of computer-assisted topographic mapping of brain electrical activity as an aid in the differential diagnosis of dyslexia is being explored.

Of radiological studies, the plain skull X ray has, for practical purposes, been replaced by computed tomography (CT, or CAT, scan). This procedure examines serial horizontal planes or "slices" of brain tissue by X rays projected from not just one direction but every point of the compass, and computes the radiodensity of each point as seen from every direction, thus revealing structures never before visible to the X ray. The use of this study is indicated whenever a structural lesion is suspected. It is also helpful in understanding the role of hemispheric asymmetry in learning disorders (Hier et al., 1978), with particular reference to verbal intellectual deficits (Rosenberger & Hier, 1980), although it is of little diagnostic use in any one case. Positron emission tomography (PET scan) promises to be of enormous value to assess focal brain dysfunction in the absence of gross structural lesion, since it employs contrast substances that are metabolically active. This technique is still in the developmental stage, however, and certain procedural requirements limit its usefulness in children. The same may be said of nuclear magnetic resonance imaging, which may well replace the CT scan when further developed.

THE ROLE OF THE NEUROLOGIST
IN TREATMENT AND INTERVENTION

Effective participation, even indirectly, in the treatment of any disorder demands some understanding on the part of the clinician of the nature of the disorder and available treatments. Much of the physician's frequent reluctance to become involved with children with developmental disabilities may derive from confusion and uncertainty on just these issues.

How, for example, do the specific learning disabilities relate to mental retardation? Most children with learning disabilities score within at least the broad average range on standard intelligence tests. Would they score even higher but for their disabilities, or does the learning disability involve something else besides intelligence?

If intelligence is synonymous with ability (i.e., aptitude, talent) for learning, the author sees no good reason to draw a distinction in kind between a learning disability and an intellectual deficit. It follows that there is reason to assume that the person with learning disability would in some way be more intelligent (more capable of learning) but for the specific deficit. The deficit of course may or may not affect performance on standard IQ tests, which are, after all, only sampling techniques for various learning abilities. That is why the author prefers to describe children with learning disabilities who have normal IQs as *otherwise* normally intelligent. Of interest to this issue is the fact that in a complete workup of what, in 1985, approaches 7,000 children and young adults with learning disabilities, the author and his colleagues have yet to find one with a full scale IQ above 150, when by chance alone they should have seen at least 30.

The learning disability, then, is most properly viewed as a talent deficit, in the face of which an important skill must, nevertheless, be acquired. The author and his colleagues explain to their patients that their task is not very different from that of the person who is determined to learn to play tennis despite a lack of talent for hitting a ball with a stick. The skill can be acquired under these conditions, but only by virtue of a great deal of hard practice and good coaching. In the process of so learning, it is quite discouraging to watch the natural athlete walk onto the court, pick up the racquet, and swing it correctly from the beginning.

The basic intervention for learning disabilities is educational, and is threefold. First, the student must acquire the skill in question despite a lack of talent. For this he or she requires remedial instruction. Second, at some point he or she must cope with academic challenges despite weak skills. For this, the child needs curriculum support. Third, and in some ways most important, he or she must maintain self-esteem and enthusiasm for learning despite the aversive educational experience of the basic skills years. For this the child requires the careful attention of a counselor and/or parent who is aware of his or her other talents.

The design of the actual remedial curriculum is left to the educator, with the understanding that few data are available to justify insistence upon a specific technique or strategy (see Chapter 1). An ongoing dialogue between the neurologist and the teacher aids in selecting interventions that make sense in view of measured deficits, and in setting up a program for monitoring their effect. An understanding of what the student faces at certain critical junctures (fourth grade; junior high school; high school or vocational school; college, if appropriate) is critical for long-term follow-up at regular intervals.

Medications (most frequently psychotropics or anticonvulsants) are best prescribed and monitored by a specialist in learning disorders, in order to insure optimal effectiveness, early detection of toxicity, and appropriate trials of discontinuation.

The physician can also be helpful with activity restrictions and driver's license certifications, waivers of language and physical education requirements, and medical requests for prosthetic aids ranging from wheelchairs to word processors.

INDICATIONS FOR REFERRAL TO A NEUROLOGIST

For children with learning disabilities being evaluated primarily by allied disciplines, the neurologist is seen as a resource for specialty referral, but such referral should not be made routinely. However, any child whose learning disorder is thought to be of constitutional origin (rather than environmentally determined) should probably have a neurological examination at some point.

In addition, certain specific symptoms or signs raise the index of suspicion for neurological dysfunction. A developmental history indicating a plateau, regression, or paroxysmal impairment of learning ability may signal an acquired nervous disease, possibly progressive and potentially treatable. A family history of nervous system disease is an indication for referral if that disease is known to be relevant to learning ability. Any observation of regression, paroxysmal impairment, or undulating acquisition of learning ability suggests neurological involvement. Any obvious asymmetry of motor or sensory function, such as focal weakness or clumsiness, or neglect of sensory input on one side, is reason for referral to a neurologist. Finally, although the simple diagnosis of "organicity" is beneath the sophistication of most modern psychometrists, certain constellations of performance deficit, particularly in timed nonverbal tasks such as the Coding subtest of the WISC-R, correlate sufficiently well with neurological deficit to warrant further study.

REFERENCES

Alexander, D., & Money, J. (1966). Turner's syndrome and Gerstmann's syndrome: Neuropsychologic comparisons. *Neuropsychologia, 4,*265–273.

American Psychiatric Association. (1980). *Diagnostic and statistical manual of mental disorders.* Washington, DC: Author.

Aram, D., & Nation, J. (1982). *Childhood language disorders.* St. Louis: C. V. Mosby.

Boder, E. (1973). Developmental dyslexia: A diagnostic approach based upon three atypical reading patterns. *Developmental Medicine and Child Neurology, 15,* 663–687.

Carroll, L. (1871). *Alice's adventures in wonderland.* London: Pennyroyal Press.

Chadwick, O., Rutter, M., Shaffer, D., & Shrout, P. (1981). A prospective study of children's head injuries. *Journal of Clinical Neuropsychology, 3,* 101–120.

Chase, C., Tallal, P., Schmitt, R. et al. (1984). A new chemotherapeutic investigation: Piracetam effects in dyslexia. *Annals of Dyslexia, 34,* 29–48.

Conners, C. (1971). The effect of unilateral alpha training on the visual evoked response in a dyslexic adolescent. *Psychophysiology, 9,* 467–470.

David, O., Clark, J., & Voeller, K. (1972). Lead and hyperactivity. *Lancet, 2,* 900–904.

DeLong, G. R., & Nieman, G. W. (1983). Lithium-induced behavior changes in children with symptoms suggesting manic-depressive illness. *Psychopharmacology Bulletin, 19,* 258–265.

Deutsch, C., Swanson, J., Warsh, J., & Farkas, L. (1984). *Neurological and pharmacological correlates of dysmorphology in attention deficit disorder.* Paper presented at the Society for Biological Psychiatry, Los Angeles.

Dodge, P. (1964). The neurological examination. In T. Farmer (Ed.), *Pediatric neurology.* New York: Harper & Row.

Duffy, F., Burchfiel, J., & Lombroso, C. (1979). Brain electrical activity mapping (BEAM): A method for extending the clinical utility of EEG and evoked potential data. *Annals of Neurology, 5,* 309–321.

Duffy, F., Denckla, M., Bartels, P., & Sandini, G. (1980). Dyslexia: Automated diagnosis by computerized classification of brain electrical activity. *Annals of Neurology, 7,* 421–428.

Eisenstein, E. M., & Cohen, M. J. (1967). Certain facts of learning relevant to the search for its physical basis. In G. C. Quarton, T. Melnechuk, & F. O. Schmitt (Eds.), *The neurosciences.* New York: Rockefeller University Press.

Finley, W., Faux, S., Hutcheson, J., & Amstutz, L. (1985). Long-latency event-related potentials in the evaluation of cognitive function in children. *Neurology, 35,* 323–327.

Frankenburg, W. K., & Dodds, J. B. (1969). *The Denver Developmental Screening Test.* Denver: University of Colorado Medical Center.

Galaburda, A., & Kemper, T. (1979). Cytoarchitectonic abnormalities in developmental dyslexia. *Annals of Neurology, 6,* 94–100.

Gascon, G., Victor, D., & Lombroso, C. (1973). Language disorder, convulsive disorder, and electroencephalographic abnormalities. *Archives of Neurology, 28,* 156–162.

Geschwind, N. (1965). Disconnexion syndromes in animals and man. *Brain, 88,* 237–293.

Geschwind, N., & Behan, P. (1982). Left-handedness: Association with immune disease, migraine, and developmental learning disorder. *Proceedings of the National Academy of Sciences, 79,* 4097–5001.

Geschwind, N., & Levitsky, W. (1968). Human brain: Left-right asymmetries in temporal speech region. *Science, 161,* 186–187.

Golden, G. (1982). Neurobiological correlates of learning disabilities. *Annals of Neurology, 12,* 409–418.

Hier, D. B., LeMay, M., Rosenberger, P. B., & Perlo, V. P. (1978). Developmental dyslexia: Evidence for a subgroup with a reversal of cerebral asymmetry. *Archives of Neurology, 35,* 90–92.

Hier, D. B., & Rosenberger, P. B. (1980). Focal left temporal lobe lesions and delayed speech acquisition. *Developmental and Behavioral Pediatrics, 1,* 53–57.

Hubbard, T., Paradise, J., McWilliams, B., Elster, B., & Taylor, F. (1985). Consequences of unremitting middle ear disease in early life. *New England Journal of Medicine, 312,* 1529–1534.

Illingworth, R. S. (1960). *Development of the infant and young child.* Edinburgh: Livingstone.

Kinsbourne, M., & Caplan, P. (1979). *Children's learning and attention problems.* Boston: Little, Brown.

Knobloch, H., & Pasamanick, B. (1962). *Etiologic factors in "early infantile autism" and "childhood schizophrenia."* Paper presented at the Tenth International Congress of Pediatrics, Lisbon, Portugal.

Knobloch, H., & Pasamanick, B. (Eds.). (1974). *Gesell and Amatruda's developmental diagnosis* (3rd ed.). New York: Harper & Row.

Landau, W. M., & Kleffner, F. R. (1957). Syndrome of acquired aphasia with convulsive disorder in children. *Neurology, 7,* 523–530.

Landrigen, P., Balch, R., Barthel, W., Whitworth, R., Staehling, N., & Rosenblum, B. (1975). Neuropsychological dysfunction in children with chronic low level lead absorption. *Lancet, 1,* 708–712.

LeMay, M. (1976). Morphological cerebral asymmetries of modern man, fossil man, and nonhuman primates. *Annals of the New York Academy of Sciences, 280,* 349–366.

Mattis, S., French, J. M., & Rapin, I. (1975). Dyslexia in children and young adults: Three independent neuropsychological syndromes. *Developmental Medicine and Child Neurology, 17,* 150–163.

Moser, H. W., & Wolf, P. A. (1971). The nosology of mental retardation. *Birth Defects Original Article Series, 7* (1).

Nigam, M., & Labar, D. (1979). Effect of hyperphenylalaninemia on size and density of synapses in rat neocortex. *Brain Research, 179,* 195–198.

O'Dougherty, M., Wright, F., Loewensen, L., & Torres, F. (1985). Cerebral dysfunction after chronic hypoxia. *Neurology, 35,* 42–46.

Orton, S. T. (1937). *Reading, writing, and speech problems in children.* New York: Norton.

Rapin, I., & Allen, D. (1983). Developmental language disorders: Nosologic considerations. In U. Kirk (Ed.), *Neuropsychology of language, reading, and spelling.* New York: Academic Press.

Rohrbaugh, J., Syndulko, K., & Lindsley, D. (1976). Brain wave components of contingent negative variation in the human. *Science, 191,* 1055–1058.

Rosenberger, P. B. (1970). Visual matching and clinical findings among good and poor readers. *American Journal of Diseases of Children,* 103–110.

Rosenberger, P. B. (1980). Neurological processes in language. In R. Schiefelbusch (Ed.), *Bases of language intervention.* Baltimore: University Park Press.

Rosenberger, P. B. (1981). The pediatrician and psychometric testing. *Pediatrics in Review, 2,* 301–310.

Rosenberger, P. B., Cowgill, M. L., & Heiman, S. K. (1977). *The verbosity of hydrocephalus: An isolated speech area syndrome?* Paper presented at the annual meeting of the Academy of Aphasia.

Rosenberger, P., & Ferraro, S. (1984). Experimental hyperphenylalaninemia and reinforcement schedule performance. *Annals of Neurology, 16,* 384.

Rosenberger, P. B., & Hier, D. B. (1980). Cerebral asymmetry and verbal intellectual deficits. *Annals of Neurology, 8,* 300–304.

Rutter, M. (1978). Diagnosis and definition of childhood autism. *Journal of Autism and Childhood Schizophrenia, 8,* 139–161.

Rutter, M. (1982). Syndromes attributed to "minimal brain dysfunction" in childhood. *American Journal of Psychiatry, 139,* 21–23.

Shaywitz, B., Cohen, D., & Bowers, M. (1977). CSF monoamine metabolites in children with minimal brain dysfunction: Evidence for alteration of brain dopamine. *Journal of Pediatrics, 90,* 67–71.

Shaywitz, B., Yager, R., & Klopper, J. (1976). Selective brain dopamine depletion in developing rats: An experimental model of minimal brain dysfunction. *Science, 191,* 305–308.

Shaywitz, S., & Shaywitz, B. (1984). Attention deficit disorders. *Pediatrics in Review, 6,* 99–109.

Sprague, R., Barnes, K., & Werry, J. (1970). Methylphenidate and thioridazine: Learning, reaction time, activity, and classroom behavior in disturbed children. *American Journal of Orthopsychiatry, 40,* 615–628.

Squire, L. (1982). The neuropsychology of human memory. *Annual Review of Neuroscience, 5,* 241–273.

Wolfensberger, W., & Menolascino, F. (1970). Methodological considerations in the evaluation of the intelligence-enhancing properties of drugs. In F. Menolascino (Ed.), *Psychiatric approaches to mental retardation.* New York: Basic Books.

Zametkin, A., Karoum, F., Linnolla, M., Rapaport, J., Brown, G., Chuang, L., & Wyatt, R. (1985). Stimulants, urinary catecholamines, and indolamines in hyperactivity. *Archives of General Psychiatry, 42,* 251–255.

APPENDIX A

MASSACHUSETTS GENERAL HOSPITAL

LEARNING DISORDERS UNIT
CASE HISTORY FORM

Please fill out this form as completely as possible, and bring it with you on the day of your child's appointment.

Date:_____

Patient:_____ Birth Date:_____
Address:_____
Phone:_____ Referred by:_____

I. PREGNANCY

1. Was your pregnancy with this child your
   1st   2nd   3rd   4th   5th   6th _____
2. When you were pregnant with this child did you have:

   Spotting or bleeding .... Yes ☐ No ☐
   Toxemia .... Yes ☐ No ☐
   Excessive weight gain............................ Yes ☐ No ☐
   Pernicious vomiting............................. Yes ☐ No ☐
   High blood pressure .... Yes ☐ No ☐
   Measles, chicken pox, mumps..................... Yes ☐ No ☐
   Infection in the first three months .... Yes ☐ No ☐
                  second three months................. Yes ☐ No ☐
                  third three months................... Yes ☐ No ☐
   Accident in the first three months .... Yes ☐ No ☐
                  second three months................. Yes ☐ No ☐
                  third three months................... Yes ☐ No ☐
   Surgery in the first three months .... Yes ☐ No ☐
                  second three months................. Yes ☐ No ☐
                  third three months................... Yes ☐ No ☐
   X rays .... Yes ☐ No ☐
   Medications, specify:_____
3. Are you:
   Diabetic? .... Yes ☐ No ☐
   Rh negative? .... Yes ☐ No ☐
4. Were there any problems with this pregnancy?_____
   _____

5. How many weeks did you carry this child?_____

Case History Form
(continued)

LABOR
1. Did you go into labor yourself?........................... Yes ☐ No ☐
2. Did your bag of waters break before labor started? .... Yes ☐ No ☐
   If yes, how long before?_____
3. How long did labor last?_____
4. Were there any difficulties with the labor?................. Yes ☐ No ☐
   If yes, explain:_____

II. BIRTH
1. Delivery
   Came out by self................................. Yes ☐ No ☐
   Forceps.. Yes ☐ No ☐
   Cesarean... Yes ☐ No ☐
   Breech .... Yes ☐ No ☐
   Birth Weight ....____lb. ___oz.
2. Was your child premature........................... Yes ☐ No ☐
   postmature........................... Yes ☐ No ☐
3. Multiple birth: Identical twin......................... Yes ☐ No ☐
   Fraternal twin......................... Yes ☐ No ☐
   Triplet............................... Yes ☐ No ☐
   Other, specify_____
4. Did the baby cry immediately at birth?.................... Yes ☐ No ☐
5. Did the baby need oxygen at birth?...................... Yes ☐ No ☐
6. Was the child placed in an incubator?.................... Yes ☐ No ☐
7. Did the baby have difficulty with sucking or crying when he
   was first brought to you? .... Yes ☐ No ☐
8. Did the baby come home from the hospital with you?........ Yes ☐ No ☐

III. MEDICAL HISTORY	0–30 days	1–12 mos.	1–5 yrs.	5 yrs. up
1. Is (was) your child's general health				
good...				
fair				
poor				
2. Has your child had:				
Any serious illness				
Specify:_____				
Jaundice....................................				
Infections...................................				
Specify:_____				

Case History Form
(*continued*)

Meningitis . . . .
Specify:_____
Seizures, convulsions, or fits. . . . .
Specify:_____
Poor weight gain. . . . .
Incubator or oxygen therapy . . . .
Specify:_____
Loss of consciousness . . . .
Head injuries. . . . .
Specify:_____
Other injuries . . . .
Specify:_____
Headaches . . . .
Specify:_____
Dizziness . . . .
Fainting or blackout spells. . . . .
Frequent ear infections. . . . .
Frequent sore throats, tonsillitis, laryngitis. . . . .
Specify:_____
Operations:
Tonsils. . . . .
Adenoids . . . .
Ear drainage tubes . . . .
Laryngeal. . . . .
Hernia . . . .
Other, specify:_____
Severe rash . . . .
Allergies . . . .
Specify:_____
Postnasal drip . . . .
Toxin exposure (poisons). . . . .
Specify:_____
Other, specify:_____

3. Does your child have normal hearing? . . . . Yes ☐ No ☐
When checked?_____
4. Does your child have normal vision?. . . . . Yes ☐ No ☐
When checked?_____
5. Are your child's immunizations up to date? . . . . Yes ☐ No ☐
6. Does your child breathe through his mouth?. . . . . Yes ☐ No ☐
7. Does your child have any dental problems? . . . . Yes ☐ No ☐
8. Does your child take any medications?. Yes ☐ No ☐
Specify:_____

Case History Form
(*continued*)

9. Other medical problems, specify:_____

_____

_____

IV. DEVELOPMENTAL MOTOR HISTORY

1. At what age did your child first do the following:

Relative to siblings

	Yrs.	Mo.	Earlier	Later
Sit alone				
Stand alone				
Begin walking				
Ride a tricycle (using pedals)				
Ride a two wheel bicycle (without training wheels)				
Button his clothes				
Tie his shoes				

2. At what age was your child toilet trained? . . . . .

Was your child difficult to toilet train? . . . . Yes ☐ No ☐

3. What is your child's hand preference?
    ☐ Right ☐ Left ☐ Neither is preferred

4. Does he do some things with the other hand? Yes ☐ No ☐
    If yes, specify:_____

5. How would you rate his bodily coordination?
    ☐ Good ☐ Fair ☐ Poor

6. During preschool years, did your child have unusual difficulty
    sitting still for any period of time? . . . . Yes ☐ No ☐
    If yes, describe:_____

_____

V. SPEECH AND LANGUAGE HISTORY

1. Description of vocal behavior as an infant
    ☐ Quiet ☐ Average ☐ Noisy
2. Primary stimulation in preschool years
    ☐ Books ☐ TV ☐ Adult Exposure
3. Parents' estimate of child's intelligence
    ☐ Above average ☐ Average ☐ Below

Case History Form
(continued)

		Relative to siblings	
Yrs.	Mos.	Earlier	Later

4. At what age did your child babble?

5. At what age did your child say his first words?

      Note actual words:_____

6. At what age did your child begin to combine words?

      Note actual phrases:_____

7. Is your child's speech difficult to understand? .... Yes ☐ No ☐
8. Does your child have difficulty following verbal instructions or commands? .... Yes ☐ No ☐
9. Does your child turn up the TV louder than average .... Yes ☐ No ☐
10 During preschool years, did your child take an interest in looking at picture books? .... Yes ☐ No ☐
11. During preschool years, did your child lose interest quickly when being read to? .... Yes ☐ No ☐
12. If your child's speech is late in developing, how does he attempt to communicate?
      Eyes .... Yes ☐ No ☐
      Hand gestures .... Yes ☐ No ☐
      Babbling.. Yes ☐ No ☐
      Baby talk .... Yes ☐ No ☐
      Others, specify:_____
13. If your child has a speech difficulty, is the difficulty more noticeable at some times?............................. Yes ☐ No ☐
14. Has your child ever had speech or hearing therapy? .... Yes ☐ No ☐
      If so, where and for how long?_____

VI. EDUCATIONAL HISTORY

1. At what age did your child enter the following grades (do not include special education, transition, or ungraded classed here):
      Nursery School .... ___Yrs. or ☐ None
      Kindergarten........................... ___Yrs. or ☐ None
      1st grade.............................. ___Yrs. or ☐ None
      2nd grade .... ___Yrs. or ☐ None
      3rd grade .... ___Yrs. or ☐ None

Case History Form
(continued)

2. At what age did your child enter any of the following:
   Ungraded Classroom .... ___Yrs. or ☐ None
   Special Education .... ___Yrs. or ☐ None
   Transition Class .... ___Yrs. or ☐ None
3. Number of "school years" spent in any of the following:
   Ungraded Classroom .... ___School Yrs.
   Special Education .... ___School Yrs.
   Transition Class .... ___School Yrs.
4. Has your child ever repeated a grade in school?............. Yes ☐ No ☐
   If yes, explain:_____
5. Has your child ever skipped a grade in school? .... Yes ☐ No ☐
   If yes, explain:_____
6. What is your child's present school placement?
   Grade:_____
   School:_____
   Teacher:_____
7. Are some subjects particularly difficult for your child .... Yes ☐ No ☐
   If yes, explain:_____
8. What are the subjects in which your child does well in school?_____
   _____
   _____

VII. BEHAVIOR CHARACTERISTICS
1. Do any of the following describe your child?
   a. Nervous .... Yes ☐ No ☐
      If yes, explain:_____
   b. Nervous habits (thumb sucking, nail biting, etc.) ..... Yes ☐ No ☐
      If yes, list:_____
   c. Frustration tolerance .... Low ☐ High ☐
      List situations:_____
   d. Temper Tantrums .... Yes ☐ No ☐
      Frequency:_____
   e. Destructiveness .... Yes ☐ No ☐
      If yes, explain:_____
   f. Overactivity................................... Yes ☐ No ☐
   g. Sleeplessness.................................. Yes ☐ No ☐
      Frequency:_____
   h. Strange and persistent fears .... Yes ☐ No ☐
      If yes, explain:_____
   i. Constipation .... Yes ☐ No ☐
   j. Feeding problems (regurgitation)................... Yes ☐ No ☐
      Other, specify:_____

Case History Form
(continued)

    k. Food idiosyncracies .... Yes ☐ No ☐
       Explain:_____
    l. Shy....................................... Yes ☐ No ☐
    m. Daydreams .... Yes ☐ No ☐
    n. Tells lies .... Yes ☐ No ☐
    o. Jealous.................................... Yes ☐ No ☐
    p. Whines/cries frequently .... Yes ☐ No ☐
2. What are your child's strengths?
    (What does he do well?)_____

VIII. FAMILY HISTORY

1. Family Profile

	Name	Age	Grade in School	Grades Repeated	Handedness (Rt. or Lt.)
a.	Mother ____				
b.	Father ____				
	Children:				
c.					
d.					
e.					
f.					
g.					

2. Has any relation of the child had a history of any of the following: (if yes, state relation to child)

                                                       Specify

    Mental illness .... Yes ☐ No ☐ _____
    Epilepsy or Convulsions............... Yes ☐ No ☐ _____
    Mental retardation.................... Yes ☐ No ☐ _____
    Difficulty learning to read .... Yes ☐ No ☐ _____
    Difficulty spelling.................... Yes ☐ No ☐ _____
    Late appearance of speech............. Yes ☐ No ☐ _____
    Speech problems
      (other than late appearance).......... Yes ☐ No ☐ _____
    Hearing difficulty .... Yes ☐ No ☐ _____

3. Parents' occupations:
    Mother:_____
    Father:_____
4. Number of languages spoken in home:_____

Case History Form
(*continued*)

5. How does your child get along with his brothers and sisters?
   ☐ Well ☐ Fair ☐ Poor
   Describe:_____
6. How would you describe the parent-child relationship with the patient?
   ☐ Good ☐ Fair ☐ Poor
   Describe:_____
7. Which parent usually administers discipline?_____
   Which discipline practices are most effective?_____
   Which discipline practices are least effective?_____
8. How does your child get along with children (other than siblings)
   ☐ Well ☐ Fair ☐ Poor
9. How does your child get along with adults (other than parents)
   ☐ Well ☐ Fair ☐ Poor

Who has filled out this case history form?
   ☐ Mother ☐ Father ☐ Both together
   Other:_____
Date:_____

APPENDIX B

LEARNING DISORDERS UNIT

Neurological Assessment

Enter name and unit number on both sides of EVERY sheet. Addressograph plate to be used when available. Name and unit number to be written distinctly when plate is not available.

(√ = normal or not involved; x = abnormal)
PRESENT ILLNESS   Chief complaint:
First noted: Progressive?   Grades repeated:
Subjects involved:
Remedial efforts:
Attention span: Hyperactivity?
Discipline at home: at school:
Relationships with siblings: with peers:
PAST HISTORY   (See Case History Form for details)
Pregnancy: Perinatal: Childhood health:
Development: Motor   Language   Social   Preschool
FAMILY HISTORY   (See Case History Form)
School problems: Mental Def.:   Psychiatric: Sinistrality:

MASSACHUSETTS EYE AND EAR INFIRMARY

Neurological Assessment
(*continued*)

($\sqrt{}$ = normal or not involved; x = abnormal)
EXAMINATION
Size: Proportions:
Head circ.:   Head shape: Features:
Personality, affect:
Verbal output: Productivity   Articulation
Fluency   Grammar/Syntax   Vocabulary
Names___/10 objects; identifies___/10 by name, ___/5 by function.
Complies with ___-stage commands.
Writing: Linguistics   Mechanics
Reading: (Material _____)   Fluency   Accuracy   Comprehension
Sample errors
Figure Construction: Gesell ○ X □ △ ◇   Clock   Union Jack
Laterality preference: Hand, write   Hand, throw   Foot   Eye
Laterality awareness: ___ errors in ___ trials:
Math skills:
NEUROLOGICAL EXAMINATION
Cranial nerves:
Optic fundi: OKN:

MASSACHUSETTS GENERAL HOSPITAL

Neurological Assessment
(continued)

(√ = normal or not involved; x = abnormal)

Tendon reflexes: Plantar responses:

Motor strength: Motor tone: Motor coordination:

Sensory:

LABORATORY DATA   (presently available)

Intelligence:

School achievement:

Language, perceptual skills:

Vision: Hearing:

Other:

SUMMARY AND IMPRESSIONS

DISPOSITION

Examiner:

Chapter 10

Practical Issues and Illustrative Cases

$\sim$

David L. Wodrich and James E. Joy

At this point, the authors hope the reader has become aware of the vast array of truly multidimensional problems that are encompassed in the concepts of learning disabilities and mental retardation. Equally numerous and complex, even when presented in simplified overview fashion, are the assessment techniques and perspectives used by the various diagnostic specialties. The enterprise of multidisciplinary assessment is indeed complicated. This complicated nature prevents the authors, as practitioners, from providing the reader with simple procedures for organizing and executing the multidisciplinary process. In fact, it could be argued that there is no one multidisciplinary process, but as many different and potentially successful processes as there are groups of practitioners involved.

In this final chapter, the authors hope to provide, through discussion and illustrative cases, some issues for consideration by those involved in assessing learners with delays. For the most part, these issues highlight options that confront the practitioner as he or she works with others evaluating children. The authors' position is that there are few absolutely correct ways to proceed and few absolutely incorrect; unique professional, geographic, financial, and interpersonal considerations prohibit issuing a single blueprint. Perhaps the one absolute that can be offered is that the more each practitioner knows about the background and training, assessment procedures, and purported professional domain of the others, the better the multidisciplinary concept works. Chapters 2–9 have been written toward that end.

FIXED VERSUS FLEXIBLE TEAMS

Consider multidisciplinary assessment from its very outset—the point at which diagnostic personnel are first sought out. At this point, parents, social agencies, and schools come forward with children who are in some way failing, either in fact or at least in the perception of those lodging the referral. However, the referral source is usually unaware of the exact nature of the child's problem. Problems may range from inherent medical disabilities such as phenylketonuria (PKU) or seizures; to information-processing difficulties; to a mismatch between learner characteristics and instructional method; to no significant disabilities but rather, overconcerned parents or teacher. The diversity of the problems exhibited and the relative lack of knowledge of those outside the diagnostic process mean that the referral agent is usually in no position to determine within whose professional domain the problem resides. Consequently, that individual is in a position neither to make a precise initial referral nor to coordinate a sequence of referrals to various professionals so that a multidisciplinary process eventuates.

One solution is to turn to what might be called a "fixed team" composed of diagnostic professionals from the various disciplines. Fixed team members (e.g., physician, psychologist, speech pathologist, audiologist, educator) are usually previously identified, have agreed upon assessment and screening procedures, and have established formats for reports and parent feedback. Often all services are provided at a single location so that travel is minimized and so that the advantages of team cohesiveness can develop (Mulvenon, 1980). Central to this approach is the assumption that the team members' pooled data are so exhaustive that no aspect of a problem and no unique disability escapes detection.

Fixed teams such as might be found at the 41 University Affiliated Facilities for the Developmentally Disabled have no doubt been advantageous for complicated and severe cases of mental retardation, although it has been recognized that such centers provide services to those with milder learning and developmental handicaps as well (Bender et al., 1984; Urbano et al., 1984). These and other specialized centers, however, cannot constitute the entire picture because so much assessment occurs in locations where perhaps only one or two disciplines are available. For example, a school may be asked to assess a struggling second grader using only its available team of psychologist and special educator; or a pediatrician working alone in his or her office may begin initial evaluation of a 3-year-old with delays by checking developmental milestones. A fixed team approach has limited value for the huge number of children with potential problems who have access to some assessment services, but do not have access to those of a specialty center. Moreover, procedural assessment of all children by all team members, a practice of some fixed teams, may be unnecessary and cost/time inefficient. Insisting, for instance, that all children who fail in school receive a neurological examination because a small number may have undetected neurological disease may be considered to be of questionable value.

A second alternative, the "flexible team" approach, is also regularly used but probably could be improved by greater knowledge of each professional's unique skills and by better communication among the assessing professionals. The flexible team approach recognizes that: 1) children are referred with heterogeneous problems requiring services ranging from few to many specialty assessments; 2) any one of several professionals working independently (psychologist, educator, psychiatrist, neurologist) may start the assessment; and 3) the initial practitioners generally choose to remain involved even though they themselves are not a part of an existing multidisciplinary team.

The flexible team approach, which has wide, implicit acceptance and usage, begins with the original contact person. For example, the school psychologist who conducts a standard evaluation is responsible for initial case conceptualization, such as assessing the prospect of the existence of unique behavioral syndromes requiring specialized expertise, or biomedical conditions requiring medical involvement. Case conceptualization of this type necessarily involves hypothesizing about the presence of conditions in someone else's professional domain (e.g., medicine, audiology), so it is essential for each diagnostic profession to possess some understanding of every other diagnostic profession. Ultimately, in this example, the psychologist must judge the necessity for specialty referral based on how much additional information is to be gained and, most important, how much each specialist might aid in accomplishing the goals of assessment (i.e., to implement intervention efforts, to plan, and to inform pertinent individuals in the child's life). Involvement by additional professionals who add nothing to intervention or planning (e.g., they simply redescribe a previously documented condition in their own discipline's jargon) represents an inappropriate referral. The flexible team process concludes with information being returned to the requesting professional (in this example, the psychologist) for integration and interpretation, intervention plan formulation, and information sharing with family or teachers.

For the sake of clarity, consider the example of a slow developing 5-year-old boy, who is about to enter kindergarten and was recently evaluated by a school psychologist. Intellectual assessment revealed a Verbal IQ of 52, a Performance (nonverbal) IQ of 68, severe self-care delays, and no kindergarten readiness skills. The psychologist also noted that the child appeared physically atypical, prompting concern about a biomedical syndrome with genetic etiology. Questions also arose about auditory acuity based on both parent comment and observation during testing. The school psychologist decided to refer the child to a developmental pediatrician for physical examination and dysmorphology assessment, if necessary, and to an audiologist for a hearing examination. Specialists' findings were shared with the child's parents and returned to the school psychologist (to be consolidated with other data), and educational plans were then made in conjunction with the local special education staff. Note, however, that this child may have received the same specialty assessments but sequenced differently if he had been first examined by a developmental pediatrician rather than by a psychologist. Under such circumstances, the child's atypical physical appearance may have resulted in chromosome studies, followed by referral to a psychologist for intellectual/adaptive assessment, and then to an audiologist for hearing evaluation. Under such circumstances, the pediatrician would have shared information with the boy's parents and independently, or in collaboration with the psychologist, special educator, and audiologist, would have made intervention recommendations.

There are, of course, hazards to this informal flexible approach. Those who choose to operate from a flexible team perspective soon find a certain amount of trial-and-error is involved in locating valuable resources to whom children may be referred. Often, networks develop slowly and imperfectly over a period of years. Further, because independent practitioners seldom turn away referrals from allied professionals, some of whose judgment and professional practices are unknown, the prospect of being involved in an informal team about which one has little knowledge or over which one has little quality control is a potential pitfall of the flexible team approach. (As a minimum, one can check the referring professional's qualifications, the guidelines of which are presented in the respective chapters of this book.) Still, effective practice of the flexible team approach occurs regularly. Case studies presented later in this chapter involve successful use of both fixed and flexible team approaches.

CONSIDERATIONS FOR INCLUDING OTHER PROFESSIONALS

It is natural for each professional to value his or her own discipline's skills and techniques highly and, consequently, to argue for including his or her specialty in the assessment of virtually all learners with disability or delay. In reality, however, such professional egocentricity must be tempered by practical considerations such as time expenditure, cost, and professional availability. Clearly limits already exist or must be imposed on the number of professionals involved and how much time each one spends in the assessment. Notwithstanding this fact, there are instances in which, without the expert contribution of those from outside disciplines, one's findings may be incomplete, or worse, may be negligently wrong. A balance must be struck between absolute comprehensiveness on the one hand, and prohibitive cost and time expenditures on the other.

A reasonable aid to practitioners would be "rules" that signal which cases require additional expertise and that suggest which discipline is most likely to provide that expertise. Rules of this type are more relevant to individual practitioners working in a flexible team mode, of course, than for fixed teams in which several disciplines are always involved or in which physical proximity allows informal discussion about the need for specialty consultation. Table 10.1 is offered as a guide for deciding when and to whom to refer. It is a distillation of the most crucial points made by this book's contributing authors, who represent most of the important assessment disciplines.

The authors of this chapter appreciate that more experienced clinicians have less occasion for outside consultations. This is not to imply that seasoned diagnosticians become so competent that they know and can do everything themselves, but instead recognizes that a substantial portion of referrals are made to rule out a condition, perhaps a seizure or hearing loss, which if present would be extremely significant. Experienced clinicians often know from existing data whether hearing loss or seizure is at all likely and thus make fewer low-yield referrals. That is, even though he or she may follow the same basic rules for referring, experience has taught more precisely what the signs that trigger a referral actually look like in clinical practice.

Just as the referring diagnosticians' skills vary, unfortunately so do those in the other professionals to whom one turns for help. For instance, not all speech-language pathologists are interested in language processing skills, nor are all capable of extrapolating findings in this realm to plans that would help the youngster at school; some occupational therapists are adept at detailing remedial activities of daily living (ADL) plans for children with mental retardation, while others confine their involvement to children with physical or motor handicaps. The individual practitioner is encouraged to identify the strengths and interests among his or her team members or, if working independently, among potential professional resources in the community to whom he or she can turn on an individual case basis.

The foregoing emphasis on identifying unique handicaps should not mislead the reader; one of the real values of assessment is to provide a rational basis for intervention, and this criterion should be remembered when forming a team or making a referral. A special educator who may be perfectly competent to identify a child's attention deficit disorder, may seek confirmation and assistance from a child psychiatrist because medication may be a valuable aspect of intervention. A pediatrician may recognize a 3-year-old's mental retardation but refers to a psychologist because a detailed intellectual evaluation and interpretation will facilitate parent understanding and help determine the child's preschool education needs. A special educator, speech-language pathologist, or occupational therapist—as the person who provides direct remedial care—ultimately works out the specific drills most likely to benefit the child. His or her role in assessing the child is indispensable, although the

Table 10.1. Indices for referral

Indication	Rationale
Refer to psychologist	
Obvious delayed development 6 weeks–2 years of age	Objective cognitive measures detect only severe delays.
Suspected delayed development after 2 years	IQ measures after 2 years have good prediction.
School failure not responsive to informal intervention	IQ and academic measures can pinpoint problem for remediation and planning.
Refer to special educator	
School-age children whose initial assessment has occurred outside of school	Comprehensive delineation of the problem is impossible without educational observation and data.
School-age children in need of remedial instruction	Specific educational goals require input from a special educator.
Refer to audiologist	
Medical conditions such as otitis media with effusion, perinatal infection (TORCH), and cis platinum chemotherapy	These conditions have a high incidence of associated hearing loss.
Family history of sensorineural hearing loss	Hearing loss often has a hereditary etiology.
Child who complains of hearing difficulty or for whom examination or observation suggests possible hearing loss	Professional audiological examination can produce conclusive findings in most cases. All children are testable.
Refer to speech-language pathologist	
Preschoolers whose understanding of vocabulary, use of grammar, and articulation is one or more years delayed (refer also to psychologist for IQ testing)	May have identifiable, treatable language problem
School-age children with Verbal IQ 15 points < Performance IQ	May have identifiable, treatable language problem
Stuttering or dysfluency after age 4–5 years	Diagnosis and treatment earlier is inadvisable, may be transient

(continued)

child's condition and basic physical, cognitive, and academic parameters may have been evaluated before his or her involvement. Those involved in planning and intervention, not just those who identify and describe, warrant inclusion in a thorough multidisciplinary assessment.

A final opinion is offered before leaving the topic of team formation. In the author's view, the wise professional constantly reflects that his or her

Table 10.1. (*continued*)

Indication	Rationale
Refer to occupational therapist	
Child whose handicap includes physical limitations, severe motor problems, or requires adaptive equipment	Early assessment and intervention prevents learning of inappropriate motor habits that must be unlearned (could refer to physical therapist instead).
Child who requires detailed assessment or planning of activities of daily living	Specialized expertise often facilitates planning (could refer to special educator instead).
Refer to developmental pediatrician	
Child in high-risk population based on history (e.g., history in newborn ICU)	A definite percent have sequelae with learning/behavior problems.
Child appears physically unusual with delayed development	Dysmorphologies are relevant in identifying mental retardation.
Child with school difficulty in presence of complex/chronic medical disorders	Appropriate intervention must incorporate management of medical issues.
Refer to child psychiatrist	
Child with school problems related to suspected attention deficit disorder	Medication may be important in treatment.
Child with learning disabilities and indicators of family or parental dysfunction	Will likely need family or parent treatment if child's condition to benefit fully
Child shows unusual combination of symptoms/behaviors across many areas	Pervasive developmental disorder/ autism is often undiagnosed. Medical diagnostic statement may be required for placement. Consider anxiety, depression, or psychosis.
Child with mental retardation with evidence of emotional distress	Need to address coexisting psychiatric diagnoses
Refer to pediatric neurologist	
Child with neurological indications on psychological testing	Specific diagnosis requires consultation
Child with developmental plateau, regression, or paroxysmal recurring impairment	Must consider degenerative disorders or types of seizure activity
Family history positive for learning-related neurodisorders	Must establish or exclude same diagnosis in child
Child with history of significant central nervous system trauma	Consultation assists to establish prognosis, shape interventions

professional domain is not nearly as broad as he or she might otherwise believe, and recognizes that this is the era of specialization. Partially as a result of the explosion of knowledge and partially because of the specialty-specific method of reporting (in narrowly focused journals read by members of only one or two disciplines), it is impossible for any professional to keep abreast of important new information developing simultaneously in several disciplines. For instance, it would be unreasonable to expect any one professional to keep current on genetic research, follow the latest changes in neurotransmitters and the medications that act upon them, understand the psychometric nuances of recent multiple regression studies used to form instructional groups empirically, and keep posted on recent curriculum materials designed to teach important ADLs. Yet quite conceivably, all of this knowledge may be required to fully understand, implement intervention for, and plan for a single child with mental retardation.

TEAM LEADERSHIP

Discussion about multidisciplinary team leadership invariably raises issues of professional turf and questions the very nature of the conditions of mental retardation and learning disabilities. In the realm of learning disabilities, for instance, some have argued that the child's problems are medical and thus, assessment and subsequent intervention plans can be made best when a primary care physician is in charge (Levine, Brook, & Shonkoff, 1980). Other physicians (Griffith, 1979) have observed that reference to neurological/physical status explains only a few of the children who exhibit learning problems. Some educators and psychologists have argued that learning disability is simply an educational phenomenon and that medical assessment is relatively unimportant (McLeod, 1983; Ross, 1979).

This text is predicted on the position that no one professional group has sole entitlement to assess children with mental retardation or learning disabilities because a multitude of conditions and problems may be involved. Some of these are medical, some psychological, some linguistic, some educational, and many include elements best assessed by several disciplines. In many cases, the same problem can be meaningfully conceptualized by physiological, behavioral, or social levels, or can be thought of primarily as a perceptual, motor, linguistic, or cognitive problem, depending on the preferred professional perspective. To assert that learning and developmental problems fall solely in the purview of medicine, education, psychology, or any other discipline assumes a homogeneity of problems that is simply not the case. Moreover, adopting a single profession's perspective may confine assessment and intervention to an unnecessary conceptual straightjacket.

For a fixed team the simplest solution to the leadership problem is to agree to set aside the turf issue and to appoint a professional leader from any of the disciplines likely to be involved in most cases (e.g., special education, psychology, or medicine). This works as long as the leader appreciates the competence of the other members, so that they are used wisely, and agrees to insure that the important mission of coordinating findings into usable intervention and planning packages occurs and that parents are intelligently informed.

Things are less simple for those who form teams as needed on an individual case basis—the flexible approach. Here the key is to insure that the assessment process culminates in usable, integrated information. Generally a case or patient manager who will "own" the case is required; he or she requests consultations, draws conclusions, determines broadly or narrowly what programming or intervention is necessary, and informs parents, school, or social agencies of the findings. This person is responsible for the accuracy and thoroughness of the finished product. Often the first diagnostician involved (assuming he or she is comfortable with the task) provides this service. Exceptions might occur when a professional with a relatively more circumscribed realm of expertise (e.g., audiologist) is presented with a case in which several problems exist (e.g., hearing loss plus autism, mental retardation, and conduct problems); a decision might be made to allow someone more comfortable with the core problems (e.g., psychologist or child psychiatrist) to serve as case manager. In other cases, a significant medical condition, such as seizures, that will necessitate regular medical follow-up may lead a nonphysician to turn over case management to a physician. In other cases, it may be wisest to place case management in the hands of a nonmedical specialist such as the speech pathologist or psychologist, if recurring follow-up treatments are necessary. The point to be made here is that a case manager/professional leader should be clearly identified to all involved and should be capable of coordinating services. Professionals who find themselves involved in the multidisciplinary process and who doubt the manager's ability to explain findings clearly or to convert them into reasonable intervention options may legitimately request to participate in a planning session or an information feedback session with the parents.

MAKING INFORMATIVE REFERRALS

Just as is true any time a professional opinion is sought, the referring professional in a multidisciplinary process can help insure usable findings by clearly and concisely sharing information. A simple method of organizing referral information that involves three steps has recently been summarized by Wodrich (1984).

First, those referring are encouraged to present brief, objective descriptions of the problem, without interpretation. An example might be: "This 4-year-old has been observed by his parents to rock incessantly since 6 months of age; he reportedly has no receptive or expressive language; he is bowel and bladder trained; and recently he has appeared insensitive to sound, and has screamed intermittently for brief (20-second) intervals without apparent cause."

Second, the referring professional conveys his or her working hypotheses to the receiving professional: "Originally this boy impressed me as a mentally retarded child with difficult (but at least partially learned) behavior problems; but testing shows a Wechsler Verbal IQ of 61 and a Performance IQ of 89, and some adaptive skills are near normal. The parents seemingly have used intelligent and consistent behavior management procedures, yet the child continues his disruptive behaviors and his screaming has increased. It is unclear whether this is primarily intensification of learned behavior or reflects a neurological condition undetected during regular medical care.''

Third, and most important, specific questions to be answered by the referral evaluation are made explicit. The following might be posed to a physician: ''Is this child's behavior reflecting an identifiable biomedical condition? Is this a static or progressive condition? If progressive, what is its anticipated course? Is medical intervention possible?'' An audiologist might be asked: ''Is this child's hearing adequate to understand speech sounds? Are there corrective measures or procedures to keep in mind when speaking to him?'' Perhaps a speech-language pathologist would also be consulted to answer questions about the nature of language delays, prognosis, and remedial or circumvention activities. General referrals, such as requests for ''neurological examination,'' generally should be avoided because they impart too little information about the problem the child is exhibiting, the case manager's working hypotheses, and questions that the referring professional wants answered. The point is that answerable questions are made clear by the referring professional so as to minimize confusion about what is expected of each consulting diagnostician.

RECORDKEEPING AND SHARING

No matter how configured, the multidisciplinary assessment process is time-consuming and costly, and ought to produce important data, often of enduring significance for the child. Appropriate documentation of findings, their significance, and the plans that follow from them are required in the form of written records. While it is beyond the scope of this volume to discuss report writing and recordkeeping in depth, there are two issues important to multidisciplinary assessment that require mentioning: single versus multiple document preparation, and the question of releasing written documents to parents.

On the first point, one possibility (especially for the flexible team approach) is to have each professional prepare free-standing documentation of his or her findings. The primary professional or case manager then consolidates those findings; shares conclusions, intervention options, and future direction with those who originally requested services; but may not draft a summary document of all findings and recommendations. A major disadvantage of this arrangement is the absence of a single integrating document to which one can refer back in the weeks, months, and years ahead. A minor disadvantage is that the separate reports are often redundant, each restating the child's initial problem, developmental and family history, etc., which precludes quick reading.

An obviously preferable alternative might involve the case manager or professional leader briefly restating all specialty consultations, drawing conclusions, and formalizing recommendations in a more or less comprehensive written document that could be sent to interested professionals or later referenced as a guide for case planning. Such documents seem to be fairly commonplace in fixed team settings.

Another acceptable alternative, especially for the flexible approach, is simply for the case manager or professional leader to delay preparing the report of his or her own professional findings until all other consultations have been received. This report, perhaps that of a speech pathologist assessing for language delay, then begins with a brief summary of each consultant's findings (e.g., a psychologist who rules out mental retardation, a developmental pediatrician who rules out genetic syndromes), details the case manager's or professional leader's findings from his or her own techniques, and ends with an integration of conclusions and recommendations from all of the team members. Professionals who require more detailed information about any of the specialty consultations (e.g., as the child begins kindergarten, a school psychologist requests previously obtained Wechsler scores) would be referred to the consultant's original document.

The issues of accessibility of prior records have led some professionals to provide parents with some or all professional reports. While there are obvious ethical considerations, such as misinterpretation of the meaning of technical documents (American Psychological Association, 1974), when dealing with a child with complex problems who has seen several specialists, and particularly if geographic moves are involved, a parent armed with a portfolio of all prior evaluations can seem a godsend. The authors encourage professionals to consider this issue carefully with team members and reach a consensus. Undetected disagreement on this issue, especially among loosely affiliated professionals who occasionally constitute a flexible team, can result in major embarrassment when dealing with parents. Those who choose to share documents with parents are cautioned to consider individual circumstances and parents' needs before reaching such a decision.

ILLUSTRATIVE CASES

The following cases are offered to illustrate practical problems about team formation and interprofessional referring. Examples describing both formal fixed teams and flexible teams are provided, as are examples between the two extremes. The children described in these cases have problems ranging from the common, such as uncomplicated learning disability for which specialty consultations provide relatively little yield, to the complex, such as multi-

problems that require several diagnosticians' involvement for full understanding. The cases are offered solely for pedagogical purposes; there is nothing definitive about the assessment approach, conclusions, or intervention suggestions. It is the authors' intent to present these cases in such a way as to illustrate decisions about team formation and interprofessional referral. Consequently, an in-depth presentation and interpretation of data from any discipline is omitted, as are detailed intervention plans and individualized education programs (IEPs).

Ricky

Ricky was seen by a fixed team, the core members of which were a psychologist, a psychiatrist, a special education diagnostician, and a speech/language pathologist. Associated with this team was a full array of support diagnostic personnel and laboratory facilities necessary to perform medical diagnostic procedures.

Background Information Nine-year-old Ricky was brought for assessment because of both learning failure in school and conduct problems at home. This third grader had done poorly in school beginning with Head Start, where he was described as inattentive and mildly disruptive. During kindergarten, his behavior deteriorated and he was once sent home from school because of a refusal to follow classroom rules. School officials had expressed continuing frustration over the boy's inability or unwillingness to follow rules and noted that the youngster had made only minimal academic progress during his first three years of school, despite considerable informal supplementary teacher assistance.

At home he was described as "never listening" and as representing a substantial management problem. The parents commented that their youngster was occasionally destructive of property, was noncompliant, and alienated his peers by rough play. The parents brought their son for evaluation to determine why he was failing at school and what might be done to correct the situation.

Developmental History and Physical Examination Evaluation procedures for the fixed team involved an initial contact of Ricky and his parents with the team's child psychiatrist. The parents were informed about the particulars of the team process and what they would receive in the way of information at its conclusion.

The child psychiatrist began by conducting a physical examination and collecting a health history from the boy's mother. His mother reported a full-term pregnancy with uneventful labor and delivery. Both parents noted that Ricky was extremely irritable as a neonate, and as a toddler he required little sleep. Developmental milestones were reportedly attained within normal limits, except that the youngster had a history of frequent daytime enuresis that continued to the present. The mother reported that the youngster's health was generally good.

Physical examination noted a thin child with slight facial asymmetry. There were no other physical stigmata. He had some dullness and refraction of both tympanic membranes, suggesting chronic otitis media. Neurological examination was normal except for some maladroitness.

Mental Status and Family Assessment Information about a family history of related problems, the family's values, and the child's position within the family were also collected by the child psychiatrist. In addition, the child's mental status was assessed in an interview.

The salient findings included a paternal uncle with alcohol abuse problems, a paternal aunt with attention deficit disorder, and a maternal first cousin with a history of school learning difficulties and conduct problems. The family appeared reasonably well adjusted, with Ricky being the youngest of three boys residing in the household, the eldest of whom was from the mother's prior marriage. There were hints of impulsiveness in the mother's history, such as a first marriage after a brief courtship and a history of hasty job changes. Both parents were obviously frustrated by their inability to manage the boy at home and by his persistent lack of academic progress. The parents were concerned not only because of Ricky's noncompliance and destructiveness, but also because he had seemed to become more self-critical and less self-confident during the past year or so.

Mental status assessment of the youngster confirmed the parents' concern. The youngster was restless and was obviously attuned to the fact that he was constantly in trouble at home and unable to make progress at school. Ricky was remarkably uninhibited during the interview. At times he failed to engage the examiner, at other times he talked in a peculiar "mechanical robot" voice without inflection. However, he refused to talk in-depth about his conduct at home or his lack of progress in school. His reality testing was good, his mood was apprehensive, and his affect was appropriate to the situation.

Psychological Assessment Ricky was next evaluated by the team's psychologist, who used a standard battery of psychological instruments, as was the practice whenever a child with school failure was brought to the team. The psychometric scores of this evaluation are presented in Table 10.2. The psychologist's interpretation of the data reflected a youngster with significant problems in language usage. The child was also observed to have difficulty in both understanding and interpreting verbal messages, as well as in formulating his thoughts and expressing himself verbally. The child did substantially better on hands-on tasks involving nonverbal reasoning and problem solving. He had difficulty, for the most part, on all tasks that required concentration and freedom from distraction.

Academic assessment showed a youngster incapable of competing with classmates unless provided with continued support assistance. Academic assessment was generally consistent with the boy's verbal skills. His efforts were noted to be filled with errors reflecting difficulty in applying phonics

Table 10.2. Psychometric summary of Ricky

Chronological age = 9.7   Grade placement: 3rd

Wechsler Intelligence Scale for Children–Revised

Verbal		**Performance**	
Information	5	Picture Completion	10
Similarities	6	Picture Arrangement	10
Arithmetic	4	Block Design	9
Vocabulary	6	Object Assembly	12
Comprehension	7	Coding	6
Digit Span	3		
Verbal IQ = 69		Performance IQ = 95	

Full Scale IQ = 82

Wide Range Achievement Test–Revised

Test	**Standard score**	**Percentile**	**Grade equivalent**
Reading	73	3	2M[a]
Spelling	74	4	2B[b]
Arithmetic	74	4	2E[c]

Peabody Individual Achievement Test

	Grade equivalents	**Percentile ranks**	**Standard scores**
Mathematics	2.0	4	74
Reading Recognition	1.8	3	72
Reading Comprehension	1.9	1	65
Spelling	2.2	3	72
General Information	1.9	9	80
Total	1.7	1	65

[a]Middle of 2nd grade.
[b]Beginning of 2nd grade.
[c]End of 2nd grade.

rules (e.g., he spelled "will" as "wrch"); he showed some evidence of sight vocabulary but poor decoding of unfamiliar, phonetically regular words.

Projective testing of the Thematic Apperception Test, Sentence Completion Blank, and projective drawings was completed by the psychologist as well. These procedures showed a youngster who consistently misinterpreted others' motives, and tended to see the world as angry and confrontational, while consistently viewing himself as unable to achieve positive results despite earnest effort and good intentions. The principal characters in the projective stories (Thematic Apperception Test) were unhappy, ineffectual, and ostracized by peers. On the Sentence Completion Blank form, the youngster appeared discouraged, frequently referring to himself in derogatory terms.

Speech-Language Assessment   A pediatric speech-language pathologist was the third team member to assess the child. Consistent with the previous psychological evaluation, her speech-language assessment showed the youngster to have across-the-board language problems, with the most severe problems in the areas of short-term memory and auditory processing of complex verbal messages. Ricky had deficits in language concepts, vocabulary, and knowledge of grammatical rules. His narrative organization was also delayed.

Educational Assessment As the final regularly scheduled portion of the team evaluation, Ricky was observed in his own classroom by a special educator. He was subsequently brought to the team's diagnostic classroom where he was observed and underwent detailed educational evaluation.

Criterion-referenced assessment of basic academics indicated approximately 80% mastery of first-grade reading skills (decoding and understanding), with no better than 50% mastery of second-grade reading tasks. The youngster had approximately 92% mastery of first-grade mathematics concepts and procedures, but only 35% mastery of second-grade mathematics tasks in contrast to his actual third-grade placement.

When observed in an academic setting, he was noted to have difficulty following oral directions and completing seatwork without one-to-one supervision. The maximum instructional interval in a one-to-one situation was approximately 20 minutes, and he was virtually incapable of following instruction in anything larger than a small group setting. Ricky was observed to work considerably better in a study carrel and to follow directions better when problems were demonstrated or when he was given concrete examples. Reading group, an activity with six other children, consistently produced severe restlessness and mild disruption. Significantly, he was noted to be using a reading text of approximately 2.5 grade (2nd grade, 5th month) difficulty level in his present classroom situation.

Interpretation and Additional Procedures Available data at this point suggested a youngster with significant language problems at both the information-processing and conceptual levels; severe academic difficulties in most areas, especially on tasks that required language competency and processing of verbal information; a brief attention span; conduct problems; and questionable hearing status. Ricky fit no identifiable biomedical syndrome but possibly was suffering from constitutionally based learning problems, considering the reported compatibility of his condition to family history and the chronicity of his problems.

An EEG was ordered to further assess the youngster's neurological status; it was found to be within normal limits.

Audiological assessment was suggested because of Ricky's severe language problems, and because of suspected otitis media detected during physical examination. Audiological procedures using impedance and conditioning techniques found the youngster's hearing to be within normal limits.

Final conclusions were that the youngster had an auditory/verbal learning disability that was significantly impairing language functioning and all associated academic tasks. He was also suffering from a variety of conduct problems, perhaps secondary or related to school failure.

Recommendations Because detailed psychological, speech, and special education data had been collected on Ricky, it was possible to provide a precise set of procedures designed to remedy or circumvent the youngster's problems. In this case, unlike subsequent cases, medical data are relatively unimportant in making plans for the boy's special needs. The following recommendations were made:

1. Ricky was suggested for placement in a self-contained environment for children with learning disabilities where he was to receive all basic academic instruction, with provisions for mainstreaming in art, music, and physical education.
2. Instruction was to focus on "whole word" or "look/say" approaches to reading, to emphasize developing a sight vocabulary. Additionally, it was suggested that multimodality reading approaches might be tried to gain mastery of difficult to retain words.
3. Ricky was to be provided concise, brief directions. Repetition of directions, pantomiming, or demonstrating in a visual fashion were suggested whenever feasible.
4. It was suggested that Ricky receive primary instruction in a nondistracting portion of the classroom, with a minimum of stimulating posters, bulletin boards, and the like in close proximity to his work area. Seatwork was to be completed in a study carrel.
5. Ricky was enrolled in a language stimulation program designed both to teach new vocabulary words as well as to foster a desire in him to learn new words, to monitor his understanding of new words in an environment, and to encourage him to learn that words can be a source of pleasure and interest.
6. Ricky's parents were enrolled in a behavior management program and also received weekly contact with a child psychologist to work on management procedures and family issues.
7. Consultation with an otolaryngologist (ear, nose, and throat physician) was suggested because of the youngster's otitis media.
8. A behavioral procedure designed to prompt Ricky to urinate at regular intervals during the day was instituted.

Comment Cases like Ricky's are among the most common that are encountered by diagnosticians of school-age children: significant reading/spelling problems (in this case arithmetic, too) accompanied by poor language-processing skills (Barkley, 1981; Boder, 1973; Rourke & Strang, 1983). In this case, the child has mild to moderate conduct problems that also require intervention. The bulk of assessment and programming in this case is educational and psychological (nonmedical) in nature.

Referral decisions are minimized in this case because the fixed team was previously constituted. An important referral is made for audiological and otolaryngological assessment based upon both physical examination and a large Verbal/Performance discrepancy on the WISC-R. Either factor alone may have been sufficient to trigger the referral process. The EEG was ordered as an additional precaution against neuropathological processes that may be causing the child's problem, rather than as a result of specific observed indicators.

Walter

In contrast to Ricky, Walter was seen by several professionals among whom there was no previous relationship. In this regard, the case is representative of the flexible team approach. Moreover, evaluations were interspersed over several months, another point of departure from the typical temporally contiguous fixed team evaluation.

Background Information   Walter was first identified as having developmental delay at the age of approximately 3 years when his family's concern about "slowness" prompted a visit to the pediatrician. The results of a Denver Developmental Screening Test showed delays in all areas assessed: Personal/Social, Adaptive, Language, and Motor. A referral for formal psychological testing produced nothing definitive because of the boy's lack of cooperation and brief attention span. Walter was enrolled in a preschool stimulation program from 3 to 5 years of age, an interval during which no further assessment occurred.

Psychological Assessment   At age 5 years, 8 months, Walter was enrolled in the public schools. This precipitated an immediate referral for psychological testing, primarily to determine placement needs and eligibility for special education. Although Walter was previously identified as delayed, the school psychologist quickly concluded that little definitive assessment had yet been completed. She undertook a thorough evaluation, including developmental history, psychometrics, and family assessment.

Walter lived with both parents and a younger sister who was without developmental problems. The family had no history of learning problems, developmental delays, or psychiatric or neurological disease. The mother indicated that prior to the birth of this youngster she had experienced two miscarriages. While the child was born full term, there was hemorrhaging (placenta previa) three months into the pregnancy that required hospitalization. Delivery was described as difficult, oxygen was required, and the baby was felt to do poorly postnatally, with extended neonatal care required. He had a history of recurrent otitis media.

Walter's mother reported that developmental milestones were met late; the child sat alone at 9 months, crawled at 11 months, walked at 20 months, used single words at 25 months, and composed rudimentary sentences only at approximately 36 months. The youngster was not toilet-trained until 6 years of age.

Psychological testing consisting of the Stanford-Binet Intelligence Scale, Peabody Picture Vocabulary Test, and Alpern-Boll Developmental Profile was administered at this time. Walter earned a Stanford-Binet IQ of 51, with no evidence of differential proficiency on tasks of varying content (e.g., language vs. nonlanguage). His Peabody Picture Vocabulary Test score was 53. On the Alpern-Boll the following age equivalents were earned: Physical, 3.1 (3 years, 1 month); Self-help, 3.3; Social Skills, 3.1; Academic, 3.1; Communications, 3.4. He had an IQ equivalent of 61 on this instrument.

The school psychologist suggested that Walter's problems were so great as to require alternative, special class placement, but postponed final assignment until a special educator assessed the child. She also suggested audiological assessment, based on the recurrent otitis media reported by his mother. The diagnostic impression was mild to moderate mental retardation.

Educational Assessment   A special educator who instructs pupils with mental retardation was asked to assess Walter in reference to the following question: "Do his skills better match those of educable or trainable retarded children?" A criterion-referenced assessment of readiness skills similar to those possessed by beginning kindergartners in the district's educable mentally handicapped program found Walter to possess approximately 25% of language readiness skills, approximately 20% of fine motor readiness skills, and approximately 30% of gross motor readiness skills. Moreover, the youngster's attention span and activity level appeared incompatible with the instructional objectives of the educable retarded program. Consequently, Walter began the subsequent year's instruction in a trainable mentally handicapped program.

Audiological Assessment   To "rule out hearing loss" was the referral request made of the speech-language pathologist who performed routine hearing assessment for the district. Walter's activity level and distractibility problems were of such a magnitude that a pure tone audiometric procedure was not possible. Consequently, the child was referred to a consultant to the district (a certified audiologist) who was able to assess the child using play procedures and impedance testing. With these procedures, the child's hearing was found to be within normal limits.

Subsequent Problems   For the next two years, Walter was enrolled in a self-contained trainable mentally handicapped class where he made adequate progress in a variety of self-help skills and began to acquire academic readiness skills. Nonetheless, the boy's behavior deteriorated both at home and in school. Approximately two years after the initial program enrollment, a series of unprovoked rage-like behaviors were noted at home and in school. Finally, the youngster was observed to have a grand mal seizure, which prompted an immediate referral to a pediatric neurologist.

Neurological Assessment A detailed history taken by the neurologist identified several factors as possible insults to the central nervous system, most notably the child's prenatal and perinatal course. Observing the reported atypical and delayed early development of the child, the neurologist believed prenatal and perinatal factors to be most contributory. Careful questioning of family members suggested the presence of possible absence seizures (intervals of transient inattention and unresponsiveness with no obvious motor manifestations) as well as a likely seizure etiology to the boy's episodic outbursts.

An EEG was ordered, and was found to be abnormal with definite paroxysmal activity as well as changes suggestive of moderate diffuse encephalopathy. A CT scan of the head was also undertaken without contrast and was reported to be normal. The boy was felt to have a mixed seizure disorder that was contributing to his behavior and activity level problems. He was placed on Tegretol (an anticonvulsant) but there were continuing indications of seizure activity and continuing behavior deterioration.

Psychiatric and Psychological Assessment Concerned about the behavioral aspects of the boy's case and recognizing a need to interface behavioral and neurological status, the neurologist made a referral to a child psychiatrist. The referral was made to assess the extent of conduct problems that were independent of neurological problems and to provide guidelines for psychopharmacological and/or behavioral intervention. Through interview and examination, the child psychiatrist determined that it was likely there were both neurological and behavioral causes for the boy's difficulty. When the neurologist had completed the adjustment of the antiseizure medication, the child psychiatrist attempted intervention with two types of stimulant medication and, ultimately, with a tricyclic (Elavil), which had a beneficial effect on the boy's activity level, impulsiveness, and general manageability. Assessment also indicated that an enhanced use of behavior management procedures would likely contribute to better control of the child at home. A child psychologist working in collaboration with the psychiatrist provided basic instruction on management to Walter's parents. A time-out procedure and an extremely simple incentive program were implemented at home. The psychologist also worked as a liaison to the public school to provide information about intervention strategies and medication.

Comment Although this child's case is indeed multifaceted and although the child received services from individuals operating in an informal network, ultimately, necessary services were procured and reasonably well-integrated diagnostic conclusions were reached. In this case, dual case management occurred. Delineation of Walter's cognitive ability and educational needs continued to rest in the hands of the school psychologist, with input from outside consultants that was primarily of a medical nature. Detailed recommendations for intervention were not sought from the outside sources, but rather the primary contribution was to diagnose and treat the child's unique neurological problems and insure that management approaches being used outside the school were compatible with those used inside the school. The school psychologist in this case was aware of important indications of referral and made referrals to the appropriate sources. For example, she recognized the possibility of hearing deficit based on recurring otitis media, which precipitated an audiological assessment, and she made a prompt referral to a neurologist based on the child's seizure.

Medical management of the case resided with Walter's neurologist who made necessary supplemental referrals for diagnostic assistance to clarify the problem and insure that intervention was effective and comprehensive. Without accurate medical assessment and management, Walter's educational progress and development would have been severely compromised.

Sandra

Like Walter's case, Sandra's case is generally representative of a flexible team approach. In this instance, a pediatric neurologist was the primary case manager. He accessed other consultants who treated the youngster's accompanying developmental problems so that they could help him fully understand the nature of Sandra's medical status.

Background Information At age 25 months this youngster was diagnosed as having H-flu meningitis and a porencephalic (due to abnormal brain structure) cyst. The youngster's development, which apparently had been progressing normally, ceased and the girl lost a good deal of previously acquired function. It was not until age 3 years that the child walked again, and again began speaking in single words. She accomplished the speaking of brief sentences at 3 years, 6 months, and toilet training at 5 years. At the time of the original diagnosis, 25 months, a CT scan and EEG were administered. The girl continued to be monitored by her pediatric neurologist; her seizures, generally controlled with medication, were a sequela of neurological illness.

At age 5 years, upon enrollment in kindergarten, Sandra was assessed using the Wechsler Preschool and Primary Scale of Intelligence. These scores were forwarded to the neurologist as follows: Verbal IQ, 67; Performance IQ, 76; Full Scale IQ, 68. The youngster passed a hearing and vision screening at that point. Sandra was enrolled for the next three years in a primary program for youngsters with mental retardation.

At age 8 years, with her increasing size, Sandra had become a significant management problem in the classroom. Her recurrent assaultive behavior, coupled with high activity level and short attention span, mandated placement in a more structured environment outside the public school. The psychologist at her school found her untestable using the WISC-R, which raised the ominous prospect of loss of function. This, coupled with reports of minimal academic progress and regressing behavior, prompted her neurologist to request a more detailed assessment. Sandra was placed in a hospital-based inpatient pediatric biobehavioral program where comprehensive reassessment was undertaken.

Psychological Assessment　An attempt was made to administer a standard psychometric battery while Sandra was an inpatient. This was felt to be important because the scores might represent an index of the child's functional level that could be compared, now that she was 8, with her scores earned at age 5 years. Although the girl was difficult to test because of the aforementioned conduct problems, scores on the WISC-R and the Wide Range Achievement Test were collected (see Table 10.3). In comparing current scores with those found at 5 years of age, the psychologist was concerned that the girl had, indeed, lost cognitive functioning, which raised questions about a progressive as opposed to static encephalopathy (brain disorder).

To substantiate that adaptive skills were similarly delayed and that Sandra's poor scores were not simply reflecting poor test-taking behavior, the inpatient unit staff administered an AAMD Adaptive Behavior Scale, the scores of which are also reflected in Table 10.3. Sandra clearly had significant delays in adaptive behavior in virtually all spheres. The AAMD Adaptive Behavior Scale also documented the conduct problems that had been previously observed. Her scores on the AAMD Adaptive Behavior Scale were more compatible with trainable mentally handicapped children than with educable mentally handicapped youngsters. She met the defining criteria for mental retardation.

An interview with her parents, however, was interesting in that no obvious regression in adaptive functioning had been noted at home. While the girl had become increasingly difficult to manage, she had maintained all previously acquired adaptive skills and was making slow progress, in the view of the parents. Interestingly, the parents had seen their daughter as significantly delayed at all times subsequent to the meningitis insult at age 25 months.

Speech-Language Assessment　A pediatric speech-language pathologist completed a detailed assessment while Sandra was an inpatient and noted the same difficulties in test-taking behavior encountered by the psychologist. He noted significant delays in all language areas, including: vocabulary, mastery of grammar rules, word finding, oral formulation, and narrative organization. The girl's articulation was immature and there were persisting developmental sound substitution and distortion errors. Again, comparing the youngster with her previously earned Wechsler Preschool and Primary Scale of Intelligence scores (when she was 5 years of age), the speech-language pathologist suspected loss of function.

Audiological Assessment　An audiological assessment found bilateral pure tone hearing to be within normal limits. Sandra's hearing was also assessed as adequate for speech sounds, but it was found that right ear con-

Table 10.3. Psychometric summary of Sandra

Wechsler Preschool and Primary Scale of Intelligence
Chronological age = 5.1

Verbal		Performance	
Information	5	Animal House	9
Vocabulary	4	Picture Completion	6
Arithmetic	5	Mazes	5
Similarities	5	Geometric Design	6
Comprehension	5	Block Design	6
Verbal IQ = 67		Performance IQ = 76	

Full Scale IQ = 68

Wechsler Intelligence Scale for Children–Revised
Chronological age = 8.3

Verbal		Performance	
Information	2	Picture Completion	3
Similarities	3	Picture Arrangement	3
Arithmetic	4	Block Design	4
Vocabulary	3	Object Assembly	5
Comprehension	2	Coding	3
Digit Span	4		
Verbal IQ = 55		Performance IQ = 58	

Full Scale IQ = 52

AAMD Adaptive Behavior Scale: School Edition
Chronological age = 8.3

Adaptive functioning compared to EMR[a] = 3 percentile
Adaptive functioning compared to TMR[b] = 32 percentile

Wide Range Achievement Test–Revised
Chronological age = 8.3

Test	Standard score	Percentile	Grade equivalent
Reading	<45	.03	<1
Spelling	<45	.03	<1
Arithmetic	<45	.03	<1

[a]Educable mentally retarded.
[b]Trainable mentally retarded.

tralateral and ipsilateral reflexes were absent or elevated, suggesting a right conductive hearing loss.

Special Education Assessment In the controlled special education environment of the inpatient behavioral program, Sandra was found to be frequently off-task, to work only for short instructional intervals, and to require considerable physical prompting and immediate reinforcement, sometimes with primary reinforcers. Under these circumstances, she showed some beginning kindergarten skills, such as letter production, counting, number recognition, and letter recognition. She knew most preschool concepts related to size, color, shape, and direction. With hands-on materials, her attention span sometimes approached 15 minutes. Generally, with an extremely favorable teacher-to-student ratio, the youngster was manageable and was felt to be capable of making some degree of academic progress.

Milieu Assessment   When observed in the structured day environment of the inpatient program, Sandra was observed to be frequently combative and to have an extremely high activity level. She was inattentive to verbal directions, and consistently noncompliant. A behavioral program that made isolation (time-out) the consequence of aggressive behavior was found to have a marked effect in reducing the number of hitting incidents. Similarly, an immediate time-out consequence for noncompliance quickly reduced the incidents of refusal and resistance, making the girl considerably more manageable. Modification of antiseizure and stimulant medication also had a beneficial effect on the youngster's activity level and general manageability.

Neurological Assessment   Significantly, CT scans repeated while Sandra was in the inpatient unit were found to be compatible with those previously conducted, and reflected no progressive neurological disease. EEG findings similarly suggested no new abnormalities.

Conclusions   It was concluded that Sandra was a youngster with mild mental retardation secondary to neurological illness of a static nature. It was believed that the youngster's intellectual or adaptive functioning had not regressed, but rather that previous scores may have been somewhat inflated, with subsequent testing compromised by behavior problems. These findings were predicated on the parents' observation of their youngster's status and on neurological testing. Moreover, much of the girl's apparent lack of progress appeared attributable to deteriorating behavior, especially her uncontrollable activity level, impulsiveness, and short attention span, which predisposed her to develop a variety of conduct problems. Bringing these overt conduct problems under reasonable behavioral control and readjusting the medication that affected her activity level, ultimately made her more amenable to instruction. Due to an extreme lack of external control, a tightly organized, structured environment with a great deal of immediate feedback was required so that Sandra could make academic gains. With increased behavioral control, initial instructional objectives focused on the acquisition of simple self-care and life skills and on beginning academics. The viability of acquiring basic academics was to be reviewed for progress at regular intervals, and revised or deleted if necessary.

Comment   Sandra's case is indicative of those where a clear biomedical cause for the child's learning/developmental problems exists. Her case highlights the need for primary medical management, but nonetheless demonstrates the importance of simultaneous educational assessment and planning. In this instance, educational and behavior assessment was required not only to guide remedial efforts in those spheres, but to suggest as well how effectively the child's medical management was proceeding. As Sandra's conduct and development deteriorated, these factors pointed to the need to re-examine medical control of the case.

Harry

Like Sandra, Harry suffered from a neurological condition that medical diagnosticians can identify through examination and laboratory techniques. Unlike Sandra, however, no continuing medical intervention was required, and management and planning subsequently became nonmedical in nature. This case is also representative of a flexible team approach.

Background Harry, at 4 years of age, was referred for evaluation of developmental delay with associated behavior problems, including hyperactivity, tantrums, and destruction of toys and playthings. He was not trained for bowel or bladder control.

Harry was the first son born to healthy parents in their twenties. His early development was reportedly unremarkable with normal landmarks reported to age 1½ years. Concurrent with the birth of a sibling, at 2 years Harry began to change substantially. His language, which had been reported as normal, ceased. He became increasingly hyperactive and destructive, and at times displayed headbanging and tantrums in response to frustration.

Speech-Language Assessment Concerned about the peculiar language loss, the parents brought Harry, at age 4 years, to a speech-language pathologist. Speech and language evaluation was accomplished following the report of a normal audiological evaluation. The examiner reported severe delays in language comprehension and expression with no development of the social and cognitive prerequisites for language. Harry also showed no evidence of: understanding cause and effect relationships, functional use of objects, imitative skills, requesting behavior, or complete mastery of object permanence. It was reported that Harry appeared to be able to understand tone of voice, a few simple commands, and nothing more than the names of a few familiar objects. His language was described as simple babbling with undifferentiated vocalizations. No formal instruments could be administered. Convinced that the child's delays were not confined to language spheres, the speech-language pathologist made simultaneous referrals to a developmental pediatrician and to a psychologist.

Developmental Pediatric Assessment The developmental pediatrician learned Harry had two older sisters who were developmentally normal. Family history was negative for learning, developmental, or psychiatric problems. Pregnancy, labor, and delivery were unremarkable as well.

A physical examination, although indicating good overall health with normal height and weight, revealed the presence of several stigmata, including posterior rotation of the ears and dermatographic patterns which featured 8 of 10 fingerprints as whorls. An undescended testicle was also noted. Laboratory studies included evaluation of metabolic status (it was normal) and chromosome studies, to look for fragile-X (it was not found).

Neurological examination led to a request for an EEG. It showed diffuse slowing and sharp discharges from the left hemisphere. A CT scan revealed mild bilateral frontal lobe atrophy (reduced size).

Observation of the child was remarkable in that Harry was extremely agile and overactive with, at best, fleeting eye contact. He seemed to have a fixed "silly" smile. The child did not relate personally to the examiner and handled toys briefly with no apparent use displayed.

No discernible language was heard, although the child did make several expressive grunts. Harry seemed interested in staring at his fingers held close to his eyes. When taken outside the examination room, he wandered off without individual supervision.

Psychological Assessment Assessment by the psychologist was compromised by the child's short attention span, impulsiveness, and oppositional behavior. On a Stanford-Binet, Harry completed only one of the II-year level tasks (form board) before attempting to tear, drop, throw, or eat the test material. Similarly, Harry produced no meaningful response to the Peabody Picture Vocabulary Test, but rather displayed ritualistic perseverate behaviors. The AAMD Adaptive Behavior Scale was administered and the resultant profile showed Harry to have across-the-board impairment. He had self-care skills most like a trainable mentally handicapped youngster, and showed a variety of peculiar, resistive, and idiosyncratic behaviors.

Interview with the family revealed the child to be a source of substantial stress to the parents' relationship. His mother was found to be substantially depressed and tired of attempting to manage the child. It was learned that Harry had caused so much property damage that eviction from their apartment complex was a possibility.

Interpretation and Additional Procedures Harry met the defining criteria for infantile autism and for mental retardation. His condition was felt to be associated with static bilateral encephalopathy (nonprogressive diffuse central nervous system impairment affecting both hemispheres). Findings from the physical examination implied that the child's condition was probably due to prenatal factors, though the child did not fit any identifiable biomedical syndrome.

In addition to fixing the child's diagnosis, interpretation of the data made it clear that the youngster needed remediation. Among the areas requiring direct intervention was activities of daily living; consequently, an occupational therapy consultation was requested. Harry was found to be delayed on all gross motor parameters and to possess none of the prerequisites for beginning development of self-care skills or activities of daily living.

The youngster was enrolled in a preschool stimulation program for children with handicaps, with consultative services provided on a regular basis by specialists in speech-language pathology and occupational therapy.

Comment Though some may question the importance of medical involvement in a case of static encephalopathy, there are important reasons for including medical diagnosticians. First, thorough medical work-up rules out a progressive or treatable condition and allows educational and behavioral intervention to proceed with the assurance that no alternative medical interventions have been missed. Second, parents of children with mental retardation frequently expend considerable effort attempting to locate the cause of their child's problem and at times are uncomfortable proceeding with intervention until they feel "the cause" has been located. In this case, indicating to the parents the likely prenatal cause of the youngster's difficulty and indicating the distinct likelihood of a static condition allowed their concerns to be laid to rest and attention to be focused on the important intervention mission.

This case also demonstrates an important referral consideration sometimes overlooked by speech-language pathologists. Although Harry displayed peculiar and delayed language development, the speech-language pathologist wisely requested a prompt assessment of the youngster's overall cognitive and adaptive skills in order to rule out the possibility of mental retardation, which, in this case, was found to be the primary handicap. It is important for diagnosticians to rule out pervasive problems (e.g., mental retardation) before attempting to remedy problems in narrower skill areas such as language or motor.

SUMMARY

Those who assess children with handicapped or ineffective learning abilities must consider several issues related to the multidisciplinary process. Unless one adopts the untenable position that one can always do everything oneself, some questions must be answered: With whom will one collaborate? Under what conditions is collaboration necessary? Who will lead the collaborative effort? How will those collaborating communicate with each other and with those using assessment findings?

This chapter encourages thinking about these important concerns and offers some suggestions. Diagnosticians attempting to answer the difficult questions about individual children's etiology, prognosis, and intervention needs, however, will invariably develop their own positions, subject to continual update and refinement. It is hoped that this chapter, and indeed this entire volume, facilitates that process.

REFERENCES

American Psychological Association. (1985). *Standards for educational and psychological tests.* Washington, DC: Author.

Barkley, R. A. (1981). Learning disabilities. In E. J. Mash & L. G. Terdal (Eds.), *Behavioral assessment of childhood disorders.* New York: Guilford Press.

Bender, M., Lynch, E. W., Forness, S. R., Rotberg, J., Gardner, T. P., & Siantz, J. (1984). Interdisciplinary services used by public schools. *Applied Research in Mental Retardation, 5,* 91–98.

Boder, E. (1973). Developmental dyslexia: A diagnostic approach based on three atypical reading-spelling patterns. *Developmental Medicine and Child Neurology, 15,* 663–687.

Griffith, J. F. (1979). The neurology of learning disabilities: An overview. In M. I. Gottlieb, P. W. Zinkus, & L. J. Bradford (Eds.), *Current issues in developmental pediatrics: The learning disabled child.* New York: Grune & Stratton.

Levine, M. D., Brook, R., & Shonkoff, J. D. (1980). *A pediatric approach to learning disabilities.* New York: John Wiley & Sons.

McLeod, J. (1983). Learning disabilities is for educators. *Journal of Learning Disabilities, 16,* 23–24.

Mulvenon, J. (1980). Development of preschool interagency teams. In J. O. Elder & P. R. Magrab (Eds.) *Coordinating services to handicapped children: A handbook for interagency collaboration.* Baltimore: Paul H. Brookes Publishing Co.

Ross, A. O. (1979). *Learning disability: The unrealized potential.* New York: McGraw-Hill.

Rourke, B., & Strang, J. D. (1983). Subtypes of reading and arithmetic disabilities: A neuropsychological analysis. In M. Rutter (Ed.), *Developmental neuropsychiatry* (pp. 564–574). New York: Guilford Press.

Urbano, R. C., Forness, S. R., Lynch, E. W., Bender, M., Rotberg, J., & Gardner, T. P. (1984). Interdisciplinary evaluation: Types of children referred to UAF clinics and hospitals. *Mental Retardation, 22,* 117–120.

Wodrich, D. L. (1984). *Children's psychological testing: A guide for nonpsychologists.* Baltimore: Paul H. Brookes Publishing Co.

Glossary

AAMD (American Association on Mental Deficiency) Adaptive Behavior Scale (ABS)   A standardized interview procedure to measure adaptive behavior, generally as part of the assessment process for children suspected of having mental retardation.

Ability deficits   Hypothesized cause of academic failure arising from lack of mastery of skills or inability to perform particular behaviors (as contrasted with performance deficits).

Activities of daily living (ADL)   Basic living procedures such as feeding, grooming, and personal hygiene, frequently assessed in detail by an occupational therapist.

Adaptive behavior   The degree to which standards of personal independence and social responsibility expected for an individual of a specific age and from a particular cultural group are met. Delayed adaptive behavior is one criterion for a diagnosis of mental retardation.

Affect   Facial expression that reflects an underlying emotional mood or state.

Agnosia   Inability to recognize objects that were previously known.

Air-bone gap   The difference between hearing thresholds for air-conducted and bone-conducted sound during an audiometric assessment. A significant discrepancy in the two thresholds typically signifies a conductive hearing loss.

American Association on Mental Deficiency (AAMD)   A multidisciplinary professional group that concerns itself with issues important to persons with mental retardation, such as a definition and nosological system for mental retardation.

American Speech-Language-Hearing Association (ASHA)   National organization of speech-language pathologists and audiologists.

Amnestic   Refers to a type of neurological impairment associated with memory loss.

Angular gyrus   A brain structure hypothesized by early theorists to play a central role in ''word blindness.'' Contemporary thinkers continue to speculate about its role in dyslexia.

Articulation disorder   Any of a variety of problems with speech/sound production, such as substitution, omission, distortion, or addition.

Assessment of Children's Language Comprehension   An individually administered test that assesses the child's ability to understand increasingly complex sentences (e.g., ''show me the boat'' versus ''show me the big boat'').

Association for Retarded Citizens of the United States (ARC-US) An advocacy group that, among other services, publishes competency requirements for teachers of persons with mental retardation.

Ataxia Impaired coordination of muscle movements due to disease or damage in the cerebellum.

Athetosis Abnormal involuntary writhing movements of the extremities due to neurological damage.

Auditory attention problem Distractibility to irrelevant stimuli, difficulty maintaining auditory attention, difficulty shifting from one task to another, and slow adaptation to relevant auditory stimuli.

Auditory discrimination problem Difficulty in differentiating one sound pattern from another.

Auditory evoked potentials Changes in the EEG in response to sound that allow assessment of hearing status. The procedure is particularly helpful for use with infants, young children, or persons who are difficult to test.

Auditory figure-ground problem Difficulty in selecting the primary message from background noise.

Bayley Scales of Infant Development Individually administered assessment device suitable for children up to 2½ years of age with separate IQ-like scores produced for mental and motor development.

Behavior assessment An approach that emphasizes the importance of environmental events on behavior and direct observation of behavior in natural settings, and uses ongoing assessment data to plan and evaluate intervention programs.

Boston Naming Test Individually administered test that requires the naming of pictures on demand and is sensitive to word retrieval problems.

Boulder Model Originated at a conference held in 1949 in Boulder, Colorado. It advocates that psychologists be trained as scientist-practitioners.

Central auditory disorders Disorders of hearing and auditory information processing presumed to be caused by problems in the brain stem or temporal lobe. This disorder results in an inability to process complex speech messages, rather than an elevated threshold for sounds.

Cephalopelvic disproportion Condition in which a baby's head is too large to pass through the maternal birth canal.

Certificate of Clinical Competence (C.C.C.) Certification offered by the American Speech-Language-Hearing Association as the nationally recognized designation of professional expertise. C.C.C.-SLP denotes certification in speech-language pathology; C.C.C.-A denotes certification in audiology.

Complex partial (psychomotor) seizure Epileptic or seizure activity originating in the temporal lobe of the brain. It usually produces some degree of confusion, disorientation, or sensory distortion.

Conditioned play audiometry A conditioning procedure that teaches the child to respond to a sound stimulus with an appropriate play activity such as stacking rings on a peg. It is useful for assessing the hearing of children 30–36 months and older.

Conductive hearing loss Hearing loss characterized by an elevated threshold for air-conducted sound, typically related to disorders of the external or middle ear.

Congestive heart failure Cardiac muscle fatigue that produces body fluid accumulation and lung congestion.

Construct validity The extent to which a test measures a hypothetical construct (e.g., anxiety, motivation), as reflected by agreement between theory and empirical data.

COTA Abbreviation for certified occupational therapy assistant, an individual who has met standards, including the minimum of an associate's degree, established by the American Occupational Therapy Association.

Content validity The extent to which a test's content is an adequate sample of the attribute or trait being assessed.

Council for Exceptional Children (CEC) Advocacy group that also publishes competency requirements for teachers of children with learning disabilities or mental retardation.

Cranial nerve A group of nerves originating from points within the lower brain or brain stem.

Craniopharyngioma A type of tumor located near the pituitary.

Criterion-referenced assessment An educational assessment approach emphasizing that test items and procedures correspond directly to defined objectives rather than to norms.

Criterion-related validity Validity that is indexed by a correlation between a test and some independent criterion.

Curriculum-referenced assessment A type of criterion-referenced educational assessment that tests the learner's mastery of locally established instructional objectives.

Cyanotic heart disease Abnormal heart function or structure that gives normally pink skin surfaces a blue color due to reduced oxygen in the blood.

Cytoarchitecture Cellular structure.

Cytology Microscopic study of cellular structures and tissues.

Cytomegalovirus (CMV) Congenital viral infection occurring *in utero* that places the child at risk for subsequent developmental and physical problems based on central nervous system (CNS) damage.

Deficits in adaptive behavior One defining criterion for a diagnosis of mental retardation.

Denver Developmental Screening Test A screening instrument for preschoolers that assesses developmental competence in four areas: personal-social, fine motor-adaptive, language, and gross motor.

Developmental dysfluency Normal speech fluency or stuttering problems that resolve spontaneously without the development of secondary symptoms such as blinking and head turning.

Developmental dyspraxia Difficulty selecting, directing, and organizing the sequences of oral movement necessary for speech/sound production.

Diagnostic and Statistical Manual of Mental Disorders-III (DSM-III) A comprehensive guidebook for the diagnosis and classification of mental disorders published by the American Psychiatric Association (APA). *DSM-III* contains definitions of mental retardation and several learning disorders.

DiGeorge syndrome Congenital condition characterized by endocrine deficiencies with seizures, irregular heartbeat, and muscular problems.

Dopamine A compound that serves as a principal neurotransmitter.

Down syndrome A cluster of mental, physiological, and structural changes seen in persons with three rather than two chromosomes in the #21 pair; also called "trisomy 21" or "translocation 14/21."

Dysarthria Articulation problems related to weakness, paralysis, or severe incoordination of the oral musculature, presumably related to lesions in the central and/or peripheral nervous system.

Dyseidetic Impaired capacity for mental image formation.

Dysgraphia Difficulty in writing due to neurological impairment.

Dyslexia A disorder manifested by difficulty in learning to read despite conventional instruction, adequate intelligence, and social and educational opportunity. It is dependent upon fundamental cognitive disabilities that are generally believed to be of neurological origin.

Dysmetria Inability to halt muscle movement at a desired point.

Dysmorphic Atypical in form or development, often producing an unusual appearance.

Dyspedogogia A label used to imply that academic failures may be attributable to deficiencies in teaching, rather than to inherent disabilities in the learner.

Dysphasia A language disturbance that produces jumbled word order.

Dysphoria A subjectively unpleasant emotional state that may reflect depression, unhappiness, dissatisfaction, or irritability.

Dyssynergia Disruption of the complex programming of contractions of various muscle groups constituting a single smooth movement.

Dystonia Abnormal muscle tone, either increased or decreased.

Encephaloclastic Destructive process within the central nervous system.

Erhardt Developmental Prehension Assessment (EDPA) An objective measure of prehension, or the ability to grasp, frequently used by occupational therapists to assess abnormally developing youngsters of any age.

Error score The hypothetical portion of any person's test score that consists of all the factors, independent of the true score, that can cause scores to fluctuate. It includes such factors as guessing, fatigue, and text anxiety.

Facial diplegia Paralysis of both sides of the face.

Familial/functional mental retardation Mental retardation believed to be due to inherited limited ability or consequent to being raised in an impoverished environment. This is contrasted with organic mental retardation.

Fetal alcohol syndrome A cluster of physical abnormalities with associated mental retardation that are related to maternal alcohol consumption during pregnancy.

Fixed team approach Method of forming multidisciplinary assessment groups in which diagnosticians are identified before the process begins. Members of the team use a standard agreed upon assessment procedure for all children, and matters such as report format and fees are also agreed upon before the fact.

Flexible team approach Method of accomplishing multidisciplinary assessment by consulting professionals on an individual case basis, as problems manifested by the child require.

Gerstmann's syndrome Specific neurological disorder that impairs right-left discrimination, calculations, writing ability, and finger recognition.

Glioma A central nervous system tumor.

Goniometer A flexible instrument, similar to a protractor, that measures the degrees through which the moving joint passes in range of motion studies.

Guadalupe v. Tempe Elementary School District   A court decision that mandated the inclusion of adaptive behavior measures, that assessment not rely exclusively on intelligence tests in making education placements, and that children must be tested in their primary language.

Hamartoma   A tumor with many different cell types.

Heart murmur   Audible sound resulting from abnormal blood flow (turbulence) within the heart, often caused by structural abnormality.

Hemiparetic   Neurological weakness of one-half of a paired structure such as the arm or leg.

Homonymous hemianopia   A reduced range of vision due to specific nerve damage that causes loss of one-half the visual field in each eye.

Hydrocephalus   Enlargement of the head due to an excessive accumulation of fluid caused by obstruction of the spinal fluid pathways through the central nervous system.

Hypotonia   A reduction in muscle tone, which conveys a sense of "floppiness."

Hypoxia   Condition resulting from reduced availability of oxygen in body tissues.

Individualized education program (IEP)   A tailor-made intervention program, usually created by a special educator, designed to meet the individual needs of learners with handicaps (as prescribed by PL 94-142).

Infarction   Tissue destruction resulting from blockage of blood supply.

Instructional analysis   A formal educational process used to evaluate learner characteristics, situational factors, and requirements of the learning task.

Intraventricular hemorrhage   Bleeding into the central cerebrospinal fluid space of the brain that often occurs spontaneously. It is related to prematurity, blood vessel abnormality, or trauma.

Ipsative interpretation   The evaluation of intraindividual differences as part of the assessment process.

"Jangle" fallacy   Incorrect assumption that two tests with different names are measuring different traits or attributes.

"Jingle" fallacy   Mistaken assumption that two tests with the same name are measuring similar traits or attributes.

"Jungle" fallacy   Mistaken assumption that two highly correlated tests are measuring the same thing.

Karyotyping   Process by which a cell's chromosomes are isolated, photographed, and displayed in orderly sequence.

Kaufman Assessment Battery For Children (K-ABC)   An individually administered test of mental ability for children aged 2½–12½ years that dichotomizes cognitive processing into sequential and simultaneous components and separates these from skills hypothetically acquired through experience (called achievement).

Korsakoff's syndrome   Disorder usually due to alcoholism that leads to amnesia, confabulation (fabricated narratives), and nerve damage.

Learning process assessment   Educational evaluation of the perceptual skills (or processes) necessary for learning and the degree to which such skills are intact or deficient.

Limbic system   A group of structures deep within the brain that participate in emotional regulation.

Lipid storage disease   Abnormal metabolic accumulation of organic fats that leads to progressive tissue destruction and loss of function.

Lithium   Also called lithium carbonate, a medication effective in treatment of manic-depressive illness.

Luria-Nebraska Neuropsychological Test Battery   A neuropsychological test battery that produces scores in ten discrete subareas and is based on the neuropsychological theorizations of A. R. Luria.

Lysozomal   Refers to a particular particle within the structure of a cell.

Lytic   Destructive.

Mania   Extreme excitation of behavior and emotion that is a manifestation of manic-depressive illness.

McCarthy Scales of Children's Abilities   An individually administered test of general intelligence that not only produces a general cognitive index (IQ equivalent), but subtest scores in a variety of areas. Suitable for children aged 2½–8½ years.

Menarche   Developmental point at which menstrual cycle begins.

Microcephaly   Abnormally small head, which reduces brain capacity; often associated with mental retardation.

Milani-Comparetti Motor Developmental Screening Test   A brief, easily scored scale for the early identification of motor delays and abnormal movement patterns in children from birth to 2 years; frequently administered by occupational therapists.

Mild mental retardation   Individuals with mental retardation who have IQ scores in the range of 50–70.

Miller Assessment for Preschoolers (MAP)   A standardized preschool screening instrument designed to assess moderate to severe problems in the following areas: basic motor and sensory abilities, complex fine motor and oral-motor abilities, speech and language abilities, cognitive skills, and visual-motor integration.

Modality preference assessment approach   View of assessment that contends emphasis should be placed on identifying a learner's differential aptitude to process information, such as identifying a child who has superior verbal as opposed to spatial/mechanical aptitude.

Moderate mental retardation   Individuals with mental retardation who have IQs in the range of 35–55.

Morphogenesis   Process of organ or structural development during the period of fetal growth.

Movement Assessment of Infants   An in-depth assessment instrument typically used by occupational therapists to assess muscle tone, reflexes, automatic reactions, and voluntary movements of infants up to 1 year of age.

Necropsy   Autopsy.

Neoplastic   Refers to a tumor or abnormal cell growth.

Neurotransmitter   Chemical released at a nerve junction (synapse) that allows transmission of a nerve impulse from one cell to another.

Neurotropic   Acting upon the nervous system.

Norm-referencing   A testing approach that compares scores obtained for a particular individual with those of a representative group.

Organic mental retardation   Mental retardation presumed to be attributable to nervous system pathology or damage. This is contrasted with familial/functional mental retardation.

Oromotor   Relating to musculature of the mouth.

Otitis media with effusion (OME)   Middle ear infection with fluid accumulation. It can cause mild to moderate, fluctuant, bilateral conductive hearing loss.

Otolaryngologist   Physician who specializes in treating disorders of the ear, nose, and throat.

OTR   Abbreviation for registered occupational therapist, an individual who has met standards, including the minimum of a bachelor's degree, established by the American Occupational Therapy Association.

Paraphasia   A neurologically based language difficulty that leads to improper word substitutions.

Peabody Developmental Motor Scales   An in-depth assessment instrument typically used by occupational therapists to assess children from birth to 6 years, 11 months in the following areas: reflexes, balance, grasp, hand use, eye-hand coordination, manual dexterity, locomotion and nonlocomotion, and receipt and propulsion of objects.

Peabody Picture Vocabulary Test–Revised   A measure of receptive vocabulary that requires the child to select from four pictures the one that is associated with a spoken word. The test requires no speech from the child and is suitable for children aged 2½ years and older.

Performance deficit   Academic failure that occurs when a child possesses a particular behavior or skill (e.g., oral reading competence) but fails to display it in the classroom (as contrasted with ability deficit).

Perseverate behavior   Repetition of a meaningless word or phrase.

Personality Inventory for Children   A multi-item objective inventory completed by parents that is designed to assess children's emotional and behavioral status, and also to screen for intellectual and academic delays.

Petit mal   Seizure exhibited as a brief staring episode. Consciousness is interrupted.

Phenylketonuria (PKU)   An inherited disorder characterized by impaired metabolism of the amino acid phenylalanine, which causes mental retardation and other problems.

Phonological learning   Producing the sounds of the language.

Porencephalic cyst   An abnormal cavity within the brain substance.

Pragmatic learning   The ability of a child to alter his or her language style to meet social situations, such as learning the language of politeness and the social situation in which it is appropriate.

Profound mental retardation   Individuals with mental retardation who have IQs in the range below 20–25.

Projective testing   Any of a variety of techniques that provide the child with unstructured material, the responses to which are felt to reflect aspects of personality. These techniques were originally based on the psychoanalytic theory in which overt behavior is thought to be a manifestation of underlying needs, motives, and conflicts.

Psychomotor seizure   Same as complex partial seizure.

Psychotropic   Centrally acting medication that alters mood, attention, or behavior.

Quick Neurological Screening Test   Test consisting of items adapted from pediatric neurological exams and measures of soft neurological signs that are believed to assist in locating children aged 5–17 years who are exhibiting learning problems.

Range of motion (ROM) therapy   Therapy often provided by occupational or physical therapists designed to prevent contractures and deformities by working with body movements of children with handicaps.

Referent-based testing Assessment that is conducted in the actual setting, such as the classroom or workplace, where skill application is to occur.

Reflex arc The neurological pathway that a reflex stimulus follows from start to finish.

Reliability The consistency and reproducability of assessment data, held by many to be essential for meaningful assessment.

Seizure Convulsion.

Semantic learning Learning associated with language meaning and understanding.

Sensorineural hearing loss A hearing loss characterized by elevated thresholds for both air-conducted and bone-conducted sound, typically related to a dysfunction of the cochlea or eighth cranial nerve.

Severe mental retardation Individuals with mental retardation who have IQs in the range of 20–40.

Sleep apnea Periodic cessation of spontaneous respiration during sleep which may lead to cardiac rhythm irregularity or sudden death.

Somatosensory Referring to the body's sensory systems.

Southern California Sensory Integration Tests A battery of tests developed by A. Jean Ayres designed to measure sensory integrative abilities such as form and space perception, motor planning, postural and bilateral abilities, and sensory responsiveness. They are suitable for children 4–10 years of age.

Spasticity Abnormal neurological condition with markedly increased muscle tone and reflexes.

Spina bifida Congenital abnormality in which the lower portion of the spinal cord is incompletely covered, often resulting in lower extremity paralysis.

Standardized test Assessment method that has prescribed procedures for administration, scoring, and interpretation.

Stanford-Binet Intelligence Scale An individually administered test of general intelligence suitable for individuals from 2 years of age through adulthood.

Strabismus Uneven eye position and movement due to muscle imbalance.

Stuttering Disorders in the rhythm of speech characterized by involuntary repetition, prolongation, or cessation of sound.

Symbiotic dependency An abnormal extreme interdependence between parent and child that impairs both if they are separated.

Syntax learning Language learning dealing with order or sequences of sounds or words.

Tangible reinforcement operant conditioning audiometry (TROCA) A conditioning procedure that uses systematic reinforcement for appropriate responses to sound stimuli. It is useful for assessing hearing of children aged 36 months and older who are difficult to test.

Task analysis A method of instructional analysis that systemically analyzes the procedures or steps needed to perform a given educational skill.

Tetraplegia Paralysis of all four extremities.

TORCH complex Perinatal viral infections identified by the infective agent (T=toxoplasmosis; O=other, usually considered syphilis; R=rubella; C=cytomegalovirus; H=herpes). These conditions result in an increased incidence of handicapping conditions.

Trisomy   An extra chromosome exceeding the usual paired structure of chromosomes within a cell, producing various types of abnormal development and function.

True score   The hypothetical portion of a person's test score that reflects true knowledge or skill (as opposed to error score).

Tuberous sclerosis   Disease that causes multisystem damage due to multiple small cysts. It is especially problematic in the nervous system.

Turner's syndrome   Abnormal condition in females, usually of normal intelligence, due to a missing X chromosome. It is characterized by: short stature, broad chest with widely spaced nipples, atrophied ovaries, webbed neck, and congenital heart disease.

Validity   The extent to which a test fulfills the functions for which it is being used.

Visual reinforcement audiometry (VRA)   A conditioning procedure using an animated toy mounted atop a loudspeaker which is lighted simultaneously with the presentation of the sound stimulus. It allows the evaluation of hearing for children aged approximately 6–30 months.

Wechsler Intelligence Scale For Children–Revised (WISC-R)   An individually administered intelligence test for children 6.0 to 16.11 years that produces separate Verbal, Performance, and Full Scale IQ scores, as well as subtest scores.

Wechsler Preschool and Primary Scale of Intelligence (WPPSI)   Content and format is similar to WISC-R, but for children aged 4–6 years.

Word retrieval problems   The momentary inability to recall the name of an object or event of which the individual has previous knowledge.

Index

~